# THE STRUCTURE AND MANAGEMENT
# OF THE BRITISH WATER INDUSTRY

WATER PRACTICE MANUALS

# THE STRUCTURE AND MANAGEMENT OF THE BRITISH WATER INDUSTRY

EDITOR
Bernard J. Dangerfield

Compiled and Published by
The Institution of Water Engineers and Scientists,
London, England.

© Published by The Institution of Water Engineers and Scientists,
6-8 Sackville Street, London W1X 1DD,
England.

ISBN 0 901427 07 1

First published, 1979

*Text photoset in 9/10pt. Times*

*Printed in Great Britain
at The Lavenham Press Ltd., Lavenham, Suffolk, England.*

(02/8/94)

# ACKNOWLEDGEMENTS

The Council of The Institution of Water Engineers and Scientists acknowledges the help given in the preparation of this book by those serving the many bodies and organizations involved in the water industry and related activities.

Acknowledgements for permission to reproduce extracts and, or alternatively, illustrations from published works are included, where appropriate, as footnotes in the text.

The Council also acknowledges with gratitude the work of the Manuals Subcommittee, which was set up for the planning of this series of Water Practice Manuals. The members of the Subcommittee are: H. Speight (Chairman); T. W. Brandon; J. D. Jepson; J. E. Massey; B. Rhodes; K. H. Tattersall; A. C. Twort; and B. J. Dangerfield (Subcommittee Secretary).

# CONTRIBUTORS

The Council of The Institution of Water Engineers and Scientists acknowledges the considerable debt of gratitude which is due to the following who have contributed to the writing of this book.

## Book Co-ordinator

J. S. M. Willis,
BSc, FICE, FIWES, Divisional Secretary, Tame Division, Severn-Trent Water Authority.

## Chapter Contributors and Helpers

### Chapter 1: Historical Development of the Water Industry

Contributed by: A. B. Baldwin,
MEng, FICE, FIWES, retired; formerly Chief Executive, Yorkshire Water Authority.

H. Speight,
BSc, FICE, FIWES, Director of Resource Planning, Southern Water Authority

### Chapter 2: The Water Industry from 1974

Contributed by: S. F. White,
BSc, FICE, FIWES, Adviser, Policy Division, National Water Council.

Assisted by:

G. E. Bowyer,
BSc, FICE, FIWES, Director of Operations, Anglian Water Authority

R. Y. Bromell,
FICE, FIWES, Director of Operations, Severn-Trent Water Authority.

G. Cole,
BSc, MICE, MIWES, Chief Engineer, Ministry of Agriculture, Fisheries and Food

H. Cronshaw,
BSc, FICE, Chief Engineer, Directorate of Engineering, Welsh Office.

R. L. Harrison,
BSc, FICE, FIWES, retired; formerly Director of Operations, North West Water Authority

W. M. Jollans,
MA, FICE, FIWES, Director of Operations, Yorkshire Water Authority.

J. O. Thorburn,
BSc, MICE, MIWES, Assistant Chief Engineer, Scottish Development Department

J. A. Young,
FICE, FIWES, Director of Operations, Wessex Water Authority

### Chapter 3: Water Law

The section on the water law which applies in England and Wales was contributed by the following members of the Legal Department of the Severn-Trent Water Authority:

I. C. Sinclair,
LLB, Solicitor, Assistant Director of Administration

J. T. Rhead,
LLB, Senior Solicitor

S. J. Sullivan,
LLB, Assistant Solicitor

Assisted by:        R. B. Richardson,     LLB, Area Solicitor
                    Miss L. J. Fenner,    LLB, Assistant Solicitor
                    P. R. Craggs,         Senior Legal Executive
                    J. D. H. Broughton,   Legal Executive

The section on the position in Scotland was contributed by:
                    J. P. Williamson,     BSc, FICE, FIWES, Director, Water
                                          Supply Services Department, Lothian
                                          Regional Council.

The section on the position in Northern Ireland was contributed by:
                    H. Stevenson,         Water Service of the Department of the
                                          Environment for Northern Ireland.

## Chapter 4: Economics

Contributed by: G. L. Davies,            BSc, MICE, MIWES, Group Manager,
                                         Directorate of Operations, Southern Water
                                         Authority.

                R. N. Balmer,            BSc, MICE, MIWES, Co-ordinator,
                                         Directorate of Operations, Severn-Trent
                                         Water Authority.

                R. Banerji,              BA, MA, MBA, Chief Economist,
                                         Directorate of Resource Planning, Southern
                                         Water Authority.

Assisted by:    D. L. Walker,            MA, MSc, MICE, Deputy Director
                                         General, National Water Council.

## Chapter 5: Finance

Contributed by: R. C. North,             VRD, FCA, IPFA, ATII, Director of
                                         Finance, Wessex Water Authority.

Assisted by:    A. Routledge,            BSc, Administrative Assistant to the
                                         Director  of  Finance,  Wessex  Water
                                         Authority

## Chapter 6: Management

Contributed by: J. S. M. Willis,         BSc, FICE, FIWES, Divisional Secretary,
                                         Tame Division, Severn-Trent Water
                                         Authority.

Assisted by:    H. Speight,              BSc, FICE, FIWES, Director of Resource
                                         Planning, Southern Water Authority.

## Chapter 7: Research

Contributed by: V. K. Collinge,          MScEng, DIC, ACGI, MICE, MIWES,
                                         Director (Medmenham Laboratory), Water
                                         Research Centre.

Assisted by:    D. G. Miller,            BSc, PhD, MIChemE, FIWES, Research
                                         Co-ordinator, Water Research Centre.

                J. Moss,                 MA, PhD, Assistant Research Co-
                                         ordinator, Water Research Centre.

## Index

Compiled by: W. M. Lewis, FRIC, FIWES

# PREFACE

Both the former Institution of Water Engineers and the Society for Water Treatment and Examination held a well-earned reputation as learned societies responsible for the publication of authoritative works on water technology and science. In 1975 the common interests of these bodies led to their amalgamation and The Institution of Water Engineers and Scientists was formed. With the extensive restructuring of the public bodies involved in water management over much of the British Isles now largely completed, this Institution has again entered the book-publishing field with a wide-ranging series under the general title *"Water Practice Manuals"*.

This will appear, over a period of several years, as a series of separate books. Each will be complete in itself and will be written by teams having special knowledge and experience within the chosen subject. Where necessary the resources available within the membership of the Institution have been reinforced by specialist contributors from outside.

The books will deal mainly with the engineering and scientific elements concerned with the water cycle but they will also focus attention on subjects which, particularly in England and Wales, have now become associated with the overall management of that cycle. In recording what has become, or is likely to become, accepted current practice the books will not be confined entirely to British experience. Where relevant, references will be made to overseas practice and, in particular, to thinking and developments within the EEC.

It is appropriate, because of the far-reaching changes which have taken place in recent years, that the first book in the new series should cover the newly evolved structure and management of the water industry in Britain. It will be of interest to all seeking a working knowledge of an industry whose activities are basic to modern civilization.

The reorganization which was brought about in England and Wales by the implementation of the Water Act 1973, has created world wide interest. British practice has, over many years past, influenced the construction, operation, and management of public health engineering works overseas and the book will thus have an appeal outside the British Isles.

In due course the whole series of books will form a basic library for those concerned with the technology and science of water. Individual books in the series will attract readers both inside and outside the water industry. Despite the introduction of the new books, much of the material contained in the Institution's existing three volume *"Manual of British Water Engineering Practice"* remains valid and copies of that Manual will continue on sale until present stocks are exhausted.

# NOTE ON THE INSTITUTION OF WATER ENGINEERS AND SCIENTISTS

The Institution was established as The British Association of Waterworks Engineers in 1896 and was incorporated in 1911 as The Institution of Water Engineers. On 2nd January 1975 its name was change to The Institution of Water Engineers and Scientists preliminary to the Institution and the Society for Water Treatment and Examination amalgamating on 1st September 1975. The combined Institution now has a membership of over 5250.

The *objects* of the Institution are set out in its Memorandum of Association. In summary these are:

1. To advance water engineering and science and education therein.
2. To promote study and research work in water engineering and science and to publish the results thereof for the public benefit.

"Water engineering and science" means the application of engineering or scientific knowledge or skill to the supply of water, the management of rivers, the treatment of sewage and its disposal, and the control of pollution in relation to water.

The membership of the Institution comprises engineers and scientists, including chemists, bacteriologists, geologists, hydrologists and others concerned with the water cycle. Only persons with appropriate professional and technological experience can be admitted to corporate membership. Water engineers must be chartered engineers (most are chartered civil engineers) and water scientists must be graduates of a United Kingdom or Irish degree-awarding body. Overseas qualifications are judged on an equivalent standard.

Most members of the Institution in the United Kingdom work for public or quasi-public authorities. In England and Wales, these are the National Water Council, the ten Regional Water Authorities and the statutory water companies; in Scotland, the nine Regional and three Islands Councils together with the Central Scotland Water Development Board; and in Northern Ireland, the Department of the Environment for Northern Ireland (Water Services Branch).

Other members work in central government, research and teaching establishments, or as consulting engineers. Some members are concerned with the construction of civil engineering works as contractors, or as manufacturers of equipment such as pumps or treatment plant.

About 20 per cent of the members of the Institution are overseas, either because they are citizens of overseas countries or because they are working there on secondment from the United Kingdom.

The main function of the Institution is the provision of learned society activities, i.e. the sharing of experience and the dissemination of knowledge through meetings and publications. In the United Kingdom and the Republic of Ireland there are seven Local and two Specialist Sections, each with its own programme of papers and visits to works. In addition the Institution holds two General Meetings each year and organizes symposia.

The publications of the Institution, besides this new range of Water Practice Manuals, include a Journal (published six times a year), proceedings of symposia, and various reports.

# CONTENTS

**Chapter 3**—*continued*

**Chapter 6**—*continued*

**Chapter 7.  Research**

Chapter 1

# HISTORICAL DEVELOPMENT OF THE WATER INDUSTRY

## 1. MAN AND NATURE

THE selection of a vantage point from which to review the history and structure of what is now the British water industry does not appear to present problems. It would be equally appropriate to focus either on the physical role of the many corporate bodies discharging responsibilities prior to the 1974 reorganization in England and Wales, or on the professional disciplines and administrative systems which are themselves already been integrated over many years within those bodies. Both are relevant to the purposes of this, the first book in a series dealing with the science and technology of water-related matters, but it is to water itself that the reader's attention will first be directed. In more specific terms that direction should be to the water cycle and to the interaction of the pressures which it places on man and that man, in turn, places on it. That cycle, although long recognized and hitherto understood largely in relation to it component parts, had never previously been treated as an administrative entity. As will be explained in the book, detailed arrangements for administrative control are not identical across Britain. The system introduced by the Water Act 1973 has, however, emphasized the relationship of each part of the water cycle to the other parts, irrespective of there being all-purpose regional water authorities only in England and Wales.

If the oceans and ice-covered land masses are regarded as containing the world's water supply, then those primary expressions of natural energy, sun and wind, are the motive forces which distribute that supply throughout the atmosphere to fall as rain and, subject to the various uses and diversions made by man, to return again in due course to the sea. The distribution process, although governed by natural laws, is more capricious than a cursory appraisal of typically British weather may suggest. Extremes of flood and drought (coupled with significant differences in the location of either within the relatively small geographical area of the British Isles) have led to systems and procedures being devised for the better control of this complex natural system, which is the very basis of modern civilization.

In earlier ages, when population was restricted in comparison with present numbers and distribution, and when the water-based hygiene of some of the older civilizations awaited rediscovery, it was the over-abundance of water which produced Britain's first water-based administrative arrangements. As a result, the present day internal drainage board becomes the oldest surviving relic of the earliest kind of democratic institution responsible for water management, its lineage going back at least as far as the Lords of the Level. Their duty was to maintain the sea walls and drainage systems of Romney Marsh, an area of low-lying land in South-East England built up, in historical times, by the deposition of sediments over an originally tidal area. The lords' bailiff and jurors were a properly constituted drainage authority dating from 1232, financed by levying scots on the landowners (hence the expression "to get off scot free"). Internal drainage boards now exercise powers derived both from Parliament itself and by the common consent of those whose interests they serve and, whatever may befall their independent status in some future water reorganization, they epitomize man's corporate response to the need to control the immediate environment for his own use and safety.

A detailed understanding of the natural laws and forces required to secure effective technical performance necessarily had to await the arrival of the nineteenth and twentieth centuries. However, the assumption of specific responsibilities for drainage concentrated the available knowledge and skills of each succeeding age and thus began to create an expertise in the technology and finance of water management.

With the passage of time this expertise became both deeper and wider and, inevitably, specializations arose. In embarking on the publication of the Water Practice Manuals, The Institution of Water Engineers and Scientists, following the example set by its two predecessor bodies, is seeking to distil both knowledge and experience in a way which will enable those involved in the now several distinct fields of practice to know more of their own field and to understand something of what is happening in others.

## 2. WATERCOURSES AND HISTORY

Having used land drainage as an example of man's response to external factors, it will be appropriate to continue to set the scene by looking further at this specific aspect of the water cycle. The flow of water in surface channels, be they known locally as brooks, streams, burns, becks, dykes, rills, rivulets, or rivers, represents the "return" part of the water cycle. The "outward" part is represented by evaporation from the sea and the subsequent precipitation of rain and snow.

The surface and sub-surface watercourses so created by countless years of water flow provide both a source of water (more or less capricious in the sense that renewal takes place regularly, but not necessarily in a dependable manner) and an inevitable channel for carrying away used water and waste products. In passing, it is relevant to comment that the complexities of modern civilization have produced numerous substances which, should they escape in any way, must find their way to those watercourses as the force of gravity urges them inexorably seaward. The watercourses, particularly those on the land surface, also provide a habitat for aquatic life (from the simple algae to the higher orders of fish and aquatic mammals). In earlier days they also provided the nucleus of a transport system which, in fact, continues in existence in some localities to the present day. The history of Britain has been dependent on its watercourses and the water cycle therefore helps to identify those pages relevant to an appraisal of the past structure and management of the British water industry.

## 3. INDUSTRY AND URBAN GROWTH

The breezes of change which ushered in the Industrial Revolution were fanned to gale force by the development of canals and the utilization of both hot (the steam engine) and cold (the water wheel) water to give power to lift and to move and to pump and to manufacture. Villages grew to towns and towns into cities and no longer were the consequences of ill-considered water supply and sewage disposal arrangements confined in their effects to small numbers of people living in restricted and separated localities. Whether or not the cause was simply to ensure that the work-force necessary for industrial attainment remained alive and healthy enough to be able to work, there is no doubt that a concern for public health was made inevitable by the Industrial Revolution. The effect, however, was to focus attention on what could be done with water courses by way of providing water supplies and on what was happening to those watercourses because of their natural drainage and conveyance function. None of the established institutions was equipped to deal with the sudden burden placed upon them and most of them virtually collapsed under the strain. At their height, epidemics of water-borne disease were killing more people than all other causes of death combined. The city fathers of Liverpool were faced with the need to secure pure water supplies and to initiate a system of main drainage. In both matters they responded to the challenge and, going further, achieved the distinction of appointing the world's first Medical Officer of Health.

Parliament had to learn how Governments might best play a legislative role in the new situation which had arisen and whilst the first national census in 1801 gave a numerical datum it was almost half a century before the Waterworks Clauses Act 1847 and the Public Health Act 1848 provided a legislative foundation. Heading the march to acquire the necessary technology to deal with the situation came newly formed mechanics institutes and schools of applied mechanics, the first of which was founded in Glasgow in 1823. Such learned societies as the Royal Society, the Institution of Civil Engineers, the British Association for the Advancement of Science, the Institution of Mechanical Engineers and the British Meteorological Society all reflected man's desire for a better understanding of the forces which influenced his living conditions and his economic prosperity.

## 4. PUBLIC WATER SUPPLY

### EARLY ACTIONS

No community, be it farmstead, hamlet, town or city can exist without a dependable supply of pure water. Such a supply is a universal necessity, and for that reason the history of water supply will be the first element of the water cycle to be studied in any detail in this chapter. The engineer and the artisan were the founding fathers of modern water supply and they have now been joined by possibly a dozen or more other professions. They, however, were the first to design, construct, and operate the early works which brought into the urban home a supply of water which was adequate in quantity, reliable in quality, dependable in availability, and acceptable in cost.

A supply of this kind is so vital that, throughout English history, the most powerful contemporary authority has assumed ultimate control of water and has devolved that power in specific ways in relation to limited and closely defined functions. Kings granted charters to individuals, towns, and ecclesiastical bodies. In London, an early example was the granting of powers of water abstraction and use to the Manor of Hyde (now Hyde Park). Drake, seeking water for use in the dockyard at Plymouth, was granted powers to construct his now famous Leat to carry supplies from upland areas in the hinterland. The town of Shrewsbury was granted water rights in 1550 to bring water to Conduit Head and there are many other examples of the royal purse benefitting from the display of private initiative in responding to the need of the growing communities for a good water supply.

As time went on this initiative, now influenced by the early general legislation about water supply, began to be concentrated largely in the hands of private companies and a number of municipalities. The role of the public bodies expanded considerably in the latter half of the nineteenth century, many private companies either failing to provide satisfactory supplies or being prepared to sell their interests to the municipalities (whose own powers and responsibilities were growing) in whose areas they were operating. Other companies built up their enterprises and, with the passage of time, secured a significant proportion of the potable water supply market.

## REGROUPING

After the 1939-45 World War successive governments in Britain followed a policy of encouraging the amalgamation of water supply undertakings to provide a stronger technological and financial base from which to meet ever rising demands for water. In England and Wales there were over 2 000 water supply undertakers in 1915, but this number had been reduced to less than 950 in 1950 by amalgamation and the formation of water boards (of this latter number about 124 were water companies). In 1968 there were 276 undertakers, and in 1973 immediately prior to the reorganization of the industry there were 187 (including 30 water companies). This changing picture of the growth of large water supply units reflected, as already indicated, the increasingly sophisticated technology and management skills being called for. It was unfortunate that there was virtually no corresponding movement in the sewerage and sewage disposal side of the water cycle where, at the time of the 1974 reorganization, this service was in the hands of almost 1 400 municipal authorities of various kinds.

## ENGINEERING WORKS

That, however, is a matter which can be returned to later and it will be relevant now to think of the physical works which were being constructed for water supply purposes during the latter part of the nineteenth century and the early years of the twentieth. The construction of the canal system in the earliest days of the Industrial Revolution created a need for impounding reservoirs to make good the loss of water from the canals by lockage and leakage. Such reservoirs were relatively small, but so were many of the water supply impoundments built in upland catchments where rainfall was usually abundant and each succeeding winter's rain was generally more than sufficient to achieve refilling before the onset of the summer. In the British Isles 141 dams over 15 m high, many of which continue in service, were built between 1850 and 1900, and a further 114 in the succeeding 50 years. That at Vyrnwy is noteworthy as being possibly the first masonry dam to be wholly dependent on a stress analysis design which predicted no tension arising within the dam structure.

## LESS ENGINEERING

It is salutary to think that the middle of the twentieth century saw a change in the public attitude towards the engineering works associated with water supplies. Whilst it was acknowledged that credit was due for the public health benefits which flowed from wholesome piped supplies, a feeling began to grow that the water undertakings were fueling their aspirations with the dictum that if a reliable and wholesome supply was a good thing then a reliable, wholesome, and abundant supply must be better still. No longer could the water engineer prescribe his mixture of works construction (particularly impounding works) to be taken "as before" . . . only in larger doses!

This same situation has applied in other service industries. When most of the population already have electricity . . . or enough roads for their motor-cars . . . or the weekly magic of making their refuse and rubbish disappear from their own immediate environment, there is an increasing opposition to new power stations, or motorways, or refuse transfer stations. Once man has acquired a satisfactory domestic environment he begins to ask whether, in regard to heavy engineering works, enough is enough and, indeed, to attempt to define just how much he regards as enough. Opposition to a project by those likely to be dispossessed by its construction has long been a feature of major schemes; but a changing climate of opinion has introduced a new opposition lobby, seeking to protect the environment (as well as the individual) from both engineering works and their physical effects. In the future the environmental impact statement could well become as significant a preliminary to works construction as is the site survey.

## MORE RECREATION

A growing affluence highlights the fact that, in earlier days, with a relatively immobile population, upland reservoirs were capable of producing a bacteriologically satisfactory water. Further protection was often secured by the water industry purchasing the catchment area and so controlling the farming practices there. This was also the era of the "Private—Keep Out" philosophy which, reinforced by forbidding fencing, separated the public from physical contact with their water supply until it emerged from their taps. The increasing mobility of the public has changed this and the pressures for recreation in the countryside led to changes in thought in the 1950s and 1960s, and there is now a positive duty on the new regional water authorities to provide, whenever practicable, for recreation on reservoirs and their catchments.

## WATER TREATMENT AND PUBLIC HEALTH

Knowledge about the treatment of water before use grew with the passage of time and it is salutary to consider that the slow sand filter (an effective, if costly in terms of the land area required, means of removing bacteria) was already in regular use for water treatment before bacteria had been recognized as the cause of water-borne disease. With the arrival of the twentieth century, however, advances in methods of water treatment became more dependent on applied chemistry (and, latterly, on electronic techniques) than on advances in civil and mechanical engineering. Routine chemical analysis of London's water began in 1858 and bacteriological examination in 1885, the year in which Theodor Escherich identified the colon bacillus which now bears his name and provides a criterion by which routine water samples are judged. The need both to mechanize the laborious process of filter cleaning and to reduce the area of land required for the construction of plant having a given throughput led to the adoption both of rapid filtration (with the need to add chemical coagulants to the water) and, later, of preliminary sedimentation to remove suspended matter from the water being treated. Bolton was possibly the first undertaking to use sulphate of alumina as a coagulant and the heyday for the first time installation of pressure filters was in the years leading up to the outbreak of the First World War in 1914. During the present century the chemical approach to water treatment has grown apace with other compounds being used as coagulants and coagulant aids. The lime process and ion exchange have been introduced to soften waters whilst activated carbon, ozone, ammonia, and chlorine dioxide have been adopted in response, *inter alia*, to the need to overcome problems caused by tastes in the water passing into supply.

The dramatic effects on the incidence of water-borne disease which followed firstly the adoption of filtration and, secondly, the introduction of chlorination need no elaboration here. It is interesting, however, in passing to reflect that the chemical which has produced the greatest impact on the purity of water supplies in Britain has been chlorine, both acting as a disinfecting agent on its own and in combination with other elements. It was first used continuously in Lincoln to sterilize contaminated river water in 1904, such use being followed soon after in Shrewsbury for the supply being drawn from the river Severn. Subsequently, the techniques of chloramination and of superchlorination and dechlorination became established. When the Second World War broke out in 1939 chlorination of all drinking water was quietly instituted by the Government and is now of universal application in disinfecting water supplies.

During the 1950s moves were made to add fluorine to potable supplies on the basis that a carefully controlled amount would improve the dental health of the nation's children. Hitherto, chemicals had been added to water to protect the consumer from diseases which he could not avoid if the water he drank was contaminated. Ethical considerations were introduced, however, by the thought of adding a chemical which would reach every water consumer irrespective of his having passed the age at which its presence was believed to be effective in relation to dental decay. The fact that some water supplies already contained at least the stipulated fluorine content did little to resolve the situation. The introduction of fluorine as a routine part of water treatment has been heavily influenced by political pressures on the (health authority) bodies which must make the actual decision to fluoridate. To this extent the water undertakers stand aside from the controversy despite being the bodies which would, on a rechargeable basis, actually carry out the fluoridation process at their treatment works.

In general terms the benefits of adequate and safe supplies of potable water were brought largely to urban areas but, during the course of the Second World War, Parliament looked forward to the time when the return of peace would provide an opportunity of extending the public piped supplies into country areas. Legislative steps had, in fact, been taken in 1934 to improve rural water supplies, and the basis of the Rural Water Supplies and Sewerage Act 1944 was a system of grants which recognized the disparity in cost of distribution mains (and sewers for the used water) in urban, and in rural, areas. Accomplishment can be gauged by the fact that it was estimated that the regional water authorities became responsible for supplying 99 per cent of the dwellings in their regions with water whilst 95 per cent were, in addition to industrial dischargers, connected to public sewerage systems.

## 5. SEWERAGE AND SEWAGE DISPOSAL

### THE EARLY SITUATION

Sewerage and sewage disposal proved in 1974, with a number of notable exceptions, to be the cinderella service of the water industry and five years after the reorganization much has been done, and much still remains to be done, to rectify the legacy. The 1 366 local authorities previously responsible for this service had long since learnt that there was neither profit nor votes in sewage disposal. Nor had there been the incentive to amalgamate sewerage and sewage disposal bodies in the way that occurred in the water supply sector. Relatively few (27) joint boards existed and most were of many years standing, although such organizations were still being created only a few years before the 1974 reorganization.

The availability of piped supplies of water inevitably increases the pressures for the provision of a water-borne sewerage system, and the first areas to develop water supplies thus became the first to face up to the problems and costs of sewerage and sewage disposal. The earliest methods of disposal adopted by the local boards of health (using powers given by the Public Health Act 1848) involved either land treatment (the sewage farm) or disposal, with degrees of pretreatment ranging from virtually non-existent to elementary, to rivers, estuaries or to the sea. A Royal

Commission on Sewage Disposal was set up in 1898 and made its final report in 1915; its best remembered contribution possibly being the 30:20 standard for discharges made to rivers. This standard has continued to be applied ever since, although thinking changed during the middle years of the present century to recognize that an arbitrary standard is no substitute for the *ad hoc* consideration of the actual effects of each discharge on the river into which it is made.

## TECHNIQUES

Sewage treament (in contrast with all but the slow sand treatment of potable water) is heavily dependent on biological action, and there has been a gradual change from land treatment to more intensive methods. The contact bed, a tank filled with clinker or coke and operated on a fill-and-draw principle, was the forerunner of the biological filter which consists of a ventilated free-draining bed of media onto which the settled sewage is distributed by mechanical means. During the 1930s effort was directed at improving the efficiency of the biological filter and the recirculation of effluent and alternating double filtration were introduced at a number of sewage disposal works. In more recent years synthetic filter media have been developed and have found an application in the treatment of strong effluents.

In 1913 Ardern and Lockett, working at Manchester and using coarse bubble aeration of settled sewage, developed what is now known as the activated sludge process. In 1916 the first full-scale plant using diffused air was installed at Worcester, whilst the first full-scale mechanical aerator using a paddle unit was installed at Sheffield four years later and in 1921 a cone aerator was installed at the Bury sewage disposal works. These processes led to improved effluents, but the need to secure yet higher effluent qualities led to the development of tertiary forms of treatment (settlement being the primary treatment and filtration or aeration the secondary stage) such as microstraining, grass plot irrigation, and sand filtration.

## SLUDGE DISPOSAL

The development of more intensive treatment methods introduced (as it did with water supply) the problems associated with disposal of the resultant sludge. The sludge arising from the settlement and aeration processes of sewage treatment is some 95 per cent liquid and still presents disposal problems even after it has been digested and dewatered. Digestion results in the production of methane gas (and provides a less offensive sludge) and the anaerobic sludge digestion process was developed in the 1920s, with the world's first plant being installed in Birmingham. Mechanical dewatering by such processes as pressing, vacuum filtration, and centrifuging has largely replaced the time-honoured method of leaving the wet sludge to dry out into cake form on beds which, of necessity, are subject to the vagaries of the prevailing weather conditions.

Disposal of the sludge (in liquid or dry form) to land has agricultural attractions, provided that the levels of toxic metals within the sludge are acceptable and the sludge does not carry organisms capable of affecting animals subsequently grazing the land. Recent years have seen the growth of more extensive and more rigid methods of controlling discharges of trade effluent to the public sewers, and effort is increasingly being directed towards achieving again the principle of what took place in the original sewage farms, i.e. the return to the land of the nutrients in sewage.

Sludge derived from some disposal works on the mainland has for many years been disposed of by being taken out to sea for dumping either by boat or by submerged pipeline. Such disposal is now subject to the issue of licences by central government, and concern for the environment coupled with pressures to protect fisheries has led to the imposition of increasingly stringent conditions. In recent years the incineration of sewage sludge has tended to fall out of favour, although new incinerators continue to be installed. This method may prove to be an effective method of disposing of the sludge from urban concentrations along the coastline, should dumping at sea be subjected to further restriction.

## DISPOSAL TO THE SEA AND ENVIRONMENTAL CONSIDERATIONS

Disposal of sewage direct to the sea after only preliminary treatment removes the sludge disposal problems otherwise arising at inland works. However, the methods considered to be satisfactory for discharges to coastal waters earlier in the present century have created their own problems in relation to bacterial pollution and the deposit of sewage solids on nearby beaches, and have led to public misapprehension that all discharges of sewage to the sea are harmful unless they have been fully treated. Modern techniques for the construction of long sea outfalls, coupled with detailed scientific studies of the movement and dispersion of the discharge, make disposal to the sea an economic and environmentally attractive alternative to full treatment.

Reference to a growing concern for the protection of the environment serves to emphasize the change which has taken place since it became evident that the attitudes prevalent at the time of the Industrial Revolution could not be permitted to continue. In 1847 the practice of permitting the drainage from middens and cesspools to pass into surface water sewers was legalized and this decision did nothing to combat the growing pollution of the country's rivers. An Act of 1852 forbade abstraction of water for public supply from the Thames below Teddington weir, and in 1865 a Rivers Commission was appointed to look into means for preventing the then prevalent pollution of rivers. The Thames was about this time in a particularly bad state and was so evident by its stench that sheets drenched in disinfectant were hung over the windows of the Houses of Parliament. Particular attention was paid by the Commission to the Thames, Mersey, Aire, Calder, Severn, and Taff as the then worst polluted rivers. The resulting Rivers Pollution Prevention Acts of 1876 and 1893, however, largely disregarded the Commission's conclusion that pollution prevention and the effective management of rivers were dependent on entire river basins being placed under the control of bodies hampered by none of the artificial boundaries of local government.

## 6. RIVER MANAGEMENT

Administration of the new legislation was put into the hands of local authorities which found themselves obliged by the circumstances to create *ad hoc* bodies such as the West Riding of Yorkshire River Board, the River Dee Joint Committee, and the Lancashire River Board. The Conservators of the River Thames, by then some 40 years old, and the Lee Conservancy Board became responsible for pollution prevention, land drainage, fisheries, navigation, water abstraction and (for the Lee) flood prevention also. It is of interest to note that the Royal Commission on Sewage Disposal and the 1902 Royal Commission on Salmon Fisheries both urged the formation of local river boards under a central administrative authority. That end was slow in coming. Catchment Boards set up in England and Wales under an Act of 1930 exercised pollution control and certain drainage functions and in due course the River Boards Act 1948 created bodies charged with responsibility for some (i.e. pollution prevention, land drainage, and fisheries) of the functions necessary for the proper management of river systems. The Water Resources Act 1963 changed the

River Boards into River Authorities (amalgamating a number of the Boards in the process) and added the function of controlling the water resources of their catchments. It was not until 1973, however, that legislation created truly all-purpose river basin authorities in England and Wales. It would be wrong to suppose, however, that improvement in the quality of rivers was not being achieved before that date. Foundations were being laid, particularly in the 1960s, on which to base the new thinking and action of the all-purpose authorities. ✗

## 7. POLLUTION PREVENTION

The pollution prevention powers available to the River Boards and River Authorities stem from a series of Acts passed between 1951 and 1961, which required consents to be secured before discharges could be made to rivers and, for new discharges, to tidal waters. The principles of the earlier Act were reflected in legislation covering Scotland and the Border Rivers. Conditions attached to the consents were seen as a way of ensuring that discharges did not overtax the natural purification capability of the receiving waters. In the event, however, there was a reluctance (which if not actually encouraged was connived at by central government in times of economic strain) to take enforcement action against local authorities as dischargers of sewage effluent except in the more flagrant cases. To some extent, this was a political reflection of the recurring need to impose restraints on public spending, but the end-product was that of passing on to the regional water authorities a number of sewage disposal works which were either incapable of meeting their consent conditions or which could only be made capable by the injection of capital, expertise and enthusiasm.

Despite this, the decade of pollution prevention legislation did enable a substantial foundation of control procedures to be built in preparation for the powers given by the Control of Pollution Act 1974, which, at the time of writing (April 1979), is becoming available to the regional water authorities in instalments.

## 8. LAND DRAINAGE

It would be misleading to pass too quickly over the other functions of land drainage and fisheries which featured as part of the responsibilities of the river boards and river authorities. Reference was made earlier to the long-established importance of land drainage which, in the contemporary context, is related to protecting low-lying land from inundation either by freshwater or by the sea. Land drainage works may therefore include sea walls and groynes, together with sluices to keep out the tide, but the protection of the coastline against erosion as such is the responsibility of the respective maritime local authorities. In specific locations the distinction may not be readily apparent, but the river engineer has developed his own expertise (and jargon) drawing upon the centuries when manpower, coupled with the forces of nature themselves, was the only physical resource available to combat flooding. The advent of mechanical plant has, as with other branches of civil engineering, vastly increased the potential for land drainage improvement works and their importance to the national economy has been reflected in the manner in which substantial grant income was (and still is) made available by Government.

Increasingly, urban development with its preponderance of impermeable areas has led to higher rates of flood run-off and the need either to construct river channel improvement works or to ensure that washlands can accommodate flood waters temporarily without risk to property or life. Earlier land drainage legislation has now been consolidated in the Land Drainage Act 1976 (see also Chapter 3).

## 9. FISHERIES

Reference is made briefly later to fishing as a recreational use of water, but it is self-evident to state that fishing is dependent on the existence of a fishery, i.e. waters free of pollution and capable not only of sustaining fish life but also of providing the environment in which fish will breed and grow. In such a fishery the laws of nature prevail and the art and science of fishery management imposes on the natural situation an artificial one in which particular species of fish are encouraged in order that the angler may be able to find satisfaction in his sport. Some fisheries are operated for commercial purposes, particularly for the netting of salmon and sea trout in estuarial waters, and the rights and privileges involved can be of considerable antiquity.

The responsibility for fisheries exercised by the various statutory bodies which feature in this review mirrors two aspects of contemporary (in regard to the framing of the relevant legislation) society, i.e. the value of game fisheries as an interest attached to land ownership, and the way in which fish act as a natural system for monitoring pollution. Both aspects emphasize the importance of clean rivers and both are supported by the need to regulate fishing methods and to control pollution. Earlier legislation covering the period from 1923 to 1972 has been consolidated in the Salmon and Freshwater Fisheries Act 1975, and, whilst brief reference has already been made to pollution control legislation, detailed aspects of the legislation are contained in Chapter 3.

## 10. TECHNOLOGICAL CHANGE

Steam power gave way to the electric motor for water supply purposes in 1894, and the combination of electric power and the centrifugal pump transformed the ability to move water effectively from place to place. Less striking as a technological development, but equally essential to the controlled movement of water, are the developments made in the materials used for pipes (developments which owe much to the corresponding need in the gas and oil industries to move their products along pipelines also). Cast iron, spun iron, steel, concrete (and its reinforcement variants), asbestos cement, plastic, light gauge copper, and stainless steel have all made their appearance and, in conjunction with equally numerous alternative methods of jointing, have given the movement of water a regional connotation.

The engineering structures associated with the movement and control of water have been influenced firstly by the introduction of reinforced concrete and, subsequently, by the development of pre and post-stressing techniques. Earth movement by mechanical plant, whether for the cutting of drainage ditches or the creation of reservoir embankments, has moved from one dimension to another of completely different magnitude in less than half a century. In less than half that time, however, developments in the twin fields of telemetry and electronic computation and control have introduced a new era not only in water supply and sewage disposal but in the control and management of river catchments generally.

The growth of chemical knowledge and analytical techniques has been a significant factor in the treatment of both clean and dirty water. The longstanding need to produce potable water from the sea has led to techniques of desalination which, if applied in few places in Britain, have led elsewhere to the desert blossoming and supporting a life-style differing significantly from that existing there for centuries previously.

## 11. RESOURCE TECHNOLOGY AND DROUGHTS

The effect of droughts upon reservoir yield has turned the 19th century predictions of dry weather flows into the present day understanding of hydrology and hydrogeology. With that understanding the last 30 years have seen the unconventional firstly become acceptable and then become conventional itself. The regulation of rivers by releases from surface storage and the use of groundwater to augment river flows are no longer unusual. The need over the years to introduce an increasing number of different kinds of water supply sources has brought with it the attendant ability to use them in conjunction with one another and so secure increased yields.

Nevertheless, droughts have had their effects on the ability to maintain water supplies and the analysis of their nature and frequency has introduced new thinking about the standards of reliability to be expected and paid for by the customers of the water industry. Droughts such as that in 1933-34 and 1975-76 were marked by an absence of winter rainfall and had extensive effects, whereas a shortage of summer rain (such as occurred in 1959) could be accommodated with little more than inconvenience. The actual impact of a drought on the water consumer, however, has varied within Britain simply because rainfall deficiency has not been universal nor (as between succeeding droughts) has it necessarily been felt in the same geographical areas. At such times not all water supply units have, in fact, been affected when their resources were at the point where augmentation was already being contemplated. There have, of course, been instances where augmentation had long been sought, but long opposed for a variety of reasons.

Government reaction to the effects of drought and to the importance of piped water has been marked by the introduction of legislation to meet special needs with special powers. Indeed, had it not been for the ability to "think big" provided by the 1974 reorganization in England and Wales the 1976 drought would have affected many more communities than it did. Nevertheless, the severity of the effects of that drought were seen by Government as calling for the introduction of such sweeping measures as were contained in the Drought Act 1976.

## 12. RECREATION

Possibly the one feature in the water scene which changed particularly rapidly in the 15 or so years preceding the recent reorganization was the growth of organized recreation on reservoirs and adjoining areas. Some water supply undertakers had long permitted fishing in their impounding reservoirs but recognition now had to be given to the popularity of dinghy sailing, the growing ownership of motor vehicles, and the increasing call for leisure facilities generally. This led to new thinking about the compatibility of public use of the water surface before public consumption of the water itself. The 1973 legislation opened the recreational door wider in requiring provision to be made for the use of what had been widely referred to as "the fourth dimension" in the gestation period of that legislation. Navigation (for recreational purposes) had been a feature of a number of rivers (notably the Thames) for many years and the natural association of rivers with fishing was, of course, another recreational use of long standing. Consideration of the relationship of fisheries to fishing introduces questions as to whether a good fishery leads to active fishing, or whether the active presence of a body of anglers introduces pressures to maintain, develop, and improve the fishery. Whatever may be the correct answer (if, indeed, there is such an answer), the long-standing importance of fisheries has already been referred to. King Henry VIII was reputed to have a liking for chub as a delicacy and in the middle ages a number of deeds of apprenticeship limited the frequency with which a master might serve his apprentices with salmon!

## 13. SUMMARY

This review commenced with a reference to the antiquity of the administrative bodies responsible for land drainage matters. It is appropriate, therefore, that it should conclude with a brief summary, covering some 50 years, of the various bodies which have now given way to the present structure within the water industry. Water supply was, as has been stated, partly the province of private companies and partly that of public bodies of one form or another. Both decreased in number and grew in size with the passage of the years. Sewerage and sewage disposal was entirely municipal, whilst responsibility for land drainage, pollution control and fisheries lay, again, with public bodies of various forms. The gradual concentration of "river" functions through catchment (1930) to river (1948) boards and then to river authorities (1963) marked a progression towards the integration of all water functions on a catchment basis, which was accomplished in England and Wales in 1973. In Scotland a somewhat different structure (in which full control of all functions by a single catchment body does not feature) has arisen in response to a background reflecting less acute pressures on water resources. Yet another background situation has led to yet another variation in the administrative structure adopted in Northern Ireland, where water matters are under overall control by Government. Details of the situation in Scotland and Northern Ireland are featured in Chapter 2 and it is sufficient here simply to reiterate what was said at the start of this chapter, i.e. that it is to the water cycle and to the interaction of the pressures that it places on man and man places on it that we must look when considering the aquatic significance of what has happened during the past century and a half.

Chapter 2

# THE WATER INDUSTRY FROM 1974

## 1. PREAMBLE

THIS chapter is an account of the water industry's organizational structure in the spring of 1978, four years after the implementation of the Water Act 1973. It deals with the structure of water authorities in England and Wales against the background of the Ogden Report, published in June 1973, which formed the basis of the initial top structure of most of the water authorities. Since 1974 several of the authorities have made, or are considering, structural changes of some significance in the light of their experience, and the reader should bear this in mind. It will be some time before they will have fully settled down. Nevertheless, the conclusion can be drawn that the Ogden recommendations have generally been implemented and the water authority structure hereafter described is not likely to be uncharacteristic for some years to come.

The chapter also deals with the role of the water companies and local authorities in relation to the water authorities; it deals with the structure at national level and with the very different structures in Scotland and Northern Ireland. In some respects the water authorities in England and Wales represent a compromise between the local authority orientated structure in Scotland and the fully nationalized structure in Northern Ireland.

Throughout the chapter references to the Secretary of State mean in England the Secretary of State for the Department of the Environment (DoE), and, in Wales, the Secretary of State of Wales. References to the Minister mean the Minister of Agriculture, Fisheries and Food (MAFF).

## 2. WATER AUTHORITIES—ENGLAND AND WALES

### WATER AUTHORITIES—STATUS

The water authorities are unlike any other bodies in the U.K. Although they are independent statutory organizations fully equipped with powers to carry out their functions, in some ways they have similarities to the nationalized industries. As with the electricity and gas industries the chairman and some of the members are direct appointments by the Government. Ministers are empowered to give directions of a general character in respect of their functions; the arrangements for control of capital expenditure are similar, and forward planning is subject to their general approval. These characteristics are in contrast to the situation before 1974, when control of the local authority water undertakers was exercised principally through detailed loan consent procedures and by statutory control of powers to raise revenue. These controls have now been removed and in their place have been substituted more general constraints such as those of the Price Commission.

The formation of a central co-ordinating body, the National Water Council, adds to the resemblance to a nationalized industry. Many of the major policy decisions of

TABLE 2.I. Statistics of Water Authorities: Year 1976/77

| Authority | Anglian | Northumbrian | North-West | Severn-Trent | Southern | South-West | Thames | Wessex | York-shire | Welsh |
|---|---|---|---|---|---|---|---|---|---|---|
| Area, km² | 27 360 | 9 190 | 14 850 | 21 500 | 10 950 | 10 880 | 13 100 | 9 620 | 13 500 | 21 400 |
| Resident population, in thousands | 4 760 | 2 700 | 7 000 | 8 200 | 3 800 | 1 350 | 11 700 | 2 250 | 4 500 | 3 000 |
| Average daily water supplied, tcmd | 890 | 385 | 2 260 | 1 672 | 550 | 346 | 2 240 | 300 | 1 150 | 870 |
| Supply by companies | 490 | 390 | — | 350 | 470 | — | 1 020 | 350 | 45 | 60 |
| Length of main river, km | 6 500 | 1 424 | 4 828 | 3 220 | 2 700 | 1 342 | 3 880 | 2 291 | 1 200 | 5 355 |
| Total length of water mains 4″ diameter +, km* | 35 800 | 13 400 | 33 200 | 42 600 | 19 500 | 11 400 | 43 700 | 16 400 | 25 700 | 21 100 |
| Total length of sewers 6″ diameter +, km* | 23 000 | 10 900 | 30 600 | 38 500 | 13 800 | 5 200 | 50 700 | 8 800 | 16 100 | 11 400 |
| Sewage treatment works below 50000 population† | 1 148 | 376 | 604 | 1 072 | 413 | 491 | 417 | 322 | 602 | 878 |
| Sewage treatment works above 50000 population† | 24 | 2 | 46 | 35 | 10 | 2 | 32 | 4 | 14 | 6 |
| Revenue expenditure, £million | 118 | 32 | 131 | 153 | 66 | 34 | 189 | 41 | 92 | 82 |
| Capital expenditure, £million | 80 | 59 | 77 | 75 | 39 | 19 | 84 | 23 | 49 | 33 |
| Employees | 6 700 | 2 320 | 9 200 | 10 650 | 4 090 | 2 530 | 11 910 | 2 260 | 6 280 | 5 600 |

*Report of Standing Technical Committee on Sewers and Water Mains, 1978, "A National Assessment".
†Report of Standing Technical Committee on Wastewater Treatment, 1978.

the water authorities are taken jointly, and such matters as training and research are undertaken co-operatively.

Nevertheless, some of the characteristics of the constituent bodies remain. A majority of the membership of the authorities are local authority delegates; a considerable proportion of revenue continues to be raised as a charge based on property values; there are strong links with local authorities rather than with the national bodies; and sewerage, land drainage, and fisheries continue principally to be dealt with at a local level in many areas.

The local authority representation is in contrast to and takes the place of the nationalized industry model in which consumer councils represent "consumer" interests.

The ambivalence between a nationalized industry and a local authority service was further compounded in a 1976 White Paper in which it was proposed to strengthen

**Fig. 2.1.  Regional water authority boundaries—England and Wales**

*Source:* National Water Council

the centre of the industry, while at the same time the local authority membership of the authorities would be increased.

## WATER AUTHORITIES—GENERAL

The water authorities vary considerably in size and population served, but perhaps even more significantly in their geographical characteristics. Table 2.I is intended to illustrate these variations. Fig. 2.1 shows the boundaries of the authorities in England and Wales. At one extreme is the relatively compact Thames area with 11.7 million people, at the other is the predominately rural South-West area with a population of only 1.3 million. The largest in area, the Anglian Water Authority, has only average population and no major conurbation; yet it has the greatest length of main river, one of the longest lengths of coast line in England and, correspondingly, the greatest land drainage problems. The Yorkshire and the North-West Water Authorities have inherited massive problems in water pollution control, but are relatively well supplied with water resources. The South-West Water Authority has the reverse problem, particularly because of the influx of holiday makers in the summer. The Welsh Water Authority has ample water resources but because of the topography the transfer of water is often difficult and costly. The matching of water supply and demand in many points of the Welsh Water Authority area needs to be achieved on a more localized basis than in England.

## WATER AUTHORITIES—BOUNDARIES

The constituent parts of the water authorities were the former water undertakers and the river authorities, together with certain constituent parts of local authority organizations. There were relatively few coincident boundaries. To permit an orderly transition in the short time given for implementation of the 1973 Act, water undertakers were assigned to particular water authorities *in toto*. Their boundaries had been influenced by geographical and political circumstances, but only rarely had river catchment limits been one of these factors. The river authority boundaries, on the other hand, were almost wholly catchment-based and in most areas sewerage systems were contained within the catchment limits.

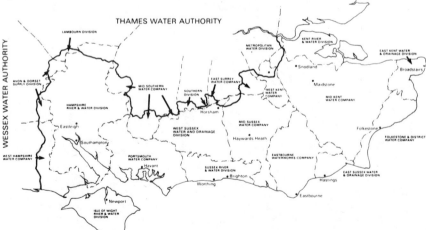

**Fig. 2.2. Southern Water Authority—areas of water divisions and water companies**

The result has been that the water authorities have different boundaries for their major functions, although in principle they are intended to be catchment-based bodies. The situation is further complicated by the retention of the water companies, whose boundaries are not in many cases wholly within one water authority's area.

Two maps illustrate the position at the date of writing (1978):—

Fig. 2.2, is a map of the Southern Water Authority area showing the boundaries for water supply in relation to the Authority's area. This is an authority where water companies supply the bulk of the area.

Fig. 2.3, is a map of the Yorkshire Water Authority's southern boundary. It is as complex as that of the Southern Water Authority, yet no water company is involved.

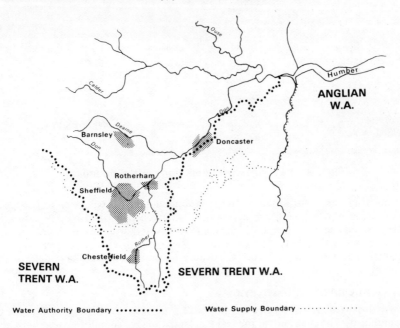

**Fig. 2.3. Yorkshire Water Authority, southern boundary**

The Water Act 1973 (Section 8) enables a water authority in consultation with any other water authority, in the interests of rationalization, to alter any boundaries of their area for the purpose of any function and to transfer any property. Authorities are charged to give priority to boundaries which are different for different functions.

Boundary problems arise in tidal waters where some estuaries form the border between water authorities. The estuaries principally concerned are the Humber, Thames, and Severn. Under the Clean Rivers (Estuary and Tidal Waters) Act 1960 seaward limits were prescribed to all estuaries in England and Wales for the purpose of bringing discharges to them under control. In the case of the estuaries mentioned above, two or more authorities are involved in the control of water quality. In each case joint committees (see below) have been set up through which control is exercised jointly. Fig. 2.4 is a map of the Severn estuary showing the seaward limits of control and the authorities involved.

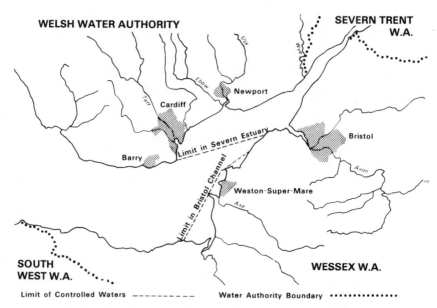

**Fig. 2.4.   Severn estuary pollution control boundaries**

Under the Control of Pollution Act 1974 water authorities will be given powers of control over any trade effluent or sewage discharged from land by pipe into tidal waters outside controlled waters. The controlled waters will include the sea up to 3 miles beyond LWMOST. The exercise of such control must ultimately create a national or international dimension, because the water authority boundary in one sense becomes limitless.

### WATER AUTHORITY—CONSTITUTION

The chairman of each authority is appointed by the Secretary of State and is paid by the authority. The chairman of the regional land drainage committee, who must also be one of the people appointed to the authority by the Minister, is also a paid appointment.

The total membership is determined by the Secretary of State and the Minister within fairly detailed statutory requirements which, in outline, are:

—   The Minister may appoint from two to four members who have relevant experience in agriculture, land drainage, or fisheries.
—   The Secretary of State may, subject to the following constraints, appoint any number of members who have experience of matters relative to the functions for the authority.
—   A metropolitan county council with more than one-quarter of the population resident within the authority's area may appoint two members, and the district councils within that county may also jointly appoint two members.
—   Non-metropolitan county councils with more than one-quarter of the population may appoint one member, as may the relevant district councils.
—   Smaller counties and their districts may appoint one member between them, provided that not less than one-sixth of the population resides in the county.
—   In all cases there shall be a majority of local authority appointed members.

Table 2.II shows how these rules have worked out in practice.

2 ORGANIZATION FROM 1974 19

## TABLE 2.II

| Water authority | Appointed by Secretary of State (including chairman) | Appointed by Minister | County Councils | District Councils | Total |
|---|---|---|---|---|---|
| Anglian | 13 | 4 | 9 | 9 | 35 |
| Northumbrian | 7 | 2 | 5 | 5 | 19 |
| North-West | 10 | 3 | 7 | 7 | 27 |
| Southern | 7 | 2 | 5 | 5 | 19 |
| South-West | 5 | 2 | 4 | 4 | 15 |
| Severn-Trent | 17[1] | 4 | 11 | 11 | 43 |
| Thames | 18 | 4 | 19[2] | 17[3] | 58 |
| Wessex | 5 | 2 | 4 | 4 | 15 |
| Yorkshire | 9 | 3 | 7 | 6 | 25 |
| Welsh | 11 | 4 | 10 | 10 | 35 |

*Notes.* 1. includes a member from Welsh Water Authority
2. includes 10 Greater London Council members
3. includes 10 London Borough members

## Authority Committees—Constraints

Water authorities may arrange for the discharge of any of their functions by a committee, a subcommittee, or by an officer. They may also arrange for another water authority to do so, and two or more authorities can discharge any of their functions jointly or by a joint committee. Unless the authority or authorities concerned otherwise direct, a committee may itself delegate the functions to a subcommittee or an officer.

The constitution of the committees is fixed by the appointing authority or authorities but, if it is intended to co-opt members, at least two-thirds of the members must be members of the authority or authorities.

The important exception to these facilities is the statutory land drainage committee, which is appointed in a different manner. Also, the two-thirds rule does not apply to advisory committees.

## Statutory Committee for Land Drainage

The Water Act 1973 prescribes that the water authorities shall exercise a general supervision over all matters relating to land drainage, including making of charges and precepts and raising capital, but that they shall otherwise arrange for the discharge of their land drainage functions through a regional land drainage committee. The authorities may give directions to these committees if their activities appear to affect other functions of the authority.

The membership of the land drainage committee is also limited by the terms of the Act. In England the Minister appoints the chairman and a number of other members, two members are appointed by the water authority, and a number of other members are appointed by the constituent councils. The latter must be in a bare majority and unless the Minister otherwise determines, the numbers shall be not less than 11 and not more than 17. Within these criteria and subject to Ministerial approval, the water authority determines the total number of the committee. The members appointed by the Minister must have had experience in land drainage, in agriculture, and in particular matters which affect the region or part of the region. In Wales these powers are exercised by the Secretary of State for Wales. It was a first duty of every regional land drainage committee to submit to the relevant water authority a scheme for the creation of local land drainage districts, each with a local land drainage committee. The scheme would set out the constitution, functions, and procedure of the local committees and would be submitted to the Minister.

All the water authorities have set up a regional land drainage committee. The numbers of members vary from 13 in some of the smaller authorities, to 21 in the case of Thames. Most of the regional committees have set up local land drainage committees corresponding to the previous 29 river authority areas.

### Statutory Fisheries Advisory Committee

Under Section 28 of the Salmon and Freshwater Fisheries Act 1975 every water authority is required to set up a regional fisheries advisory committee and such local advisory committees as it considers necessary. The regional committee has the function of advising the water authority on its functions relating to maintaining, improving, and developing salmon, trout, freshwater and eel fisheries. The local advisory committees are intended to include people interested in fisheries in the area concerned.

In most cases the regional advisory committee reports to an "amenity" fisheries and recreation committee of the authority, but where such a committee does not exist it reports to a water management committee or a committee of similar name. In all authorities except Severn-Trent and Yorkshire local advisory committees have been set up, usually covering an area corresponding to the old river authority areas. In the case of Severn-Trent the regional advisory committee has been enlarged to include the local interests. The Yorkshire regional committee is advised by a regional fisheries consultative association.

### STATUTORY ARRANGEMENTS
### Water Companies

Under the Water Act 1973 the water authority normally discharges its duties in connection with the supply of water through a water company within the area of the company. Arrangements made with the company include provision for the management and operation of sources of supply, bulk supply by or to the company, and may also deal with the company's charges for water supply. Other provisions include the submission of rolling capital works programmes dealing at least with source works, treatment works, trunk mains and notification of changes in treatment methods. Liaison has in many cases been established to ensure common practice in charging, application of bye-laws, and dealing with rural water supply grants and grants received from MAFF.

Subject to the above arrangements the companies carry on much as before the Act and in some respects resemble independent single-purpose divisions of the authorities. Although the arrangements made are sometimes referred to as "agency" arrangements, the companies are not in fact agents, being statutory bodies in their own right and with their own powers and duties.

### The Sewerage Function

Section 15 of the Act required every water authority and district of London borough council to endeavour to make arrangements for those councils to undertake the sewerage function within their area.

The arrangements required the councils to prepare and carry out annual programmes for approval by the relevant water authority, to vest any public sewers in the water authority, to provide vehicles and equipment, to undertake any legal proceedings, and to provide for transfer of staff to the authority in the event of the ending of the arrangement. The water authority reimburses the councils for the expenditure incurred.

In the case of new towns, the Act includes as "relevant authority" whichever of the following bodies is selected by the water authority, i.e. the development corporation and any district council within whose area the town is wholly or partly situated.

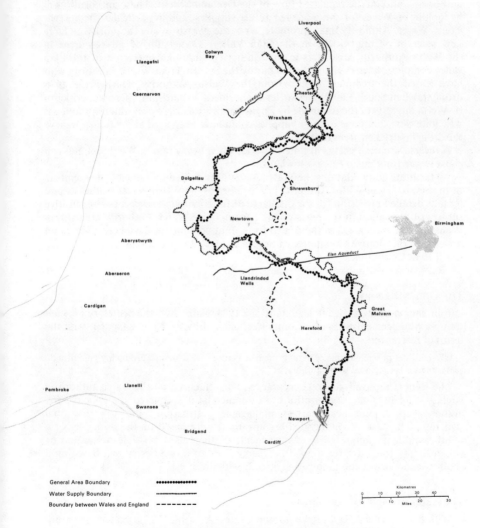

| General Area Boundary | ●●●●●●●●●●●●●●● |
| Water Supply Boundary | ...................... |
| Boundary between Wales and England | – – – – – – – |

**Fig. 2.5.   The Welsh Water Authority boundary**

## The Welsh Border

The catchments of the Dee, Wye, and Severn all straddle the Wales/England border (Fig. 2.5). The catchments of the Wye and Severn in particular diverge considerably from the national boundary. The upper Severn catchment is in mid-Wales, while most of Herefordshire lies within the Welsh Water Authority area. Local authorities in Wales and the Welsh Water Authority are administered by the Secretary of State for Wales through the Welsh Office. All other water authorities are administered by the Secretary of State for the Environment and the Minister.

The North-West and Severn-Trent Water Authorities are especially dependent on supplies of water from reservoirs in Wales, which were financed by their constituent authorities, and on the regulated flow of the Dee and Severn. These authorities will be looking to Wales for some of their future supplies, and in particular the Severn-Trent Water Authority may promote with the Welsh Water authority a large new reservoir, Craig Goch, in the Elan Valley. Ownership of all resources in the Welsh Authority area vests in that authority, although operation of the Elan valley complex of reservoirs is carried out by the Severn-Trent Water Authority who have leased the treatment works from the Welsh Authority. During the 1976 drought, when South-East Wales suffered considerable hardship, there was criticism by Welsh interests of the use made by English authorities of Welsh water, although it was quite clear that none of these supplies could have been used at the time to relieve the drought-stricken areas in Wales.

A reverse situation occurs at time of flood, when heavy rain in Welsh uplands can cause severe flooding in English lowlands.

To facilitate good relations the Water Act 1973 provided that one of the members of the Severn-Trent Water Authority is a member of the Welsh Water Authority and it made detailed provision for the discharge of functions with respect to the sensitive subject of recreation in the parts of the Severn-Trent Water Authority area within Wales. The powers given in the Act to form joint committees have been used to set up a Dee Consultative Committee, a Severn Estuary Joint Committee, and a Craig Goch Joint Committee.

## THE OGDEN REPORT

During the passage of the bill leading to the 1973 Water Act, the Secretary of State set up a Management Structure Committee, chaired by Sir George Ogden, with the terms of reference:—

> "To consider possible forms of management structure with a view to producing guidance on this matter for regional water authorities".

The Report received general acceptance and influenced all the water authorities while setting up their organizations. Recommendations covered three fields: the authority itself, the headquarters management structure, and the divisional structure. The basic recommended organizations were based on the principles of a multi-disciplinary approach to management, of the fullest possible delegation of responsibility for water functions to divisions, and of a two-tier system based on a central headquarters communicating directly with divisions.

## The Authority and its Committees

Within the criteria laid down in the Water Act, the Management Structure Committee felt that the requirements of each authority were sufficiently common to enable it to put forward a single structure. It assumed that full advantage would be taken of the facilities in the Act to delegate functions to committees, subcommittees, and officers. In forming committees it felt that membership should be as small as possible in relation to the overall strength of the authority, and that each member should serve on a least one committee. The suggested committee structure is shown in Fig. 2.6.

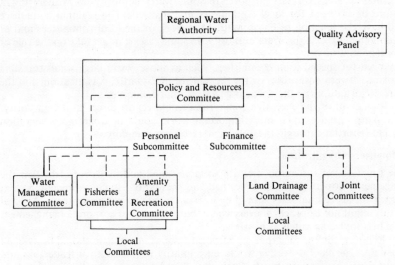

**Fig. 2.6.   The Ogden Report recommendations: committee structure**

Because the authorities would be required to monitor their own discharges, thereby acting as both gamekeeper and poacher, particular importance was attached to the water quality advisory panel. It was recommended that the panel should derive its power direct from the authority, to achieve the necessary degree of independence. The panel would be responsible for providing published water quality reports on the authority's own performance as well as that of outside bodies. The membership of the panel should be separate from that of the water management committee.

The policy and resources committee would be the central committee, chaired by the chairman of the authority. Its responsibilities would include the corporate planning of water and financial resources, priority of objectives, the formation of water control policy, the raising of revenue and expenditure estimates, and the relationships with the National Water Council and local authorities. It was considered that this committee would have only two subcommittees, one dealing with personnel matters and the other with finance. The chairman, and possibly the vice-chairman of the other executive committees, should automatically be members.

The water management committee would have responsibility for operations and new works in relation to water conservation, water supply, sewerage, sewage disposal, and pollution prevention and would reflect the multi-disciplinary approach of the authority.

The statutory fisheries committee and the work of the amenity and recreation committee would be closely related and the report mentioned that there might be advantage in combining the two into a single main committee with separate interests pursued in subcommittees to facilitate contacts with various fishery, amenity, and recreational groups.

All the land drainage functions must be administered through the regional land drainage and local land drainage committees. The intention was that a local drainage district administered by the latter would correspond with a river authority area, but the Report mentioned the possibility, in one or two parts of the country, of amalgamating areas for this purpose. In some water authority areas there might therefore be no need for local committees and districts. The regional committee would have the function of co-ordinating the work of the local committees and of providing the link with the water authority. In some cases it might take on the role of the local committees.

The need for special joint committees, such as those where large water transfers take place between authorities or for the control of estuaries, was mentioned in the Report. In all authorities there would be a staff joint committee.

On some matters the executive committees would report direct to the authority, but in many instances their most important work would be done in co-operation with, and reporting through, the policy and resources committee.

**Headquarters Organization**

The functions of the authorities are so interrelated and interdependent that the Management Structure Committee had no hesitation in recommending that management at regional level should be by a corporate management team. At local level this might not be practical everywhere, but the spirit of corporate management should be adopted as widely as possible.

The Report recommended that the corporate management team should be as small as possible. The chief executive would be primarily responsible for leadership and co-ordination, and would be the main link between the authority itself and its officers. The team should in all cases include the director of finance. Because technical disputes between interests of the different services should not be taken to top management, it was recommended that responsibility should be taken over by a single director of operations on the team. To relieve him of the burden of planning functions, at least in the initial stages when these might become neglected through the pressure of day to day preoccupations, a director of resource planning should be appointed.

Although the Report recognized the need to set up viable and independent scientific departments within each authority, it felt that the needs for representation in the management team varied according to the size and water quality problems of the authority. It recommended directors of scientific services in the cases of Thames, Severn-Trent, North-West, and Wales and, because of its heavily polluted rivers, Yorkshire might qualify. In the case of the other authorities the chief scientific officer might rank as an assistant director in the resource planning department.

Similar reasoning led to the recommendation that there might be a need to include a director of administration in the team to relieve the chief executive, especially in the earlier days.

The Management Structure Committee came out very strongly against the appointment of deputies to any posts, considering these would be a contradiction to the principle of corporate management. They made certain recommendations about the structures of the directorates. In particular:

—    The functions of water supply, sewerage and sewage disposal and river management carried out by the director of operations should each be represented by an assistant director.

— The directorate of resource planning should be divided into two parts, research and resources, but in some authorities a central information unit could be located here as well as the scientific services mentioned above.
— The chief scientific officer would have a dual role, firstly in connection with the executive functions of the authority, and secondly in connection with publicly reporting in an impartial manner on the authority's performance in maintaining and restoring water resource quality. Because of this duality, in the smaller authorities, he should have freedom to report independently to the corporate management team on water quality questions.

## The Divisional Structure

The Management Structure Committee found that the timetable for reorganization and implementation of the Act was too short for it to give detailed consideration to the divisional structure. However, local multi-disciplinary voluntary teams of officers concurrently reviewed the individual working units in different areas and made recommendations about their regrouping into river divisions, sewerage and sewage disposal divisions, water supply divisions, and in a few cases multi-purpose divisions.

The Committee restricted its role to considering the relations between divisions and headquarters, and to preparing a model scheme for delegation of powers from the authority to divisions. The model would be particularly useful during the early years of the authorities, and at the same time would be a concrete expression of the strongly held view that responsibility for the different water functions should be delegated to the fullest extent consistent with efficiency and economy.

The report envisaged that each division, as an entity, would report through the director of operations to the management team at headquarters. There would, however, be functional lines to the other regional directorates to the divisions with a free flow of advice and information. The multi-functional approach in divisions should be encouraged by the divisional manager, but a designated senior officer should be enabled to ask that an occasional decision be referred upwards and that he be free to consult his functional chief at headquarters.

Beyond giving general advice the report did not express any view in favour or against multi-purpose or single-purpose divisions.

## IMPLEMENTATION OF OGDEN REPORT

### Committee Structure

The authorities have generally followed the recommendations of the Ogden Report in setting up their committee organization, but each has made adjustments to suit individual circumstances.

### Policy and Resources

With the exception of Southern, South-West, and Wales, all authorities have set up policy and resources committees. The Southern Water Authority has only 19 members and formally decided to deal with relevant matters at the full meetings of the Authority. The policy and resources committee of some of the other authorities also consists of the full membership. To compensate for the lack of this committee the South-West and Welsh Authorities have finance committees supplemented by establishment committees which, to some extent, act together as a substitute. In the case of the South-West the finance committee includes all members of the Authority and is clearly a key committee.

## Operations and Resource Planning

The majority of authorities have water management committees dealing with operational aspects of the full water cycle, the exceptions being the Northumbrian which has a planning and works committee, the South-West which has a water control and quality committee, and the Yorkshire where water management matters are dealt with by the policy and resources committee. The Welsh Authority has a separate resource planning committee, and the Yorkshire Authority has a resource planning advisory panel.

## Water Quality Panel

There are some departures from the Ogden recommendations for a water quality advisory panel. Most authorities have set up a small panel of members who are not members of executive committees concerned with water management and have in some instances arranged for direct access to the director of scientific services. The Anglian Authority has a water quality consultative group "to provide a forum for discussion between scientific disciplines on problems of water quality and management. Membership of the Group includes representatives of agricultural, scientific and individual interests in the region together with Authority scientists". This Authority further comments in its first annual report:

> "The Ogden Committee proposed the establishment of a quality advisory panel to provide an independent check on water quality. However, the Authority considered that the panel would be largely dependent on reports from the Authority's officers or from consultants paid by the authority and that neither of these sources could be regarded as wholly independent. It was accordingly provided that the director of scientific services should be required to report to the Authority on water quality independently of his fellow chief officers and of any committee".

In the case of the Thames Authority, the water quality panel reports to the policy and resources committee but this exception is more a reflection of the size of the authority than of any question of principle. The Northumbrian Authority did not consider it necessary to set up a water quality panel.

## Amenity and Recreation

Most authorities have set up amenity, recreation and fisheries committees, in one case incorporating the statutory advisory fishery committee, but the North-West and Anglian Authorities have contented themselves with advisory committees only. The Anglian Authority has added a regional recreational advisory committee, and the North-West has a recreational advisory subcommittee of the water management committee. Where an authority has an executive amenity, recreation and resources committee, the statutory fisheries committee acts as its source of advice.

## Liaison

All the authorities have recognized the great need for effective liaison with and understanding of their operations by local authorities and the general public, and it is in measures to meet this need that there is the greatest variation between authorities.

Some authorities such as the Anglian have broadened the formal committee structure to incorporate special advisory committees dealing with sensitive areas such as water quality and recreation. Others, such as the North-West and Southern, have attempted to establish a multiplicity of informal relationships at all levels with local authorities, recreational interests, such organizations as the CBI, NFU, and CLA, and of course the press. The Yorkshire and Wessex Authorities have gone further and have set up formal consultative machinery. In the Yorkshire area there are five local authority consultative committees and further committees established with the Yorkshire and Humberside Economic Planning Council and Chambers of Commerce within the region. The Wessex Authority has three local advisory water committees which act as additional channels of communication between the Authority and its consumers.

These arrangements are still developing and the lessons learnt during the first few years experience are being digested.

## HEADQUARTERS STRUCTURE

The authorities have without exception formally adopted the principle of corporate management recommended by the Ogden Committee. The teams vary in size from four to seven and the roles are shown in Table 2.III.

### TABLE 2.III

| Authority, in order of population | Chief Executive | Director Operations | Director Scientific Services | Director Resource Planning | Director Finance | Director Administration | Others | Total |
|---|---|---|---|---|---|---|---|---|
| Thames | 1 | 1 | 1 | 1 | 1 | — | — | 5 |
| Severn-Trent | 1 | 1 | 1 | — | 1 | 1 | — | 5 |
| North-West | 1 | 1 | 1 | 1 | 1 | 1 | 1 | 7 |
| Anglian | 1 | 1 | 1 | 1 | 1 | 1 | — | 6 |
| Yorkshire | 1 | 1 | — | 1 | 1 | — | — | 4 |
| Southern | 1 | 1 | — | 1 | 1 | 1 | — | 5 |
| Welsh | 1 | 1 | 1 | 1 | 1 | 1 | — | 6 |
| Northumbrian | 1 | 1 | — | 1 | 1 | 1 | — | 5 |
| Wessex | 1 | 1 | — | 1 | 1 | — | — | 4 |
| South-West | 1 | 1 | — | 1 | 1 | 1 | Director Fisheries and Recreation | 6 |

The size of the team is clearly not related to the size of authority, but Table 2.III shows that the Ogden recommendation that the medium and smaller authorities do not justify a full director of scientific services has been followed. The further recommendation that the chief scientific officer in such authorities should be disassociated from operational matters has been followed in all except the Yorkshire Authority, where he has been incorporated in the staff of the director of operations. In some smaller authorities arrangements have been made for him to report direct to the chief executive and in theory to by-pass the corporate management team. The intimate relationship between the senior staff at headquarters tends to reduce the significance of this distinction; access to the water quality panels is of greater importance.

Although in principle the management team takes all corporate decisions and makes joint recommendations, there is evidence that practice varies and depends in part on management style. The Welsh Authority has gone so far as to relate particular committees to individual directors, a practice similar to that of predecessor river authorities.

In most cases chief executives have, as Ogden recommended, taken direct responsibility for a limited number of functions. The nature of those functions varies from authority to authority and probably reflects personal proclivities, but generally chief executives have retained personal control over personnel and establishment matters.

Fig. 2.7 compares the outline headquarters structure of three authorities and illustrates the basic adherence to Ogden. Perhaps the most apparently significant difference is in the reporting lines of the divisions. The most common arrangement is that the divisional manager reports to the director of operations, but in others they report to the chief executive. The distinction is probably more apparent than real; there are inevitably such a number of links between individual directors at headquarters and the divisions that the formal reporting lines tend to lose importance except for major policy decisions. The latter are in any case the result of corporate decisions of the management team, endorsed by the authority.

The nature of the links between headquarters and divisions is discussed in some detail below.

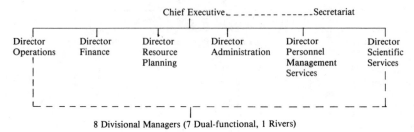

**NORTH WEST WATER AUTHORITY**

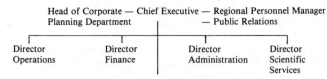

**SEVERN-TRENT WATER AUTHORITY**

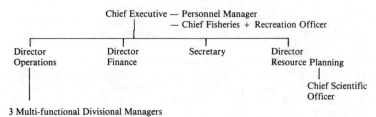

**WESSEX WATER AUTHORITY**

**Fig. 2.7. Regional Water Authorities—typical management structures**

Headquarters establishments vary widely; the actual size depends not only on the size of the authority but on other factors such as the degree of devolution to divisions, the degree to which centralized services are provided, the geography of the region, and to some extent on the organizational history. Comparisons without detailed consideration of these matters are relatively meaningless.

The duties performed at headquarters include "services" afforded to divisions. One authority, Wessex, describes these services as:

(1) *Regional Control Centre.*—Headquarters provide a 24 hr service for receiving information of operational failures, either by telemetry or by telephone, of pollution incidents, and of anything which may affect the Authority's work and for calling out any divisional staff who may be required.

(2) *Radio Network.*—Headquarters are designing and providing the radio communication network for the whole region, excluding the provision of mobile sets in divisional vehicles.

(3) *Purchasing.*—Headquarters negotiate regional contracts for the supply of a wide range of materials and equipment.

(4) *Operational Research.*—Headquarters provide analyses of pipe networks to identify low pressure points and lengths of mains of inadequate capacity, and analyses of interconnected supply systems to determine the most economical method of operation.

(5) *Legal Services.*—Headquarters provide all legal services for the divisions.

(6) *Financial Services.*—Headquarters provide all money required by the divisions, provide all insurances, and operate the superannuation arrangements.

(7) *Computing Services.*—Headquarters are providing the bulk of computing services for the divisions and will replace remaining existing divisional arrangements during the next 12 months or so. The divisions have terminals connected to the Authority's computing facilities.

(8) *Biological Services.*—Headquarters provide a regional biological service to all divisions.


## DIVISIONAL STRUCTURE

The headquarters role is that of policy formation, planning, financial control, and monitoring performance. The essential operational unit is the division. The relationship between headquarters and divisions is complex, as the inspection of the instruments of delegation of the authorities given below shows. Such an examination not only illuminates this relationship, but it clarifies the roles of headquarters staff and in some cases the relationship between divisions.

It is first necessary to set out the variations in the arrangement of divisions and this is done below:—


| Authority | | Divisions |
|---|---|---|
| Northumbrian | : | Two multi-functional divisions sewerage and sewage disposal (S and SD), water supply, land drainage<br>One multi-functional division water supply, land drainage. |
| Welsh | : | Seven all-purpose divisions based on catchments. |
| Yorkshire | : | Seven multi-functional divisions—water supply, S and SD, control of pollution.<br>One regional rivers division—land drainage only. |
| North-West | : | Seven multi-functional divisions—water supply and S and SD. One regional rivers divisions—all aspects of management. |
| South-West | : | Three all-purpose divisions |

| | | |
|---|---|---|
| Thames | : | Five multi-functional divisions—water supply and S and SD. |
| | | One multi-functional division—S and SD, and river management |
| | | One water division (single-purpose) |
| | | One public health division (single-purpose) |
| | | One river management division. |
| Severn-Trent | : | Eight all-purpose divisions. |
| Wessex | : | Three all-purpose divisions. |
| Anglian | : | Five river management divisions |
| | | Seven S and SD divisions |
| | | Eight water supply divisions  } all single-purpose. |
| Southern | : | Four multi-functional divisions—water supply and river management (one being completely all-purpose) |
| | | Two drainage divisions—S and SD |
| | | Three multi-functional divisions water supply and S and SD. |

A multi-functional division carries out two or more functions of the authority at division level. An all-purpose division carries out all the functions of the authority, within its area. The chosen arrangements reflect to a considerable extent the geographical characteristics and history of each region. With the exception of Anglian, all authorities have gone a considerable way towards the multi-functional approach recommended by Ogden. Those who have not gone all the way have done so for different reasons. In the Northumbrian, Southern, and Thames areas the existence of the water companies complicates the pattern and the Thames Authority of course has to cope with the immense problems of water supply and sewerage and sewage disposal in the Greater London Area. North-West and Yorkshire Authorities have created separate rivers divisions, in the former case separating the control of pollution function from that of the provision of services.

The Anglian Authority, in its first annual report, gave its reasons for not going the way of the others:—

"The former river authorities and water undertakings comprised over half the organization. They were already in full working order and continued to operate without drastic change. Immediate problems were, therefore, largely confined to sewage and attention could be concentrated on them. There is almost a complete absence of experience in managing multi-functional divisions and their advantages and disadvantages have not been demonstrated yet. Sewage has traditionally been a cinderella among local authorities. With the increasing need to recycle water its importance is now greatly enhanced. The formation of sewage divisions has led to high morale among the staff concerned who have injected enthusiasm and knowledge into a service which had, in some cases, been neglected".

Nevertheless, the Authority seems to be keeping an open mind on the subject and has not ruled out the multi-functional approach altogether.

## Divisional Structure—Delegation and Relation with Headquarters

The following analysis is based on the actual instruments of delegation to divisions of the authorities. These instruments, modelled in the Ogden Report, must be viewed against a background of control by annual budgets and specific directions from the corporate management teams to divisional managers. The divisions do not work in a vacuum and informal communication is plentiful. In addition, the authorities call regular meetings between divisional directors and members of the management teams, and divisional managers play their part in influencing headquarters policy. Their essential importance is reflected in their high status within the authorities.

The instruments of delegation are not exciting reading, but they are illuminating documents about the management of the water authorities. The Ogden approach, subject by subject, is usually followed, but with some variations in subject headings. In a number of instances, authorities do not think a subject is worth mentioning so its inclusion below does not assure its inclusion in the instruments of a particular authority.

(a) *Issue of Consents.*—Divisions are usually fully responsible for control of trade effluents to sewers and consents under the Land Drainage Acts. In some authorities they may issue abstraction licences (e.g. Wessex up to 5Ml/day) and consents to discharge to inland waters (e.g. Wessex up to 0.5 Ml/day), in other cases all such licences and consents are issued by headquarters or, in the North-West the rivers division has overall responsibility.

Usually, the director of scientific services or in the case of the smaller authorities, the director of resource planning, is the referral officer.

(b) *Authentication of Documents.*—The divisional manager usually has delegated powers to sign, subject to limitations (e.g. in Severn-Trent to contracts up to £110000). Usually, the director of administration is the referral officer.

(c) *Land and Property Transactions.*—There are considerable variations between authorities. In some cases all proposals for purchase of land must be dealt with by the director of administration; in others land and property of small value may be bought up to a given limit. Most divisional managers may settle compensation claims up to a given value and sell surplus plant and equipment (in Severn-Trent up to £1 000) and most can grant tenancies, again up to a given amount. In all cases the director of administration or his equivalent is the headquarters officer concerned.

(d) *Legal Matters.*—Most legal matters are dealt with at headquarters, including promoting Bills and Orders, applying for confirmation of bye-laws, conveyancing, legal proceedings, etc. Divisional managers can often deal with less complex matters, such as applying for planning permission, application for powers to enter on land and to lay mains, preparation and completion of contracts up to given limits, preliminary steps towards prosecutions, etc. Headquarters legal sections under directors of administration are generally responsible.

(e) *Contracts and Tenders.*—Divisions are responsible for the execution of contracts, direct labour works and control and supervision. In most cases they can accept tenders subject to certain limitations such as value and closeness to estimated or budgetted costs. Directors of operations deal with these matters in headquarters.

(f) *Appointment of Consultants.*—This is usually reserved to directors of operations.

(g) *Action in Emergencies.*—The divisional manager is usually responsible for all action in an emergency, subject to any preplanning procedures agreed with directors of operations. Arrangements are made for notification to headquarters.

(h) *Reservoir Safety.*—Not many authorities mention this subject, but North-West makes provision for divisional managers to keep the statutory records and the director of operations to appoint the statutory panel engineers for construction and inspection of reservoirs.

(i) *Personnel Matters.*—Complements are invariably a matter for headquarters, but usually recruitment and appointments to fill vacancies up to specified grades is the responsibility of the divisional managers. Within those grades variations in grading, increments, etc., can be dealt with in divisions who also deal with proposals for changes in complement, dismissals, sickness allowances, medical examinations, incentive/bonus schemes, etc., at local level. Accounting and pay are sometimes delegated to the divisions; personnel and management services directors are generally responsible at headquarters.

(j) *Training.*—Overall schemes and programmes of staff training are usually developed and agreed at headquarters, but divisions put forward their own training programmes and implement those related to manual training. Divisional managers may usually approve attendance at training courses, up to prescribed limits of duration.

What the above does not give is a feel for the operational management task of the divisions, which are responsible for the actual provision of the water services and the execution of the water authority functions. The divisions are large and complex organizations in their own right. Most of them are more than comparable in size and financial responsibility with the predecessor water undertakers and sewerage and sewage disposal authorities.

### Divisional Structure—Organization

*Multi-purpose Divisions.*—The headquarters of most multi-purpose divisions are fairly similarly organized and to some extent mirror the head office organization not only in structure but in the establishment of divisional corporate management teams.

The model establishment of the Severn-Trent divisions is a typical example.

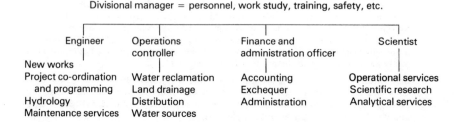

Divisional manager = personnel, work study, training, safety, etc.

| Engineer | Operations controller | Finance and administration officer | Scientist |
|---|---|---|---|
| New works | | | |
| Project co-ordination and programming | Water reclamation | Accounting | Operational services |
| Hydrology | Land drainage | Exchequer | Scientific research |
| Maintenance services | Distribution | Administration | Analytical services |
| | Water sources | | |

The divisional corporate management team consists of the manager, engineer, operations controller, divisional scientist, and the finance and administration officer.

The Southern and Wessex Water Authority divisions are somewhat similarly organized, except that the divisional scientist works to the operations controller thereby further reflecting the headquarters structure.

In the three water authorities mentioned, new works design and construction is delegated to divisions, together with short term planning within the guidelines provided by medium and long term plans and general policy of the authorities. The engineering divisions are fully multi-functional.

The department of the finance and administration officer is similarly organized in the three authorities, and the degree of delegation from headquarters is similar. The main differences between the divisional organization of the three authorities lie in the way the executive functions are organized under the operations controller. In the Severn-Trent area the functions of water supply, sewage disposal, and river management are organized on a single-purpose basis, but subdivided into districts in much the same way as the larger water undertakers were organized before the 1974 reorganization.

The Wessex Water Authority has gone the whole hog and has subdivided each division into three similar multi-purpose districts where the district manager is responsible for all the operational functions. The organization under the divisional operations manager (controller) is shown below:—

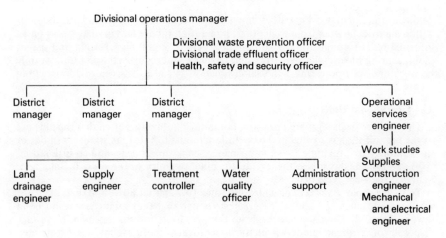

In a pre-1974 water board the district manager was often of superintending status, but in these multi-functional districts the manager is a senior professional man with considerable responsibility.

The Southern Water Authority divisional organization is complicated by the high proportion of the area served by water companies. The multi-functional principle has been followed as far as possible down to the second tier at divisional level, thereafter a single-purpose basis applies within the division. As with the Severn-Trent Authority, single-purpose districts have been formed where the division is too large for effluent control to be exercised from the divisional headquarters.

There are other variations: the North-West Authority has separated the river management function (including pollution control) into a regional division. The other individual functions are controlled on a single-functional basis from the divisional headquarters without a further sub-division into districts. The Yorkshire Authority has organized land drainage on a regional basis, but the other functions are carried out at divisions on a single-purpose basis.

*Single-purpose Divisions.*—It should be clear from the above that the only fundamental difference between multi-functional and single-functional working is the level within the structure at which the various functions come together. The choice has been determined by historical and geographical factors. The Thames Water Authority consciously set out to build on what existed before 1974, and this resulted in a wide variety of structures including both multi-functional and single-functional divisions. This was probably inevitable in the case of this Authority which included the Greater London area.

Only the Anglian Water Authority, for the reasons given earlier, adopted single-functional divisions. This Authority has a widely dispersed population in a particularly large area, and the balance between the functions in each area varied so widely that if multi-functional divisions had been set up an equally varied number of divisional structures would have emerged from the 1974 reorganization. The Authority has a large number of divisions and the tendency will be to amalgamate where this is convenient. Some of the divisions are able to exercise their functions directly from divisions headquarters, but in most it has been necessary to sub-divide the divisions into districts, each under a district manager.

Single-functional working does not entail the complete isolation of divisions within a particular area from each other; integration takes place in many ways on an informal basis through the use of common depots, common servicing and use of plant, sharing of specialist expertise, and frequent and regular consultation not only between divisions performing the same function but also between divisions within an area.

## The Operational Units

This chapter deals with organization, but it must not be forgotten that the purpose of the organization is to enable the operational units to fulfil the statutory duties of the authority by providing them with finance, back-up services, and co-ordination. At the end of the day it is at the level of the plant operator or the sewer maintenance man that the work is carried out.

To such people changes in organization since 1974 matter little, and their places of work remain much the same. The greatest change that they might see would be in sewage disposal. The tendency to group the operation and management of sewage disposal works, already underway in the larger local authorities, has been accelerated and the very important expert backup to operational control is increasingly centralized. This has undoubtedly brought about greater efficiency in operation, but it has meant that plant operators may have to be more mobile than before and are undoubtedly subject to greater supervision.

Pollution control since 1951 has been organized on a catchment basis and with the setting up of the river authorities under the Water Resources Act 1963 pollution control officers have been used to working on a semi-regional basis. Only their reporting lines will have changed.

The authorities have given a considerable degree of authority to divisions and this has extended to give some freedom to districts and operational units in respect of purchasing and operating policies. It is to be expected that central purchasing and the imposition of common operating policies will develop, and there will be a gradual trend to multi-functional operation at least to the district level. At the national level the implications of multi-functional working are being considered in relation to the protection of water quality both in source and in public supplies. These deliberations will eventually set a framework within which water authorities can integrate working below district level, but it is unlikely that dramatic changes will take place.

## CONTROL OF AQUATIC POLLUTION

### Gamekeeper—Poacher

The development of the present water authorities has been traced earlier. In England and Wales the integration of the river authorities, water undertakers, and local authority sewerage and sewage disposal services has combined the role of one of the major abstractors from water resources with that of the licensing authority and one of the largest dischargers of polluting matter with that of the controlling authority responsible for river health. In Scotland these roles are still separate and are described later.

The role of the water quality advisory panels in the water authorities is to monitor water quality and the performance of the authorities' own works and those of private dischargers. In this they act as the authorities' watch dog and through the publication of comprehensive information can do much to reassure the public and private dischargers that the authorities are acting fairly in respect of their own discharges.

The arrangements vary from authority to authority, but the chief scientific officer
has direct access to the panel in almost every case. Further, in most authorities the
divisional scientific officers have direct access to him and they supervise and
administer the river inspectors. In this way the chief scientific officer exercises a
degree of independence and in addition determines the sampling programmes and
has the authorities' laboratories under his control. Some authorities set up rivers
divisions which perform much the same duties as the antecedent river authorities.
This preserves the separation of the control of pollution function from the executive
function but the tendency to multi-purpose divisions has reduced the number of such
divisions. Each authority publishes comprehensive information under the aegis of
the water quality advisory panels covering water quality in source, in supply, and of
effluents.

As an example, the North-West Water Authority publishes the following:—

Analyses of source raw water quality
Analyses of treated water supply and water in distribution
Bacteriological examination of water in source and in distribution
Performance of sewage treatment works in relation to consent conditions
Quality of industrial effluents to surface waters by individual catchment
Analyses of samples of river water quality throughout the region

It is chiefly when priorities for taking action are being determined that difficulties
arise. As the Southern Water Authority's Water Quality Advisory Panel puts it in
the 1975 report: "In recommending action in respect of the Authority's own
operations the Panel has had to face the fact that restrictions on capital expenditure
are greater than for many years past and that proposals for action may therefore
have to join an ever lengthening queue".

This selection of priorities for improvement of river water quality is a matter for
the corporate management team of each authority. The team works within a framework of a formal planning procedure set out in Section 24 of the Water Act 1973.
Each water authority must survey the water in its area and prepare action plans for
long and medium terms including restoring or maintaining the wholesomeness of
rivers and other inland and coastal waters in its area. These plans must be regularly
reviewed and updated, and they include quality objectives and assessment of the
means of attaining those objectives. Public accountability is achieved by the
requirement under the Act to prepare programmes for the discharge of functions,
over a period of not more than seven years, for submission to Ministers for their
approval. In carrying out those tasks local authorities must be consulted and reports
must be made available to the public.

These requirements for openness will be augmented when Part II of the Control of
Pollution Act 1974 comes into operation. Water authorities will be required to
maintain registers containing, among other things, prescribed particulars of
applications for consents to discharge effluents, of consents issued and conditions
attaching to them, and of samples and analyses of effluents and receiving waters. The
registers will be open to the public. Water authorities may, under regulations made
under the Act, be required to submit applications for their own discharges to the
Secretary of State.

In the light of all the information which is available to him, a private discharger
will be able to assess whether he is being fairly treated in relation to the water
authority's control of its own works. He has the right of appeal to the Secretary of
State in respect of conditions attached to new discharges or in the case of a modified
or revoked consent to an existing discharge.

## The Role of Government

The powers of direction and determination of appeals held by the Secretary of State cannot be maintained without adequate information, and in order to exercise his duties of promoting national policy in connection with the control of pollution, he requires to monitor the condition of inland and coastal waters and assess the effect of discharges on water quality and of measures taken and expenditure incurred on remedial works.

The River Pollution Surveys of the Department of the Environment are carried out at intervals of two or three years and through a system of classification of river water quality assess national progress towards cleaner rivers. These surveys include information about the condition of discharges largely similar to that published by the water authorities quality advisory panels.

This information is complemented by a scheme of monitoring of river quality in much greater detail at key points, mainly the points of discharge of major rivers into tidal waters, and is known as the Harmonized Monitoring Scheme. Thus an assessment can be made of the total polluting load discharged into estuaries by inland waters and this can be combined with information available upon direct discharges of effluents to estuaries and coastal waters to give the total of potential polluting load discharged to the sea.

Control of dumping at sea is the responsibility of the Ministry of Agriculture, Fisheries and Food, the Welsh Office, the Department of Agriculture and Fisheries for Scotland, and the Department of the Environment for Northern Ireland; the port of loading and not the origin of the waste governs the licensing authority. Control is exercised under the Dumping at Sea Act 1974 which implements the Oslo Convention (1972) and the London Dumping Convention 1972. The control of direct discharges to estuaries and the sea will be governed by the Control of Pollution Act 1974 which, when implemented in full, will be administered by the Water Authorities, the River Purification Boards, and the Department of the Environment of Northern Ireland. At present discharges to certain defined estuaries are controlled by various Acts which the Control of Pollution Act will broadly supersede. The Department of Trade is the lead department for administering legislation relating to international conventions for the prevention of marine pollution by discharges from ships, including oil, chemicals, and garbage: it is also responsible for the organization of the U.K. response to oil spillages at sea either from tankers or from offshore oil installations.

Government is becoming increasingly involved in EEC measures designed to control pollution. Five directives have an immediate impact:—

—  *Quality of Surface Water for Drinking* classifies sources from which water is taken for treatment for public supply. Surface water having physical, chemical, and micro-biological characteristics falling short of mandatory limiting values should either receive appropriate minimum treatment or may not be used for the abstraction of drinking water. Lower quality water may in exceptional circumstances be used provided that suitable processes including blending are used to bring the quality of the water up to the standards for drinking water.

—  *Discharges of Dangerous Substances to the Aquatic Environment* deals with all discharges into inland surface waters, coastal waters, and groundwaters and requires member states to authorize and prescribe emission standards for certain categories of substances and to reduce pollution caused by others. The Council of Ministers can lay down either emission standards or quality objectives. In the latter event the Commission must report to the Council every five years.

— *Quality of Bathing Water* requires that any stretch of bathing water, as defined in the directive, meets the prescribed EEC standards and where they do not comply they must be brought up to the standards by December 1985.

— *Quality of Fresh Waters to Support Fish Life* requires within a two year period following the notification of the Directive (21st July 1978) that member states should designate salmonid and cyprinid rivers.

— *Quality of Water for Human Consumption* requires that, with certain exceptions, member states shall apply listed values for toxic and microbiological parameters.

Further directives have been issued in draft form including the quality of water for agricultural use, waters favourable for shellfish growth, and the protection of groundwater against pollution caused by certain dangerous substances.

Government departments, principally the DoE, MAFF, and DHSS are responsible for the U.K. input to the formulation of all these directives, and close liaison and consultation with the water industry, local authority, and industry has become essential. By and large existing U.K. pollution control legislation enables these directives to be implemented, but the existing U.K. monitoring systems will have to be tailored to meet the requirements of the European Commission for information relating to conformity with the directives.

### Emission Standards and Environmental Quality Objectives

Many of the disagreements within the EEC on pollution control, particularly those between the U.K. and the other countries, arise from differences of approach to the subject.

By and large the continental countries prefer to regulate by means of arbitrary standards placed on all emissions of a similar nature, regardless of their effect on the environment. This approach has the merit of simplicity and apparent equality between dischargers but it has the grave disadvantage that it ignores the effect that the emission has on the environment; for example, it ignores self-purifying capacity of a receiving stream to accept a discharge of sewage effluent. The other major disadvantage is that in many cases it may be cheap and relatively simple to improve a particular emission to a standard very much better than that prescribed, but it might be very expensive to ensure that another emission meets the standard. Water source quality requirements vary considerably from river to river, depending on the use to which the water is put. In the situation where choice must be exercised to allocate limited financial resources, it is clearly better to tailor standards of individual discharges to achieve a particular river quality objective or objectives.

Nevertheless, the quality objective approach requires a full knowledge of a river and all discharges. It requires careful planning and control, and it requires the confidence of all dischargers. It is likely that, for some time, the recommendations of the Royal Commission will continue to influence quality standards applying to sewage works effluents.

Quality objectives are being developed in relation to intended use, and will include limiting values for surface water for drinking and agricultural use.

### The "Polluter Pays" Principle

A logical solution to the problem of deciding which discharges to clean up first might well be to make a charge proportionate to the effect a discharge has on a receiving stream. The choice could then, in theory, be left either to pay up or to spend money on treatment plant, change a process, or direct the pollution elsewhere. Although the approach may appear to be attractive in principle, legislation is not immediately available to allow it to be carried out, and there are disadvantages:—

(i) The polluter must be subject to overall limits to the pollution he causes, otherwise his payment gives him a licence to pollute possibly beyond the receiving capacity of the stream.

(ii) It is not easy to fit into the quality objective approach because the element of choice given to the discharger makes it difficult to plan stream quality.

(iii) Although those who pollute most should pay most, those who have established themselves in a site favourably placed to make responsible use of the receiving capacity of the natural environment should not be penalized when they achieve standards appropriate to their situation.

## Control of Discharges of Trade Wastes to Sewers

This deserves a brief mention because increasingly restrictive consent conditions imposed on direct discharges of trade effluents to streams has resulted in diversions to sewers. An industrial discharger has a right, subject to the consent of the water authority concerned, to drain into public sewers. The authority is empowered to impose quality and quantity conditions on the discharge, and to charge for conveyance and treatment. Some industrial discharges so received cause difficulty at the sewage treatment works and can lead to unsatisfactory discharges to rivers. On the other hand, some are easier to treat as admixtures to sewage. They are a significant element in planning for control of river water quality and considerably complicate the calculations involved.

Although district councils and London boroughs have a statutory right to carry out the sewerage function under arrangements made with the water authority, this right does not extend to control of discharges of trade wastes to sewers. Only exceptionally does the council carry out such work on behalf of the water authority.

## 3. THE WATER COMPANIES

### GENERAL

It was explained earlier that the water companies remain much as they were before 1974. There are 30 companies in all and a number of non-statutory water undertakers with the status of private suppliers. The greatest concentration of companies is in the South-East of the country, but one of the largest (the South Staffordshire Waterworks Company) is in the Midlands and companies supply about 60 per cent of the water distributed in the Northumbrian region. Table 2.IV is a schedule of the companies and gives some indication of their size and importance. In total they supply a population of 12 million people, they have an annual income approaching £100 million, and they employ a workforce of nearly 9000 employees.

An indication of the scale of the companies' undertakings is that the revenue expenditure of the largest is equivalent to that of one of the three Wessex Water Authority multi-purpose divisions, but the average is perhaps a third of this amount.

Each company is constituted like a normal commercial enterprise and operates under the various Companies Acts. The board of directors is usually small, for

TABLE 2.IV.   Statistics for Statutory Water Companies

| Company | Population, thousands | Area, km$^2$ | Supply, m$^3$/day |
|---|---|---|---|
| Bournemouth and District | 229 | 352 | 5 500 |
| Bristol | 942 | 2 391 | 290 000 |
| Cambridge | 233 | 1 173 | 54 000 |
| Chester | 106 | 132 | 26 000 |
| Cholderton and District | 2.5 | 20 | 500 |
| Colne Valley | 754 | 386 | 230 000 |
| Corby (Northants) and District | bulk supply to British Steel | | |
| East Anglia | 214 | 1 310 | 69 000 |
| Eastbourne | 190 | 826 | 52 000 |
| East Surrey | 335 | 733 | 98 000 |
| East Worcestershire | 217 | 777 | 53 000 |
| Essex | 1 339 | 1 538 | 350 000 |
| Folkestone and District | 141 | 410 | 42 000 |
| Hartlepools | 101 | 90 | 55 000 |
| Lee Valley | 980 | 2 227 | 250 000 |
| Mid Kent | 492 | 2 056 | 117 000 |
| Mid Southern | 590 | 1 500 | 165 000 |
| Mid Sussex | 225 | 1 040 | 58 000 |
| Newcastle and Gateshead | 783 | 4 802 | 244 000 |
| North Surrey | 456 | 526 | 136 000 |
| Portsmouth | 630 | 868 | 203 000 |
| Rickmansworth and Uxbridge Valley | 564 | 601 | 202 000 |
| South Staffordshire | 1 249 | 1 507 | 325 000 |
| Sunderland and South Shields | 580 | 342 | 126 000 |
| Sutton District | 281 | 100 | 68 000 |
| Tendring Hundred | 115 | 352 | 24 000 |
| West Hampshire | 141 | 696 | 33 000 |
| West Kent | 140 | 240 | 29 000 |
| Wrexham and East Denbighshire | 131 | 689 | 37 000 |
| York | 161 | 340 | 46 000 |

example there are only six in the South Staffordshire Waterworks Company and five in the Rickmansworth and Uxbridge Valley Water Company, and they are selected in the normal way by the shareholders. Yet the companies are subject to the stringent financial constraints contained in the Third Schedule of the Water Act 1945. These are designed to ensure that any surpluses are applied to a reduction of charges. These limitations can be summarized as:—

   (1)   statutory control on the maximum rate of dividend;
   (2)   share capital must be issued by auction;
   (3)   limits on reserve and contingency funds;
   (4)   limit on the carrying forward of surpluses to succeeding years.

Although it has been argued that these limitations could inhibit enterprise, they are inevitable in the case of monopoly suppliers and have the effect of very much narrowing the distinction between the companies and other publicly owned utilities.

Relations with the water authorities are governed under statutory arrangements entered into between the two parties "whereby the company undertake to act on behalf of the authority for the purposes of (the supply of water) and provision is made for such incidental supplementary and consequential matters (including matters of a financial nature) as the authority think desirable''. These arrangements may include provisions for the management of sources of supply, bulk supplies, and the company's charges for the supply of water. The Water Act 1973 gives the water authority powers to require the companies to survey consumption and demand, to formulate proposals for meeting future requirements, and to report to the water authority. In some cases companies collect miscellaneous service charges on behalf of the water authority.

The companies are, of course, subject to other controls such as the licensing of their sources of supply and in planning for the development of new resources. Good informal relationships have been developed through the medium of *ad hoc* regional committees which in most cases provide effective liaison. Most companies are subscribing members of the Water Research Centre and they participate fully in the work of the NWC committees dealing with manpower, safety, productivity, etc. They are also represented on and are active contributors to the DoE/NWC standing technical committees.

## STRUCTURE

The traditional management structure of the companies consists of a triumvirate of clerk (administrator), engineer, treasurer (accountant) in the larger companies and a diarchy of engineer and treasurer/accountant in the smaller. There are signs that in the circumstances after the 1974 Act this pattern is changing. In particular, the importance of the waterworks chemist is becoming recognized and in the Essex Water Company he is included in a corporate management team very similarly constituted to the divisional management teams of some of the water authorities.

Typically, the headquarters staff of a company is divided into two main groups with the engineering and technical staff somewhat separate from the remainder dealing with administration, establishments, personnel, revenue collection and accounting, etc. The engineering branch usually consists of a new works and supply division and one or more water distribution divisions, but the arrangements vary, particularly where there is a multiplicity of smaller sources of supply.

In practice, there is little significant structural difference between the organization of a company's services and that of a single-purpose water supply division based on the historical structure inherited from the predecessor water undertakers.

## WATER COMPANIES ASSOCIATION

The 28 larger water companies are members of the Water Companies Association, which has the primary purpose of encouraging and facilitating the efficiency, the exercise of powers, and discharge of responsibility of the companies. The Association has its own permanent officers and its own private offices in London. Perhaps its most important role is in the operation of a Central Pensions Fund available to the staff of every company. The fund gives pension rights and benefits not less favourable than those enjoyed by water authority employees.

The association is managed by an executive committee constituted of one representative of each member company, and has various committees to enable it to form and present the corporate views of the companies.

## 4. THE SEWERAGE FUNCTION

The Water Act 1973 (Section 15) gave district councils and London boroughs the right to perform the sewerage function on behalf of water authorities. This is done under the terms of agreements under which the councils are required to:—

*(a)* prepare and annually revise a programme of sewerage works for their area;

*(b)* undertake any such programme of works approved by the water authority;

*(c)* provide personnel, vehicles, and equipment to undertake sewer maintenance and operation.

In return the water authorities reimburse the councils for expenses incurred in the discharge of the function.

Not all district councils have taken on the function. In rural areas in particular there is a close relationship between the maintenance and operation of the sewers and of the sewage disposal works. In a number of districts with a preponderance of rural areas the water authority carries out the sewerage function itself. Other notable exceptions are the Greater London Area, where the trunk sewerage system is operated by the Thames Water Authority, and the trunk sewerage system of the former Upper Tame Main Drainage Authority which is now operated by the Severn-Trent Water Authority. Where the sewerage function is undertaken by the water authority, it is usually performed as part of the work of a multi-purpose division.

Because local government reorganization took place concurrently with that of the water industry, a number of district councils took over sewerage as a "new" function from municipal undertakings.

Although little has been published about sewerage construction, operation, and maintenance under the Section 15 agreements, it is important to appreciate that they take up a considerable part of the water authorities' budgets. The proportion varies widely from authority to authority, but the range is between 6 and about 15 per cent. As much as one-third of the total capital expenditure of a water authority can be under the control of the district councils, although the average is much less than this.

As well as dealing with the sewerage function, district councils perform a number of related duties:—

  (i) Septic tank and cesspool emptying.
 (ii) Obtaining and maintaining sewer records.
(iii) Maintaining certain ditches and watercourses.
(iv) Drain and private sewer clearance.
 (v) Maintenance of highway, as highway authorities.
(vi) Operation and maintenance of surface water pumping stations.
(vii) Gully emptying as highway authorities.
(viii) Maintenance of certain sewers, drains, etc., on council housing estates.

In addition, the councils carry out such operations as adoption of sewers and vesting them in the water authorities, guarding against building over sewers, and other actions of a similar nature in connection with looking after the interests of the water authorities. The position of New Towns under the 1973 Act is not clear, and there have been disputes over the precise meaning of the relevant section. Development Corporations constituted under Section 34 of the New Towns Act 1965 can exercise the sewerage function.

Sewerage districts vary widely from scattered rural areas to those of densely populated boroughs. Organizations to deal with the function vary equally widely, but there are certain features which apply fairly generally in all but the larger towns. These are the relationships with highway maintenance and, to a lesser extent, with waste collection duties of the councils. Traditionally, highways and sewerage maintenance has been carried out from common depots with common vehicles and equipment and in some ways local authority reorganization has strengthened these ties by reducing the functions operated by district councils.

In many councils direct involvement in sewerage is limited to operation and maintenance. New works are designed and constructed under the supervision of consulting engineers. This has limited the need for large establishments under the chief engineer or surveyor at district council headquarters; the main operations are directed from a central depot or from a number of local depots. This is especially true of rural areas.

At the other extreme, particularly in metropolitan districts, the sewerage system is operated by a single-purpose team backed by full scale design offices capable of designing and supervising the construction of the largest sewers. Such expertise is not available to many of the divisions of the water authorities. In those areas the maintenance and operation of the larger sewers is highly skilled and needs adequate training and expert supervision.

Although, normally, the elected district councils oversee the work of their chief engineer and other officers in carrying out the sewerage function, in practice the supervision is fairly nominal. Only in the event of a dispute between their officials and those of the water authority is a council likely to have to take a positive role.

At the present time water authorities exercise relatively little control on the revenue expenditure side of the sewerage agencies. Gradually tighter control can be expected. The water authority divisions deal with the district councils, mainly in connection with capital expenditure or new works. Because of the general lack of sewerage expertise at divisional level, water authority headquarters become more involved with the function than would otherwise be the case.

It would appear that in some areas the agency arrangements work reasonably well, in others they are very unsatisfactory, not only from the water authority point of view. The control on expenditure can be haphazard and information from the district councils on the performance of the function is often inadequate. The present concern about the state of the nation's sewers requires an urgent and co-ordinated examination of the situation. This is needed not only to determine optimum maintenance and replacement, but also to avoid panic measures.

## 5. LAND DRAINAGE

### GENERAL

Under the Land Drainage Act 1976 land drainage is described as "the drainage of land and the provision of flood warning systems". The function includes flood protection and sea defence and, in particular:—

(1) Work to improve the channel and limit flooding in designated stretches of streams known as "main river".
(2) Such works as the East Coast sea defences and the Thames Barrier.
(3) Supervision of watercourses not designated as main river.
(4) Development and operation of inland and coastal flood warning systems.
(5) Drainage of land for agriculture.

Coast protection works to limit erosion on the coast, in practice land not subject to flooding, and public health act drainage works are not included; both are the responsibility of the relevant local authority.

Although land drainage is a highly significant activity, it is carried out with a relatively small proportion of water authority staff and expenditure.

The total number of water authority land drainage staff in England and Wales is of the order of 5000 and the water authority revenue expenditure was about £35 million in 1976-77. This figure represents under 4 per cent of the total. As might be expected, the proportion is highest in the Anglian Water Authority where it rises to nearly 7 per cent. This Authority has 6 425 km of main river and has to look after 1 308 km of sea defences, including tidal rivers.

In addition, the internal drainage boards spend something of the order of £11 million per annum. Figures are not available for local authority expenditure, but it is not likely to be very large.

## WATER AUTHORITIES

With the exception of those areas covered by single-purpose divisions, e.g. Yorkshire and Anglian Water Authority areas, the water authority land drainage work is carried out as part of the normal operations of a multi-purpose division and the type of organization mentioned earlier in this chapter applies. In the Anglian Authority area the river divisions are organized in a similar way to the predecessor river authorities, and land drainage is dealt with accordingly. In the Yorkshire and the North-West Water Authority areas land drainage is dealt with by a regional single-purpose division.

Water authorities are responsible for all the items listed above, and in all cases the function is the responsibility of the statutory land drainage committees. The accounts—revenue and expenditure—are separately kept. Revenue is raised by precepting on the relevant local authorities and internal drainage boards, and is calculated to cover the expenses of the service. There is, therefore, a clear distinction between it and other functions of a water authority.

The description of the work given above gives some indication of the complex relationship between water and local authorities due to the overlap of responsibility for drainage where rivers are not "mained" and for coastal protection matters. A further complication arises in connection with the use of river flood plains for development, housing, roads, etc., and conflict can arise between the water and planning authorities. Thus, although land drainage is primarily dealt with at divisional level, headquarters staffs are continually involved.

A storm tide warning system was set up by the Government after the disastrous East Coast tidal flooding in 1953. It is operated by the Ministry of Defence in conjunction with the Meteorological Office and is co-ordinated by MAFF. Different levels of alert have been arranged. If a particular division of the coast is in danger, warnings are sent to the relevant water authority and to the police who decide what action to take. Local authorities are, of course, concerned and civil and voluntary aid is available to water authorities where their resources are inadequate to deal with a potential emergency.

Under Section 24 of the Water Act 1973 water authorities are required to survey their areas for land drainage and to report to the Minister. These surveys include the recording of flood plains and of areas in danger of inundation by tidal waters or from arterial watercourses. Medium and long-term plans are to be drawn up, evaluated, and rolled forward year by year. By and large, such work is dealt with at regional headquarters and is in many ways related to the work of the resource planning department.

## INTERNAL DRAINAGE BOARDS

At the time of reorganization of the water industry in 1974 there were 321 Internal Drainage Boards (IDBs) with a combined income of £4.5 million and covering a total area of 1¼ million ha. The biggest concentration was in the valley of the Great Ouse, Lincolnshire, Essex, and Kent and in the Humber hinterlands.

The Land Drainage Act 1976 defines IDBs and their functions as follows:—

> "For the purpose of the drainage of land there shall continue to be within water authority areas, districts known as internal drainage districts and for each such district there shall be a board known as an internal drainage board, which shall be a body corporate.
> "Internal drainage districts shall be such areas as will derive benefit or avoid danger as a result of drainage operations.
> "An internal drainage board shall exercise a general supervision over all matters relating to the drainage of land within their district and shall have such other powers and perform such other duties as are conferred or imposed on internal drainage boards by this Act".

Those boards constituted since the Land Drainage Act 1930 consist of members elected by all the drainage ratepayers in the district under a weighted vote system, whereby the number of votes cast is related to the assessable value of the property held by the voter. For example, if the value is less than £50 he is entitled to only one vote and if it is more than £1 000 he may cast ten votes.

A member of a board must be an owner or an occupier of land of minimum specified area within the district, or he must be nominated by the owners of such land.

Boards generally supervise all matters relating to drainage of land within their districts, they maintain and improve existing works, and they can construct new works. Their income is derived from a drainage rate and they receive grants from MAFF for works of improvement and new works. The powers are permissive and they are not under any legal obligation to drain, but should their affairs become unsatisfactory the relevant water authority may petition the Minister.

Water authorities may at any time submit to the Minister (or the Secretary of State for Wales) for confirmation schemes for the transfer to them of functions of any drainage body or for the reorganization of internal drainage districts. Since 1974 there has been a gradual process of rationalization of the IDBs. It is MAFF policy that the districts should be of sufficient size to be effective. Some boards are very small and are run by the part-time efforts of someone who is, perhaps, a local solicitor; the works might be carried out by a contractor and the board might only employ one or two full-time maintenance workers. At the other end of the scale are quite large organizations headed by a clerk and a fully qualified engineer and with a qualified design staff. Water authorities may attempt to eliminate the former category of undertaking and may themselves act as the boards of districts within their regions. In the latter event revenue is raised in the same way as that of an internal drainage board, and the water authority is "answerable" to the ratepayers of the particular district.

## FIELD DRAINAGE

There is a close relationship between field drainage systems and the water levels in ditches, dikes, and streams. This close relationship has been recognized by Parliament. It was the reason for the creation of the earlier land drainage and catchment boards and for the creation of the statutory land drainage committees. The farming community is well represented on the water authority local land drainage committees, and both field and land drainage interests are looked after by the same government department and advisory services.

## 6. THE NATIONAL LEVEL IN ENGLAND AND WALES

NATIONAL WATER COUNCIL

### Status and Functions

The Council was set up by the Water Act 1973 and is an independent statutory body with statutory functions to perform in its own rights; its expenditure is defrayed by the water authorities. The status and role of the Council are set out in its first report:—

> "The constitution of the Council and its statutory duties are set in the Water Act at the broadest level in terms of it being the national centre for consultation, advice and co-ordination in respect of ten separate autonomous statutory Authorities. This framework set by Parliament reflects the desire of Government to be able to consult on occasion both formally and informally through a single national point of contact. But the Authorities have a practical need for co-operative activity in any event. They all have to face the same range of policy and planning questions and need at the very least a common understanding of them (even if not agreement); they also need to develop some operational methods and techniques in concert and to transmit useful ideas from one to another in order to save effort and public criticism by not inventing and re-inventing the wheel ten times over.
>
> "In practice the relationship between a constitutionally weak central body and constitutionally strong regional bodies must understandably be somewhat delicate. It has been clearly understood by all concerned that the effectiveness of the Council depends on the commitment of all to the necessity and advantage of joint involvement of Council and Authorities. The views of individual Authorities and of the Council will not always coincide. But provided the essence of any matter is set out clearly there need be little difficulty or embarrassment in bringing together differing views and the reason for them. And so it has proved.
>
> "The formal meetings and other activities of the Council provide a forum in which Chairmen of Authorities and their appointed independent colleagues can consider together issues on which common approach or understanding is necessary. But not everything needs to be dealt with at that level. Regular meetings of officers of the Authorities and the Council are convened to consider business of mutual interest of all kinds. Individual questions may result in executive action or report to an Authority or to the Council as appropriate".

The National Water Council has set up an organizational structure to conform with its statutory duties, either explicit or derived. These cover advice on water policy; assistance in research and technical development; training and education; the establishment and operation of negotiating machinery covering pay and conditions of employment for the water industry; an information service for the benefit of the industry and all other interested parties; the operation of a superannuation scheme; and the necessary secretarial, establishment and financial servicing and regulation of the Council's domestic business, and of its involvement in joint working with the water authorities.

The Act gives the Council the power, if requested by two or more water authorities, to perform services and these may be extended to statutory water companies in England and Wales and to other bodies in the rest of the U.K.

All the above are subject to a general power of direction by the Secretary of State (or if appropriate the Minister) to instruct the Council to carry out additional functions or to discontinue any specified activity.

### Constitution

The Act provides for the Council to consist of:—
— a chairman appointed by the Secretary of State,
— the chairmen of the water authorities,

— not more than ten other members of whom not more than eight are appointed by the Secretary of State and not more than two by the Minister. This category must be persons who have a special knowledge of matters relevant to the functions of the water authorities.

There are no requirements for any statutory committees except in connection with the testing and approval of water fittings (see below).

### Relationship with Scotland and Northern Ireland

The Water Act 1973 deals with the reorganization of the water industry in England and Wales and with some exceptions the functions of the Council relate only to those parts of the U.K. None of the members of the Council has peculiarly Scottish interests, and the Council has no formal relationship with the Secretary of State for Scotland or with the Scottish and Northern Ireland water industry.

Nevertheless, there are important functions where the Council has a U.K. role. Under the provisions of Section 4 (5) of the Act the Council has implemented a scheme for training and education in the water services throughout the U.K. The scheme is governed by a committee with members representing Scottish and Northern Ireland interests and with a Scottish sub-committee. Also under Section 4 of the Act the Council has a statutory committee, including members representing the interests of the water industries in Scotland and Northern Ireland, dealing with the testing and approval of water fittings. There are also a number of informal arrangements for co-ordination. In connection with manpower services, the Council acts as consultant to DoE Northern Ireland on organization and on preparation for the introduction of incentive schemes. In addition, Scottish and Northern Ireland interests have been well represented in the technical committee structure and in advisory working groups.

### Organization

The management structure of the Council is set out below. The total staff employed is about 320: the training division strength is about 170, and staff engaged on superannuation is about 50. The total number of staff in the Headquarters in London is less than 90. Revenue expenditure was rather less than £2 million in 1976-77. This figure does not include training expenditure which is on a separate account and which is largely self-financing.

### Policy Formulation and Advice

Under Section 4 (5) of the Act, the Council has a duty to advise Ministers and water authorities on any matters relating to national policy or common interest.

The Council has elected to act with and through the water authorities and has set up a number of advisory and co-ordinating committees to deal with major policy issues.

There are two categories of committees. The first deals directly with policy matters and consists of meetings of directors of the water authorities, e.g. Chief Executives Group and Directors of Operations Group. Senior officials of the DoE are invited to attend meetings. Matters discussed include such items as common financial policy, co-ordination of views on potential legislation and on implementation of legislation, relationship with local authorities and nationalized industries, and resource development. These groups have set up a number of *ad hoc* committees and working parties to study particular problems in detail.

Chairman

Director general — Deputy director general

Secretary
Establishment
Personnel
Testing and approval
of water fittings

Policy and technical
division

Director of training

Operations, England and Wales
Operations, Scotland and
Northern Ireland
Management
Development

Director of manpower services

Industrial relations
Research and services

Head of information

Public relations
Water Information Centre

Director of finance

Financial services
Accounts
Superannuation

Staffing and services
for Water Space Amenity Commission

The second category of committees include a group of joint DoE/NWC standing technical committees, which serve the industry in the widest sense. These are composed of individuals from within the industry, from government including Scotland and Northern Ireland, and from many organizations with an interest in water matters. They have the duty of giving technical advice related to policy formulation, of advising on research needs, influencing standards and codes of practice, and of generating a common approach to technical advance within the water industry. They report to DoE and NWC jointly.

**Relationship with Other Organizations**

The most important links maintained by the Council are of course with the DoE and the formal relationship shown in Fig. 2.8 is supplemented by a number of informal links with Government Departments and Committees.

The Council is a member of EUREAU, the association of the water industries of the European Community. It participates in the work of the co-ordinating committees which, as part of their function, exert influence on the work of the European Commission.

**Research**

A further important role of the Council, in connection with the Water Research Centre, is dealt with separately in Chapter 7 of this book.

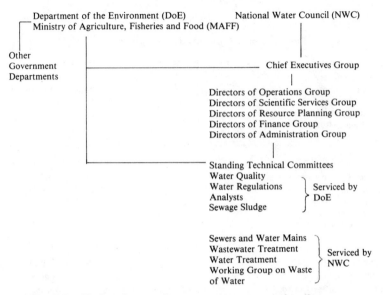

**Fig. 2.8. National committee structure—reporting lines**

### Training

The Council was required by the Water Act 1973 to formulate a scheme for education and training for the water industry. That scheme was approved in September 1974 with the objectives of advancing the training and education of employees of participating bodies, establishing and complementing a comprehensive training and education plan, and seeing to the provision of the required facilities.

The Scheme is administered by the Training Committee of the Council, which consists among others of a number of chairmen of the water authorities, members concerned with employees' organizations, members concerned with education, a Scottish water industry member, and a member appointed by the Water Companies Association. There is a Scottish Subcommittee.

The implementation of training policy and programmes is the responsibility of the Training Division of the NWC. This was formed from the basis of the staff and assets of the former Water Supply Industry Training Board. The assets included five training establishments with a total of 180 places providing a full range of residential courses. This figure has now been increased to about 250.

Apart from the provision of residential courses, the Division provides a service of training and education, advice and expertise within the water services, and operates a financial grants scheme to encourage the use of courses. Part of its work involves training staff to act as instructors "on-the-job" within the participating authorities. The Tadley Court centre concentrates on management training, which includes short-term seminars. The other centres at Millis House, Burn Hall, Melvin House, and Flint House, deal principally with technicians, supervisors, craftsmen, clerks, and operators, and are being developed in specialized fields. For example, Millis House is becoming the water industry's focal point for health and safety training.

The total staff employed is about 170, the 1976/77 expenditure amounted to about £1 700 000, and nearly 10 000 man-weeks of training were provided.

## Scheme for Testing and Approval of Water Fittings

Water undertakers make bye-laws for the prevention of waste and contamination of water supplied by them and have powers to ensure that water fittings comply with those bye-laws. Under Section 4 (5) and (6) of the Water Act 1973 the Council has established a scheme for the testing and approval of water fittings on behalf of water undertakers in the U.K. The Management Committee includes ten members appointed after consultation with the water authorities, two members appointed by the Water Companies Association, two members appointed by the Convention of Scottish Local Authorities, and one member appointed by the DoE (Northern Ireland). The Management Committee is responsible to the Council for operating the scheme and maintaining machinery for the determination of complaints about decisions of its Technical Committee. The latter is the executive committee which makes the technical decisions about compliance with bye-laws, determines test criteria, monitors the performance of test establishments, and arranges inspections of manufacturers and stock holders.

Manufacturers, designers, installers, and professional bodies concerned with water installations are represented on a Consultative and Liaison Committee, which deals with any matter arising out of the scheme and makes recommendations to the Management or to the Technical Committee.

The Scheme supervises the Council's water fittings testing station at Staines. This has an establishment of 10 and was taken over from the former British Waterworks Association in 1974.

## Manpower

The principal task of the Council's manpower staff is to service the five separate joint national negotiating bodies covering:—

| | | | |
|---|---|---|---|
| — manual employees ............ | numbering about | | 42 000 |
| — craftsmen ...................... | ,, | ,, | 4 000 |
| — staff .............................. | ,, | ,, ⎫ | 24 000 |
| — senior staff ..................... | ,, | ,, ⎬ | |
| — chief officers ................. | ,, | ,, ⎭ | 65 |

The Chairman of the Council acts as chairman of the employers' side and of the joint negotiating bodies. These bodies relate to the Regional Joint Industrial Councils and the Regional Joint Councils in each water authority area.

The Council's manpower division services a Joint Productivity Committee which has agreed a national productivity payment scheme for the industry which will be implemented when national incomes policies permit.

The water industry has set up a National Joint Health and Safety Committee. Local consultation on safety matters has been grafted on to the Regional Joint Industrial Councils and to their local Joint Consultative Committee. These arrangements fit in well with the regulations under the Health and Safety at Work Act 1974 as a basis for the required statutory safety committees. Advice on safe operational practices is organized by the issue of a series of Safety Advisory Broadsheets to encourage a common approach throughout the industry. There are arrangements to ensure that safety training with the water authorities and in the Council's training establishments is comprehensive. These include training of the employee safety representatives and supervisors.

## Superannuation

By statute the Council administers a superannuation scheme for the employees of the Council and the ten Regional Water Authorities. By agreement the scheme extends to employees of the Water Research Centre. The scheme itself is subject to the regulations governing the Local Government Superannuation Scheme.

The Council's responsibilities for superannuation are threefold: to undertake pensions administration (carried out from a decentralized office in Sheffield); to manage the investments of the Superannuation Fund; and to participate with local authority employers and the trade unions in the development of local government superannuation policy under the aegis of the U.K. Steering Committee on Local Government Superannuation.

## Finance

In addition to the management of superannuation and domestic finance, the Council's Finance Division provides a technical secretariat to support regular meetings of Water Authority finance directors and their staffs in dealing with matters where common or joint action is desirable. The management of foreign currency borrowing and the development of an industry policy on inflation accounting are two such matters that have received considerable attention.

The Council functions as agent for the authorities in relation to foreign borrowing, and in this way can combine the requirements of individual authorities to raise major loans on favourable terms. As a piece of practical machinery, loan negotiations are conducted and operating decisions taken on the advice of a small working group consisting of three water authority finance directors and the Council's finance director.

## Information Services

The information service staff of the Council collate, store, and disseminate information as a management service for the industry and provide a complementary service directed to the public. The Council presents and interprets the role, national policies, and problems of the industry to the public and media. It promotes, contacts, and exchanges information with water and other public service organizations, institutions, associations and research bodies.

The Council's Water Information Centre affords information within and outside the industry, and its publications include the Council's weekly bulletin and a bi-monthly journal *(Water)*.

## WATER SPACE AMENITY COMMISSION

The Commission was set up under Section 23 of the Water Act 1973 and is an independent statutory body in its own right. Its function is to advise the Secretary of State on the formulation, promotion, and execution of the recreational and amenity aspects of the national water policy. It is also responsible for advising and assisting the water industry on all matters relating to water recreation and amenity.

Although it is an independent body, its membership includes the ten chairmen of the water authorities and its chairman is also a member of the National Water Council. This common membership maintains a strong relationship between the two bodies and the Commission is serviced by the NWC. All the other members are appointed by the Secretary of State.

The Commission forms an integral part of the water industry. It sees its tasks as co-ordinating and promoting activities in connection with water space within the control of the industry as the amenity arm of the Council and as the link between the water industry and amenity and recreational interests in general.

In addition to co-ordination through its own regular meetings and through the membership of the chairmen of the water authorities, the Commission promotes training seminars and conferences and has set up a number of working parties. It publishes a quarterly journal and has issued advisory and information leaflets. It has initiated a research programme.

## GOVERNMENT DEPARTMENTS

### Department of the Environment

The Secretary of State for the Environment, the Secretary of State for Wales, and the Minister of Agriculture, Fisheries and Food have the duty of promoting and securing the effective execution of a national policy for water. The Secretaries of State deal with the full range of the functions of the water industry, except for land drainage and fisheries in inland and coastal waters. The Secretaries of State also have the duty of collating and publishing information relating to the demand for water and of actual and prospective water resources.

The Water Act 1973 gives general powers of direction to the Secretaries of State, but these have never been used. Policy is developed formally and informally through the constant dialogue which takes place at all levels between the Department and the Welsh Office on the one hand and the National Water Council and regional water authorities on the other. The Secretaries of State, with the Minister of Agriculture, Fisheries and Food, have the duty of appointment of the Chairmen and prescribed numbers of members of the Council and the regional water authorities. Under Section 24 of the Water Act 1973, the Secretaries of State have the duty of examining and approving regional water authorities' periodical reviews, plans and programmes, thereby exerting considerable influence upon the level of capital expenditure. In addition, EEC Directives might have an increasing influence on the functions and expenditure of water authorities.

In the Department of the Environment, water industry sponsorship rests with the Water Directorate which is also concerned with certain aspects of water pollution control. Matters concerning solid and toxic wastes disposal are dealt with by the Air, Noise and Wastes Directorate and the assessment of toxic substances, chemical information system, notification of new chemicals and environmental monitoring are dealt with in the Central Directorate on Environmental Pollution of which the Water Data Unit forms a part. The latter is responsible for co-ordinating data collection needed by Government Departments.

The Water Directorate comprises six divisions. Three are under the chief water engineer and these deal with water authority plans and programmes (national strategy and investment), technical matters (committees, water bye-laws, civil emergencies and special studies), and statutory matters (grants, certain appeals and coast protection). The other three divisions deal with water industry structure (organization, legislation, financial policy and accounts, and the British Waterways Board), and administrative and technical aspects of water pollution control (principally, Part II of the Control of Pollution Act and EEC Directives concerning water quality).

The chemical division deals primarily with water quality matters. It services the Standing Technical Advisory Committee on Water Quality, and it advises on EEC directives concerned with water quality and on water quality monitoring in England and Wales.

The Water Data Unit, at Reading, is an integral part of the Directorate General and is responsible for co-ordinating data collection needed by Government Departments, for obtaining, processing, and archiving information, and publishing information in connection with the Secretary of State's statutory duties. The Unit is responsible for the River Pollution Surveys and for the collection and processing of data in connection with the Harmonized Monitoring Scheme and *ad hoc* water quality surveys.

There is constant communication at all levels between the DGEP and the water industry both in connection with policy matters and with technical matters.

### Central Water Planning Unit

The Unit was created when the Water Resources Board was abolished in 1974 to act as an idependent source of advice on national and strategic planning to both Government and the National Water Council. In this it continues the role of the Water Resources Board in examining alternative strategies for water resource development. The strategies are not only concerned with the development of new sources of supply, but also with making the optimum use of existing sources including problems associated with re-use of water and with the development of planning techniques of general application to the water industry.

The staff are civil servants numbering between 50 and 60. They include a large proportion of professional engineers and scientists, supported by a small administrative section. The work of the Unit is supervised by a small Steering Committee representing the National Water Council and the Departments concerned. The Committee is chaired by the chairman of the Council and includes the Director General of the Council and the Director General of DGEP (DoE). This structure has given the Unit a degree of independence in its work and in its reporting.

### Ministry of Agriculture, Fisheries and Food

*Land Drainage.*—The Minister of Agriculture, Fisheries and Food is responsible for general land drainage legislation, and for securing effective administration of land drainage policy in England. Equivalent matters in Wales are dealt with by the Secretary of State for Wales.

The Minister is jointly responsible with Secretaries of State for broad matters such as the setting up of water authorities and himself appoints 2 to 4 members to each authority. Regional Land Drainage Committees are chaired by one of these members.

The Land Drainage Act 1976 consolidated previous land drainage legislation and includes the following matters in which the consideration and consent of the appropriate Minister may be required:—

(a) Main river maps, and variations to them. These indicate watercourses which are "main river" and therefore the exclusive responsibility of the water authority for improvement and maintenance.

(b) Schemes submitted by water authorities for the creation, abolition, amalgamation, or alteration of the boundaries of internal drainage boards and responsibility for the preparation of statutory orders and maps associated with these schemes.

(c) Confirmation of the bye-laws of drainage boards.

(d) Various functions in relation to drainage rating.

The Minister is empowered to make grants to water authorities and other drainage authorities towards the costs of improvement of existing drainage works or the construction of new works. This applies also to the grant aid of sea defences for protection against tidal flooding. The cost of the provision of flood warning systems by water authorities is also eligible for grant aid. Expenditure on flood alleviation schemes for urban areas is substantial. Currently, there is in progress the massive Thames Tidal Barrier and associated schemes for the protection of London. About one-half of the total area of agricultural land in England and Wales depends on underdrainage and ditches and the Ministry's Land Drainage Service, which is a part of the Agricultural Development and Advisory Service, plays a vital role in the promotion of effective drainage as well as promoting research into improved ways of flood protection. In addition to grant aid towards the cost of works, advice is provided to farmers and drainage authorities. The Field Drainage Experimental Unit, at Cambridge, plays an essential part in the research and enjoys an international reputation.

The Land Drainage Service has an important role in crop irrigation in England and Wales which, in some 20 years, has developed to an area irrigated in a dry season of about 90 000 ha. Besides grant aid and advice to the farmer, essential information and advice is provided for the water authorities to help meet their duties of planning water resources and granting individual licences.

*Fisheries.*—The Fisheries Department of MAFF has overall responsibility for all matters relating to fisheries including conservation of stocks, fish processing, prevention of marine pollution, fish farming, and interference with fishing activities.

On the more specific question of the relationship with the "water industry" there are two major fields:—

(i) salmon and freshwater fisheries matters; and
(ii) the relationship which control of marine pollution necessarily bears to pollution controls in rivers, streams and pipeline discharges.

Salmon and freshwater fisheries are controlled essentially under the Salmon and Freshwater Fisheries Act 1975 which places a statutory duty on water authorities to maintain, improve, and develop their salmon, trout, freshwater and eel fisheries, and to establish advisory committees to help in the discharge of these duties. The Minister of Agriculture (jointly with the Secretary of State of Wales where appropriate) appoints a fisheries representative to each water authority. It is usual, although not mandatory, for this appointee to become Chairman of the Regional Fisheries Advisory Committee.

On pollution matters, the National Water Council is represented on the Marine Pollution Monitoring Management Group which is chaired by a scientist from the Fisheries Research Laboratory at Lowestoft (of MAFF). This Group is in broad terms responsible for U.K. programmes of monitoring of the marine environmental monitoring groups, for which the DoE is responsible for co-ordination.

Water authorities, with DoE and MAFF, will work together in operating the provisions of Part 2 of the Control of Pollution Act 1974, when that is brought into operation.

## Welsh Office

The office of the Secretary of State for Wales was established in 1965 and since then Welsh local authority affairs have come within his jurisdiction, including functions relating to water supply, water pollution, and other water services. Under the Water Act 1973, the Secretary of State for Wales shares with the Secretary of State for the Environment and the Minister of Agriculture, Fisheries and Food the responsibility for formulating the policy for water services in England and Wales, and has full responsibility for administering the Act in Wales.

The Government Department which serves the Secretary of State for Wales is the Welsh Office. The Secretary of State's functions under the Water Act 1973, and other legislation relating to water services excluding land, drainage, and fisheries are exercised on his behalf by two divisions of that Department—the Directorate of Engineering and the Local Government Division. Among their responsibilities is the control of the capital expenditure and the long term planning of the Welsh Water Authority. Land drainage and fisheries functions are carried out by the Welsh Office Agricultural Department.

## 7. THE WATER INDUSTRY IN SCOTLAND

### INTRODUCTION

The organizational structure of the water industry in Scotland is separate and distinct from that in the remainder of the U.K. The Secretary of State for Scotland has overall responsibility for national water policy, and this is exercised mainly through the Scottish Development Department, one of the five Departments which make up the Scottish Office. Another of the Departments, the Department of Agriculture and Fisheries for Scotland, is responsible for fisheries and certain aspects of land drainage. At local level, water supply and drainage have remained a local authority responsibility and are among the functions of regional and islands councils, while river pollution prevention is the responsibility of river purification boards and the islands councils.

### CENTRAL GOVERNMENT

The principal water supply duties of the Secretary of State for Scotland are those given to him by the Water (Scotland) Act 1946. These are to promote the conservation of the water resources of Scotland and the provision by local authorities of adequate supplies of water, to secure the collection and publication of data relating thereto and to appoint an advisory committee (the Scottish Water Advisory Committee) to advise the Secretary of State on these matters.

The statute governing sewerage and sewage disposal is the Sewerage (Scotland) Act 1968. The act provides a comprehensive code governing the provision of sewerage services by local authorities and regulating the discharge of trade effluent to public sewers. It replaces the provisions relating to sewerage in the Burgh Police (Scotland) Acts 1892 and 1903, the Public Health (Scotland) Act 1897, and in certain local Acts.

So far as river purification is concerned, the Rivers (Prevention of Pollution) (Scotland) Act 1951 provides that it shall be the duty of the Secretary of State to maintain and restore the wholesomeness of the rivers and other inland waters and the tidal waters of Scotland. It also provides for the appointment of the Scottish River Purification Advisory Committee, whose task is to advise the Secretary of State on matters relating to the cleanliness of the rivers and other inland waters and tidal waters of Scotland and to the prevention of pollution of these waters.

Under the terms of the Local Government (Scotland) Act 1973, local authorities are required to obtain the consent of the Secretary of State to their capital expenditure. It is by this means in the fields of water supply and drainage that authorities' programmes are monitored.

In addition to these statutes, the Secretary of State has certain powers and duties conferred on him by various U.K. Acts which convey to him powers and responsibilities which are similar to those of his colleagues. Examples of such Acts are the Dumping at Sea Act 1974, and the Control of Pollution Act 1974. The Secretary of State has, in general, similar responsibility to his colleagues elsewhere in respect of nagivation, water recreation, etc.

Within the Scottish Development Department, the Water, Sewerage and Pollution and Engineering Divisions are the divisions concerned with the above functions.

The drainage of agricultural land and its protection from flooding are among the responsibilities of the Department of Agriculture and Fisheries for Scotland. The Department promotes work either by grants paid under the Land Drainage (Scotland) Act 1958 or, more generally, by its Farm Capital Grant Scheme. Interest in freshwater fisheries in Scotland is concentrated on salmon and trout, and the ownership of rights to fish is in private hands. District Salmon Fishery Boards representing the owners of salmon fishing rights regulate salmon fisheries in terms of the Salmon Fisheries (Scotland) Acts 1862 to 1868.

In its international dealings the U.K. is usually represented by a single "lead" department which co-ordinates the views of all interested departments. Thus, for instance, on EEC matters related to water supply and environmental pollution, the Department of the Environment is normally the "lead" department, incorporating the views of the Scottish Office among others.

## LOCAL AUTHORITY ORGANIZATION PRIOR TO 1975

Prior to the reorganization of local government in Scotland, which took place in May 1975, public water supply was, from 1968, the responsibility of 13 regional water boards and the Central Scotland Water Development Board. This latter authority was constituted to provide new major bulk supplies to the boards serving the populous central belt, and was made up of representatives of the boards in that area. The regional water boards were the successors of the 126 local water supply authorities which existed until the coming into force of the Water (Scotland) Act 1967.

Sewerage and sewage disposal were the responsibility of 234 local drainage authorities comprising the four cities, 21 large burghs, 176 small burghs, and 33 county councils.

River purification was, for the well populated areas, the responsibility of nine river purification boards set up under the Rivers (Prevention of Pollution) (Scotland) Act 1951. In the remainder of the country 12 local authorities, 10 county councils and two large burghs, were the river purification authorities.

## REGIONAL COUNCILS

The locally elected authorities were constituted under the Local Government (Scotland) Act 1973, and they are responsible for roads, education, water, sewerage and sewage disposal, strategic, and in some cases all planning and a variety of other local authority functions. There are nine regions and in all but two of them (Strathclyde and Lothian) there is a single engineering directorate dealing with both water supply and sewerage. The areas of the regions are shown in Fig. 2.9. The

**Fig. 2.9.  Scottish administrative areas**
............... = Region or Islands area
——————— = River Purification Board
*Source:* Scottish Development Department

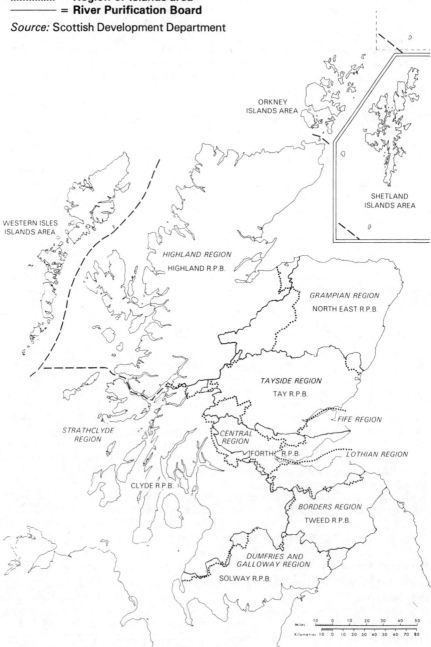

boundaries are administrative rather than hydrological, but the divergences between
the two are not such as to cause any serious problems. In two cases, the 1973 Act
provides for "added areas" for water supply purposes.

The populations of the regions vary from almost 100 000 (Borders) to over 2 500 000
(Strathclyde). Similarly, their areas range from 1 305 km$^2$ (Fife) to 25 130 km$^2$
(Highland). In general, the functions of the regions for public water supply and
sewerage and sewage disposal are similar to those of water authorities elsewhere in
the U.K., but there are a number of significant differences, most of which are due to
an absence of responsibility for the overall management of water resources at local
level. There is, for instance, no general licensing of abstractions of water in
Scotland, and supply authorities acquire water rights by means of Water Orders
made by the Secretary of State under the Water Acts. The other major difference
lies in the financing of these services which, in Scotland, are integrated with other
local authority services and funded from rates as well as water charges.

## CENTRAL SCOTLAND WATER DEVELOPMENT BOARD

The role of this separate bulk supply authority was preserved under the Local
Government (Scotland) Act 1973. The area of the Board comprises the limits of
supply of the Borders, Central, Fife, Lothians, Strathclyde, and Tayside Regions.
Bulk supplies are given to four of the constituents from its two major sources, Loch
Turrett and Loch Lomond. The Board has recently commissioned an extensive
survey of the water resources of its area (within which live almost 80 per cent of the
population of Scotland) to identify demands and alternative ways of meeting them
over the next 50 years or so. It remains to be seen what the precise pattern of
development as between local and bulk supplies will be, but already the existence of
the Board has done much to promote integration and flexibility in the use of sources
in Central Scotland.

## RIVER PURIFICATION BOARDS

At the time of local government reform the nine existing boards were disbanded
and seven new boards were created with responsibility for the whole of Scotland,
except for the areas of the Western Isles, Orkney and Shetland. Membership of
boards comprise one-third representing regional councils, one-third representing
district councils, and one-third appointed by the Secretary of State to represent the
interests of agriculture, fisheries, and industry. Boards are financed by precepts
levied on the regional councils whose areas lie, wholly or partly, within the Boards'
areas. The recommendation of the Royal Commission on Environmental Pollution
that estuaries should not come under the control of more than one pollution control
authority has been recognized and the board areas are based on catchment
boundaries as shown in Fig. 2.9. The general duties of the boards are to promote the
cleanliness of the rivers and other inland waters and tidal waters in their areas; to
conserve, as far as practicable, the water resources of the areas; and to exercise for
those purposes the functions conferred on them by the 1951 Act. The principal
function of boards is to grant consents, subject to such conditions as they think fit,
to discharge to the various waters and to carry out such survey and sampling work as
is necessary to determine the overall pollution situation.

## ISLANDS COUNCILS

There are three such councils—the Orkney, Shetland, and Western Isles Islands
Councils. Within their areas they are responsible for all local authority functions

including water supply, sewerage and sewage disposal and, in addition, prevention of pollution. Thus, it was recognized in the reform of local government in Scotland that while there was advantage in maintaining the separate river purification role for the more populous areas, in these remoter parts this could not be justified, bearing in mind the small populations involved and the generally good state of the waters.

### DISTRICT COUNCILS

Another level of local government in Scotland, excluding the areas of the islands councils, consists of 53 district councils. Their functions include development control, housing, waste collection, and other matters unrelated to the water industry. They are, however, involved to some extent as they are responsible for environmental health and thus for assessing any health risks associated with a particular water supply.

### NATIONAL WATER COUNCIL

In general, the remit of the NWC does not extend to Scotland. It does, however, have U.K. roles in respect of its scheme for training and for the testing and approval of water fittings (see above).

### FUTURE DEVELOPMENTS

At the time of writing (1978) the fate of the Scotland Bill remains unresolved. Were it to come into force, most of the Secretary of State's functions related to the water cycle would fall to the new Assembly. There is other change in prospect which is more certain. Implementation of Part II of the Control of Pollution Act 1974 would extend the already extensive control of purification authorities to all waters within the three mile limit, and also make further changes aimed at greater public awareness of and participation in the processes of pollution control.


## 8. THE NORTHERN IRELAND (DoE) WATER SERVICE

### GENERAL

Over 591 Ml of water a day is supplied throughout Northern Ireland (NI) to about 90 per cent of the population. The most important source of supply is Lough Neagh, one of the largest natural inland lakes in the British Isles. The Lough covers an area of 383 km² and it is estimated that if the top 25 mm were skimmed off a total of about 10 000 Ml of water would be collected. About one-third of all water supplied is taken from the Lough.

The Water Service of the DoE Northern Ireland became the sole water and sewerage authority on 1st October 1973, as part of the general reorganization of Local Government. The Department took over the statutory responsibility of some 79 local authorities and joint water and sewerage boards. The water and sewerage staff are classed as civil servants and the undertaking is unique because it goes beyond the usual "nationalized" concept. Water policy is formulated within the Department and is promulgated through the normal government process. This appears to work satisfactorily and parallels the formation of policies for roads and town and country planning which are also direct functions of the Department.

The functions dealt with in the Water Services are water supply, sewerage, and sewage disposal. There is no specific pollution control function, but the Department has powers to control discharges and to regulate abstraction of water.

## LEGISLATION AND FINANCE

The Water Act (NI) 1972 places a duty on the Department to promote the conservation and cleanliness of water resources. The Act also empowers the Department to make water management programmes and to make regulations controlling the abstractions of water.

The Water and Sewerage Service (NI) Order 1973 places a duty on the Department to supply and distribute water and to provide and maintain sewers for draining domestic sewage, surface water, and trade effluent and to make provision for effectually dealing with the contents of its sewers. The Department is also obliged to supply wholesome water for domestic purposes. The Order sets out the rights and duties of owners and occupiers of premises in relation to water and sewerage services.

The Water Charges Regulations (NI) 1973 provide for the levying on owners and occupiers of premises of charges for the supply of water, and for the proper provision and maintenance of adequate drains, sewage disposal facilities, service pipes, and water fittings.

The Water Regulations (NI) 1974 provide for standards for the provision of water fittings and pipes. The regulations replace the water byelaws of the former local authorities.

There is no legal obligation on the Department to balance revenue with expenditure. The services are financed with money voted by Parliament, and expenditure forecasts are included in the annual budget. The prescription and collection of charges for metered water supply is carried out by the Department, but other revenue is collected at divisional level.

## ORGANIZATION

The Water Service is headed by a Director at headquarters, with two divisions. The first, under the chief engineer, deals with water resources and planning, engineering services, communications, and management advisory services. The other, under an assistant secretary, deals with policy, administration, legislation, finance, and manpower.

A small scientific section reports within the chief engineer's command.

In the field there are four multi-functional divisions centred in Belfast, Ballymena, Craigavon, and Londonderry. Each water division is self-contained and has an administration/finance section and a planning and new works section. The structure is not dissimilar to that of a multi-functional water authority division in England, except that there is no suggestion of formal corporate management.

A further resemblance to the English divisions is in the delegation of responsibility to the divisional water managers by means of a statutory authority under the Water and Services (NI) Order and Regulations 1973. The divisional water manager and two senior officers in each division become "authorized officers", and have authority to sign specified instruments on behalf of the Department.

Each division has a scientific officer who, in common with other divisional officers, has informal lines of communication with headquarters, but the line of command is through the divisional manager in all cases.

## PUBLIC ACCOUNTABILITY

The Water and Sewerage Services (NI) Order 1973 set up the Northern Ireland Water Council consisting of 15 persons appointed by the head of the Department.

The members are chosen to reflect a wide spectrum of opinion and industry; commerce, agriculture, angling, and the trade unions are represented. Members hold office for three years and are eligible for reappointment. The Council advises the Department on all major policy questions and on the development of long-term water resource planning. It also advises on the amenity and recreational aspects of water use.

The executive decisions of the Department can affect many interests outside the Water Services. In England and Wales the Department is, in effect, the public watch dog and appeals against actions of the water authorities are taken by the Secretary of State. The NI Department is not in a position to hear appeals against its own actions and a special commission has been set up to solve the difficulty. This is the Water Appeals Commission established under the Water and Sewerage Services NI Order 1973. The Commission consists of persons appointed by the Secretary of State for Northern Ireland, i.e. a chief commissioner and such number of other commissioners as the Department, with the consent of the Department of Finance, determines. The jurisdiction of the Appeals Commission may be exercised by any of its members.

Where, in pursuance of the Water and Sewerage Services (NI) Order and Regulations 1973, any application or appeal is made to the Appeals Commission, the Commission is statutorily obliged to report its decision to the Department. The Department is empowered under the Order to vary a decision of the Appeals Commission or to substitute for it a new decision. The Department has not, so far, varied or substituted any such decision and it is unlikely to do so save in exceptional circumstances and with Ministerial approval.

## 9. THE INTERNATIONAL SCENE

### EUROPEAN COMMUNITY INSTITUTIONS

The Council of Ministers consists of ministers of each member state and are appointed by governments. Different ministers can represent their country depending on the subjects likely to arise on a particular agenda. The Council does not initiate legislation, but it is the basic decision-making body. Because its decisions are reached by compromise, some national interests are inevitably compromised. It is sometimes quite difficult to get sufficient interest taken in major technical problems in this political atmosphere.

The Commission itself consists of 13 members appointed by Governments on a four-year renewable basis. The Treaty requires that they act independently of national interest and this they have achieved to a greater extent than generally appreciated. The Commission is served by a body of permanent civil servants organized into directorates general. In addition, there is a department named the Environment and Consumer Protection Service which is in effect a directorate in its own right and is of particular interest because it produces the draft directives on water quality mentioned earlier in this chapter. Another directorate, DG XII, deals with research, science, and education; its research programme includes a fairly comprehensive list of environmental subjects.

The European Parliament (Strasbourg) consists of delegates appointed by the member states. Soon direct elections will take place. The body's powers are limited, but it is expected they will gradually increase over the years. At the time of writing (1978) its main power is to be able to dismiss the Commission given a two-thirds majority and to overrule the Council on certain budgetary matters if a 60 per cent vote can be obtained.

The Court of Justice acts in parallel with and not superior to national courts. In cases of community law national courts must refer to the Court for preliminary rulings. The prime function is gradually to secure by its decisions uniformity of interpretation of community law in the national courts. It also deals with cases where the Commission proceeds against a member state or proceedings by one member state against another.

A Committee of permanent representatives of each member state prepares the groundwork for Council meetings and the individual members provide a link between Brussels and member states for information and lobbying generally.

Features of the system are:—

(1) Balance between the Council of Ministers and the Commission.
(2) Relative unimportance of Parliament.
(3) Principle of veto in decision-making leading to the need for compromise by all rather than by majority rule.
(4) A functionalist approach, where work is started in fields where something can be achieved rather than by determining needs and priorities in an organized way.
(5) Economic objectives, i.e. monetary union and free trade within the Community, are paramount.
(6) A lack of understanding of technical issues within the Commission brought about by the dearth of professional representation within the permanent civil service. On the other hand, the staff is very sensitive to and aware of political issues.

The last three features named appear to be those that give rise to most difficulties in the U.K. They lead to the production of apparently unimportant directives and an apparent lack of an objective approach.

However, it is believed that the main difficulty with the Commission itself is common to most international activity, that is, the difficulty of communication between peoples with widely different background and approach in solving commonly experienced problems. It is almost always true that whenever people properly qualified to deal with a problem meet in a Community context, agreement can be reached.

## WORLD HEALTH ORGANIZATION

The World Health Organization (WHO) is one of the specialized agencies in relationship with the United Nations. Through this organization, which came into being in 1948, the public health and medical professions of more than 130 countries exchange knowledge and experience and collaborate in an effort to achieve the highest possible level of health throughout the world.

WHO is concerned primarily with problems that individual countries or territories cannot solve with their own resources. For example, the eradication or control of malaria, schistosomiasis, smallpox, and other communicable diseases, as well as some cardiovascular diseases and cancer.

Progress towards better health throughout the world also demands international co-operation in many other activities: for example, setting up international standards for biological substances, for pesticides, and for pesticides spraying equipment; compiling an international pharmacopeia; drawing up and administering the International Health Regulations; revising the international lists of diseases and causes of death; assembling and disseminating epidemiological information; recommending non-proprietary names for drugs; and promoting the exchange of scientific knowledge.

In many parts of the world there is need for improvement in maternal and child health, nutrition, nursing, mental health, dental health, social and occupational health, environmental health, public health administration, professional education and training, and health education of the public. Thus, a large share of the Organization's resources is devoted to giving assistance and advice in these fields and to making available—often through publications—the latest information on these subjects. Since 1958 an extensive international programme of collaborative research has added substantially to knowledge in many fields of medicine and public health. This programme is constantly developing and its many facets are reflected in WHO publications.

The WHO standards for drinking water quality are generally recognized by water undertakers in the U.K. as reliable guidelines, and they are often quoted as evidence of wholesomeness although they have no statutory basis. What is even more significant is that they are being used as the basis for discussion for standards prescribed in EEC directives.

## INTERNATIONAL CONVENTIONS

There are now a number of international agreements of considerable importance to the water industry. The Oslo and Paris conventions have already been mentioned. These agreements are arrived at voluntarily by the participating governments, and are enforced through national laws or by internal voluntary arrangements. The latter can be very effective in the U.K.; other countries prefer the regulatory approach.

## INTERNATIONAL STANDARDS-MAKING BODIES

The International Standards Organization (ISO) is of long standing and many of its standards are widely used and respected. Because of the large number of countries participating it also takes a long time for a particular standard to be agreed and published. It is especially successful in producing standards relevant to the conduct of international affairs, for example in world meteorology or in shipping. A number of the British Standards now widely used in the water industry have been harmonized and are now identical or technically equivalent with the ISO Standards.

The comparatively new European Standards-making body, CEN, has fairly close links with the European Commission and its standards are quoted in a number of directives as deeming to satisfy.

The membership of CEN is wider than that of the Community but it is roughly coincident with Western Europe including Austria, Spain, Portugal, and the Scandinavian countries.

It does not appear to produce standards any faster than ISO, perhaps for the reason that its standards could have more legal force within the Community. Although there is a great deal of activity of interest to the U.K. water industry amongst its technical working groups, few standards have yet been produced in the water field.

## EUREAU

EUREAU is the voluntary organization representing the water industries of the European Community. It is a non-profit-making body with the aims of studying problems arising out of all aspects of the "clean" water function of proposing and encouraging their solution, of representing the common interest and, particularly, to make the European Commission aware of the problems. The headquarters and the small secretariat is in Brussels and the President is appointed in rotation. The Council meets three or four times a year, but it has a number of technical and policy committees which meet more frequently. EUREAU has close links with the Commission and especially with DGIII.

## INTERNATIONAL WATER SUPPLY ASSOCIATION (IWSA)

The IWSA was founded at Harrogate in June 1947, at a meeting convened by the British water interests to secure concerted action in improving the knowledge (technical, legal, and administrative) of public water supplies; to secure a maximum exchange of information on research, methods of supply of water, statistics, and all other matters of common interest to encourage better understanding between those engaged in the public supply of water.

The water supply interests of each participating country are represented by a national committee and the organization comprises a General Assembly, an Executive Board, a Scientific and Technical Council and its standing committees, and a Secretariat. The General Assembly is composed of the official representatives of the member national committees of the Association and its functions are to approve applications for membership, to determine the policy and scope of the Association, and to consider reports and recommendations of the Executive Board.

## 10. REFERENCES

In compiling this chapter the following publications have been used as sources of references.

Department of the Environment (available from H.M.S.O., London).
    1973, "The new water industry management and structure".
    1974, "European Community—a guide to the literature and sources of publications".
    1976, "Pollution control in Great Britain—how it works".
    1977, "Environmental Standards—a description of U.K. practice".
National Water Council
    Annual Reports for 1974-75; 1975-76; and 1976-77.
    1975 *Water,* June, "Training and education in the water industry".
Central Water Planning Unit: Annual Reports.
Water Companies Association: Annual Reports.
Water Space Amenity Commission: Annual Reports for 1973-74 and 1975-76.
Water Authority Annual Reports for 1974-75 and 1975-76.
Reports of the River Pollution Surveys of England and Wales 1970 to 1975. Available from H.M.S.O.
Rickmansworth and Uxbridge Valley Water Company, Annual Report for 1976-77.
South Staffordshire Waterworks Company, Annual Report for 1976-77.
Bailey, D. A., 1976, *Chemistry and Industry,* 2nd October, "Consequences to industry of the recent water
    legislation".
Banks, D. H., 1976, *Public Health Engineer,* September, "Management and operation of functions within
    the East Sussex Water and Drainage Division".
Bray, P., 1976, *Water,* May, "Anglian—fastest growing region in the country".
Buckenham, J. R., 1977, *Water,* May, "All about EUREAU".
Jordan, A. G., 1977, *Public Administration,* Autumn, "The origins of the Water Act 1973".
Okun, D. A. 1977, "Regionalization of water management", Applied Sciences, Barking, Essex.
Roberts, K. F., 1975, *Journ. I.W.E.S.,* 29, 261, "Reorganization—reflections after a year of change".
    1977, *Water,* September, "The safety game: implications for Health and Safety at Work Act for the water
    industry".

# Chapter 3

# WATER LAW

## 1. INTRODUCTION

### VARIATIONS IN THE U.K.

THIS Chapter consists mainly of a review of the law which applies in England and Wales. There are separate sections which describe variations applying to Scotland and Northern Ireland.

### "SECRETARY OF STATE"

Where used, the term "the Secretary of State" refers to the Secretary of State for the Environment, unless otherwise stated. In Wales, the term refers to the Secretary of State for Wales. The definition and responsibilities of Government Ministers in relation to water matters are defined in Section 1 of the Water Act 1973.

### GENERAL BACKGROUND

It will be appreciated that, within the scope of a Manual such as this, it is impossible to present any comprehensive review of the manifold aspects of the law relating to water and water authorities. The Water Act 1973, which set up the Regional Water Authorities in England and Wales, merely transferred to the new authorities responsibilities which included water supply, sewerage and sewage purification, pollution prevention and control, water resources, land drainage, flood prevention and fisheries, and created some duties in respect of recreation. It did not, however, provide any new basic legal framework for the exercise of these activities, which continue to be governed by the body of law which existed prior to the 1973 Act, subject to such amendments as have taken place since then.

However, there are many fields of vital importance to water authorities and statutory water undertakers which are not covered by the Acts which deal with their primary activities. These, together with the mass of case law which has grown up over the years and of which the principles are still applicable, and the many Ministerial Orders and Regulations, as well as the general body of the law which in one way or another affects the water industry, make it possible only to draw attention in a general way to some of the more important matters. For more detailed information and advice, legal opinion should be consulted.

### LOCAL ACTS AND ORDERS

Most water authorities inherited from their predecessors powers originally granted by private or local Acts and Orders (the difference being that an Act is passed by Parliament, while an Order is made by a Government Minister under powers specifically contained in a general Act of Parliament). Similar local enactments apply to water companies.

These local enactments may prescribe the area within which the authority may operate; authorize works and the acquisition of lands; and generally regulate the management of the authority and its undertakings. In the case of water companies, the enactments may incorporate the Companies Clauses Acts, prescribe the amount of capital that may be raised and the maximum dividends payable, and place a limitation on any reserve and contingency funds and on the balance which may be carried forward at the end of the year.

Because of their inheritance of such local enactments, water authorities frequently find that they enjoy detailed powers which vary over their region, applying piecemeal to the areas of operation of their predecessor authorities to whom the powers were originally granted.

## ACQUISITION OF POWERS

Where water authorities (and water companies) require additional local powers it is now usual to seek these by way of Order. The procedure for doing so is relatively simple, and is described in detail in the various Acts, according to the particular power to be sought.

The procedure by way of private Bill in Parliament (a Bill is, in effect, an application for powers; as soon as these are granted it becomes an Act), although now infrequently used is still available. It is recognized that in some cases (for example, where special powers not available under general Acts are required, or where common rights over land are concerned) the private Bill procedure presents some advantages.

## PRINCIPAL STATUTORY PROVISIONS

Apart from the common law, the law relating to water authorities is largely contained in the statutes listed below. The most important ones are those marked with an asterisk (*).

Many of these statutes have been subject to considerable amendment since they were first enacted, and it is likely that further amendments will be made from time to time. It is often difficult for anyone but a professional lawyer to discover what is the exact state of the statute law from time to time, and the layman should beware of relying on out-of-date or Queen's Printers copies of the statutes without taking professional advice.

**Water Authorities**
*Water Act 1973

**Water Supply**
Reservoirs (Safety Provisions) Act 1930
*Water Act 1945
Water Act 1948
*Public Utilities Street Works Act 1950
Reservoirs Act 1975
Drought Act 1976
Water Charges Equalization Act 1977

**Sewerage and Sewage Purification**
*Public Health Act 1936
*Public Health (Drainage of Trade Premises) Act 1937
Public Health Act 1961

**Land Drainage**
*Land Drainage Act 1976

**Pollution Prevention**
Rivers (Prevention of Pollution) Act 1951
Clean Rivers (Estuaries and Tidal Waters) Act 1960
Rivers (Prevention of Pollution) Act 1961
*Control of Pollution Act 1974

**Fisheries**
Salmon and Freshwater Fisheries Act 1975

**Water Management**
*Water Resources Act 1963
Water Resources Act 1968
Water Resources Act 1971
Water Charges Act 1976

## 2. WATER RESOURCES

### DEFINITIONS

For a proper understanding of this aspect of water law, it is first necessary to consider how the law defines water resources. Under Section 2 of the Water Resources Act 1963, it is provided that *"water resources . . . means water for the time being contained in any source of supply"*, which in turn is defined to include both inland waters and underground strata. Inland waters include rivers, streams, lakes, ponds, and watercourses including drains, sewers, and passages through which water flows with the exception of public sewers, water mains, and supply pipes. However, lakes, ponds or reservoirs, or groups of them which do not discharge to any other inland water and are not fed by water in underground strata are excluded from the definition of source of supply.

The 1963 Act was the first comprehensive legislation in this field, being brought into force with the formation of river authorities as recently as 1965. Earlier statutory provisions were of a sporadic and rather general nature, mainly as an adjunct to water supply legislation, e.g. the general duty of the Secretary of State under Section 1 of the Water Act 1945 to promote the conservation and proper use of water resources and to formulate a national policy relating to water. Otherwise, in so far as water resources were regulated at all, control depended upon the common law and the rights and duties of riparian owners.

### GENERAL STATUTORY DUTY OF WATER AUTHORITIES

The general duty of river (and now water) authorities in relation to water resources as established by the 1963 Act and now re-enacted as Section 10 of the Water Act 1973 is *"to take all such action as the Authority may from time to time consider necessary or expedient . . . for the purpose of conserving, redistributing, or otherwise augmenting water resources in their area, or securing the proper use of water resources in their area, or of transferring any such resources to the area of another water authority"*. It is interesting to note that the Section goes on to provide specifically that desalination schemes are to be regarded for this purpose as augmenting water resources.

### SURVEYS AND MINIMUM ACCEPTABLE FLOWS

Part III of the 1963 Act contained requirements as to surveys of resources and demands, and as to hydrometric schemes to be carried out by river authorities under the aegis of the former Water Resources Board. These provisions have largely been repealed by the 1973 Act and replaced by the much wider duty of water authorities to carry out surveys under Section 24 of that Act and the abolition of the Water Resources Board, but the provisions relating to minimum acceptable flows in Sections 19 to 22 of the 1963 Act remain largely intact. The basis for control of surface water resources was to have been these minimum acceptable flows, which can be determined by the water authority after consultation with interested parties and subject to the approval of the Secretary of State. Minimum acceptable flows are both fixed initially and subject to periodic review subsequently, having regard to environmental considerations, public health requirements, and existing lawful uses of the water concerned. It was the intention that they should then become the guiding factor in the operation of the abstraction licensing system and water resources policy generally. In practice, however, these provisions have so far been largely unused, no doubt on account of the inflexibility which a formal procedure of this kind introduces into water resource management.

## Control of Abstraction and Impounding

Part IV of the 1963 Act contains the important provisions for control of abstraction and impounding which is the principal tool through which water authorities can regulate the use of water resources. Section 23 imposes a general restriction on abstraction of water from sources of supply without a licence granted by the water authority. The Act specifies a number of exemptions from the requirement for a licence, the principal of which are abstractions from surface sources for the purposes of a domestic water supply, or for agricultural purposes (other than spray irrigation) on adjoining land, and abstractions of water from underground strata by or on behalf of an individual as a supply of water for domestic household purposes. Trial or experimental underground abstractions are also exempt from licensing, provided that the water authority's prior consent is obtained.

At the time the 1963 Act came into force in 1965, existing abstractors or those having a right to abstract under statute were entitled to a "licence of right", provided that application was made to the river authority by 1st June 1965. Such an application did not require advertisement in accordance with the normal procedure, and the river authority were obliged to grant the licence in such terms as to authorize the abstraction as existing or in accordance with the statutory entitlement claimed.

Anyone wishing to commence abstracting water from a source of supply after 1st July 1965 can apply for an ordinary licence, but can only do so if in relation to the land from which the abstraction is to take place, he is either the occupier or has a right of access, or is in the process of negotiating for one, or has compulsory powers in relation thereto. The application must be advertised in the local press and the London Gazette, giving a 28-day period for objections, and notice must be served on any navigation authority or internal drainage board affected.

In determining whether to grant or refuse a licence or whether to impose conditions on a grant, the water authority must take into account the reasonable requirements of the applicant, together with any representations which have been received by them during the objection period. Where the application is for abstraction from an inland water, or from underground strata in circumstances which may affect the flow, level, or volume of an inland water, the authority is required to take into account any minimum acceptable flow prescribed for that inland water, or, in the majority of cases where none has been prescribed, the considerations by reference to which a minimum acceptable flow would fail to be determined. Where the application relates to abstraction from underground strata, the authority shall have regard to the needs of existing lawful abstractors.

If the applicant is dissatisfied with the decision of the water authority or their failure to make a decision, he may appeal to the Secretary of State. The Secretary of State may also direct that an application or applications within a specified class be referred by the water authority to him for decision. Applications dealt with by the

Secretary of State on appeal or called in by him must be the subject of a Local Inquiry, if either the applicant or the water authority request it.

The effect of a licence is that the person abstracting water in accordance with it is immune from any legal action in respect thereof, except where such action is founded on negligence or breach of contract. Furthermore, a licence holder and anyone abstracting for domestic or agricultural purposes are defined as having "protected rights" under the Act to the extent that the water authority may not grant any further licence authorizing abstraction of water so as to derogate from those rights. Derogation in this context means abstracting water in such a way or to such an extent as to prevent the person entitled to the protected rights from abstracting to the full extent to which he is entitled. However, the only remedy available to the holder of protected rights if the authority do grant a licence which authorizes abstraction so as to derogate from those rights is to bring an action against the authority for damages for breach of statutory duty. Owners of fishing rights adversely affected by the grant of a licence other than a licence of right are subject to a special procedure whereby they may apply to the Secretary of State to have the licence revoked or varied. If, however, the Secretary of State finds that fishing rights in any particular case are adversely affected but that it is inappropriate to remedy the situation by revoking or varying the licence, the owner of the rights is entitled to compensation from the water authority.

Provisions exist for the revocation or variation of licences, either at the instance of the licence holder, or, subject to payment of compensation in certain cases, at the instance of the water authority. There is also provision for succession to licences on a change in occupation of land.

There are special procedures under the Water Resources (Licences) Regulations 1965 for the granting of licences to water authorities whereby the licence is granted or deemed to be granted by the Secretary of State. The water authority formulate proposals for the licence and advertise them as if they had been the subject of an application. A copy of the proposals is sent to the Secretary of State and if at the end of the objection period he has not directed that application be made to him and no objections have been received, the authority may proceed to give effect to the licence by resolution. If, on the other hand, objections are received, they must be forwarded to the Secretary of State and no further action can be taken until he notifies the authority whether they are to make formal application to him. If application then has to be made to the Secretary of State, he may hold a Local Inquiry and must do so if required by the water authority.

### RESTRICTIONS ON IMPOUNDING

The 1963 Act also imposes a general restriction on the construction or alteration of impounding works in inland waters after 1st July 1965 without a licence from the water authority. Existing lawful impounding works at the time the Act came into force were exempt from this control but otherwise the procedure, rights of appeal, etc., in relation to such licences are similar to those applying to abstraction licences. Generally, for new reservoirs, both impounding and abstraction licences will be necessary.

### GENERAL PROVISIONS AS TO LICENCES

The Act requires the authority to keep a register of abstraction and impounding licences and applications relating thereto, which must be kept available for inspection by the public at all reasonable hours. Other detailed requirements as to licences are prescribed by the 1965 Regulations.

ABSTRACTION CHARGES

With the wide powers given to water authorities in matters of charging by Part III of the 1973 Act, the specific provisions of the 1963 Act relating to licence fees and abstraction charging schemes have been repealed. Under Section 60 of the 1963 Act, however, abstractors are entitled to an appropriate reduction in abstraction charges if they construct or have constructed works which will or have made a beneficial contribution towards water conservation generally. In addition, under Section 63, abstractors using water for spray irrigation purposes are entitled to special charging arrangements.

POWERS RELATING TO LAND AND WORKS

Part VI of the 1963 Act contains important powers for water authorities to acquire land and carry out works for water conservation purposes. Land and rights in land may be acquired by agreement or compulsorily. Of particular advantage for large water conservation schemes, Section 67 of the Act enables the Secretary of State to make an Order authorizing the carrying out of any engineering or building operations including compulsory acquisition of land and supplementary powers such as closure and diversion of roads and footpaths. The usual type of compulsory purchase procedures apply to such orders involving service of notices, Public Inquiries into objections, and so forth.

DISCHARGE OF WATER

The Water Resources Act 1971 cleared up an unfortunate uncertainty in the 1963 Act about whether river authorities had power to make discharges to inland waters. This power was obviously essential in the case of river regulation proposals involving either regulating reservoirs or groundwater schemes. An order may be made by the Secretary of State under the 1971 Act in accordance with a procedure similar to that applying to Orders under Section 67 of the 1963 Act, whereby a water authority may be authorized to discharge water for water conservation purposes. If the Order applies to a location in a National Park, it is subject to negative resolution of either House of Parliament.

SPECIAL PROVISIONS FOR WATER SHORTAGES

Prior to 1958, the only power available to water undertakers to enable them to eke out supplies in times of shortage was to introduce a ban on the use of hosepipes for washing cars and watering private gardens under Section 16 of the Water Act 1945. This is a convenient procedure in that it may be introduced without reference to Central Government or opportunity for consumers to object, but the savings that could be achieved in times of real shortage were obviously limited. The Water Act 1958 introduced new powers for the Minister to make Drought Orders, but there were procedural difficulties, and orders could only be made to supplement supplies by bringing in temporary sources or by modifying limitations as to such matters as compensation water or prescribed flows on existing sources or abstractions; or to restrict the use of water by introducing supplies by standpipes or tankers. Only when the second type of Order had been obtained and water was actually being supplied by temporary means could the undertakers be relieved from their obligations to maintain supplies under the 1945 Act.

The more serious water shortages which arose in 1976 drew attention to the defects in the then existing legislation, and resulted in the passing of the Drought Act 1976. It completely replaces the 1958 Water Act but leaves Section 16 of the Water Act

1945 still in force. The new Act draws a distinction between the circumstances in which two types of Drought Order can be obtained, the Secretary of State merely having to be satisfied in the first case that a serious deficiency of supplies exists or is threatened, but in the second case that such deficiency is likely to impair the economic or social well-being of persons in the area. The first type of Order, under Section 1 of the Act, can include measures for increasing the supplies available but also includes an entirely new power to make an Order prohibiting or limiting the non-essential uses of water. This was in answer to the public concern over a situation where, whilst measures were being taken, for example, to reduce compensation water, with consequent serious effects on abstractors and fisheries, at the same time non-essential uses of water were continuing, and could not be stopped, such as automatic car washes, and the watering of public gardens and sportsgrounds. These and other non-essential uses of water are now specified in a direction made under the Act by the Secretary of State, which uses may be prohibited by Drought Orders under Section 1.

Orders under Section 2 of the Act in the more serious type of situation may include not only the powers previously available to supply water by standpipes and tankers, but also provision authorizing the authority to prohibit or limit the use of water for such purposes as the authority think fit. This, in effect, subject to the Order granted by the Secretary of State, can give a water authority complete flexibility in rationing water right down to the situation where in the ultimate no further water is available for distribution.

Orders under Section 1 of the Act may apply for a maximum period of six months and under Section 2 for a maximum period of three months, although the Secretary of State has power to renew any Order for a further such period. The Act provides no compensation for persons affected by prohibitions or limitations on the use of water, either in Section 1 or Section 2 Orders, but compensation is available for those affected by Orders which permit the use of temporary sources and reductions in compensation water or prescribed flows.

One interesting and important change between procedure for Drought Orders under the new Act as distinct from the 1958 Act is that the Secretary of State is no longer obliged to hold a Public Inquiry if an objection is lodged and not withdrawn. If satisfied that the Order is required to be made urgently (which of course will be the case in most applications), the Secretary of State may go ahead and make the Order provided that before doing so he does consider any valid objection. The requirement for an Inquiry in the 1958 Act was one of its most serious deficiencies in that even a quite unjustified single objection could delay the bringing in of a Drought Order intolerably. Water authorities now therefore have comprehensive legislation to meet future water shortages.

## 3. RESERVOIR SAFETY

### Reservoirs (Safety Provisions) Act 1930

This Act deals with the design, construction and inspection of *"large reservoirs"*, defined by the Act as a reservoir designed to hold, or capable of holding, more than 22 700 cu m (5 mg) of water above the natural level of any part of the land adjoining the reservoir. The Act established "panels" of *"qualified civil engineers"* (appointed by the Secretary of State), and required that an engineer on the appropriate panel be employed to design and supervise the construction of such a reservoir and to issue a certificate governing its filling and use.

The Act provides that after its commencement (1st January 1931) no large reservoir may be constructed, nor may any reservoir constructed before or after that date be altered so as to increase its capacity, if the reservoir concerned is a large reservoir or will become one, unless a qualified civil engineer within the meaning of the Act is employed to design and supervise the construction or alteration. The Act further provides for preliminary and final filling certificates issued by the design engineer to specify the level up to which the water may be stored and the conditions (if any) subject to which it may be stored.

The Act also provides that all large reservoirs, whether constructed before or after 1st January 1931, shall be inspected periodically and a report on the inspection given by a qualified civil engineer. If a report contains recommendations that any measures should be taken in the interests of safety, the undertakers are required to carry such recommendations into effect. The undertakers are also required to keep the records prescribed by the Act in relation to large reservoirs.

By Section 7 of the Act undertakers are made liable, irrespective of negligence, for damage done due to the escape of water from any reservoir constructed after 1st January 1931, under statutory powers granted after that date.

## THE RESERVOIRS ACT 1975

The 1930 provisions are to be replaced and strengthened by the Reservoirs Act 1975 when this is brought into force by Order of the Secretary of State. The new Act will place a duty upon County Councils to maintain registers of *large raised reservoirs* (as they are now to be called) and to enforce the provisions of the Act. The Act contains new powers for those Councils to take enforcement action where the undertakers responsible for the reservoir have failed to comply with the requirements as to design and supervision and subsequent inspection.

The 1975 Act makes new provision for the constitution of and appointment to new panels of "Qualified civil engineers", and limits appointments to five years. There is a new requirement that large raised reservoirs shall remain continuously under the supervision of a qualified civil engineer between period inspections, and provides for the formation of a panel of such "supervising engineers".

There are also provisions for the precautions to be taken if large raised reservoirs are reduced in capacity so that they are below the limits specified in the Act (now 25 000 cu m), or where the reservoir is to be abandoned. Local authorities have power to act themselves to remedy defects if the undertakers responsible fail to comply with notices served by the local authority, and they may also deal immediately in an emergency with an unsafe reservoir.

The liability of undertakers for damage or injury caused by the escape of water from a reservoir (which was introduced by the 1930 Act) is preserved.

## 4. WATER SUPPLY

### STATUTORY WATER UNDERTAKERS

Since 1974 the expression "statutory water undertakers" has meant the regional water authorities, statutory water companies, joint water boards, and joint water committees only. From the same date these joint bodies have only been those boards and committees on which a statutory water company is represented, and so in most cases reference to statutory water undertakers can be taken as references to water authorities or statutory water companies.

## OUTLINE OF WATER LEGISLATION AND GENERAL DUTIES

The law relating to public water supply is almost wholly contained in the following Acts, together with the more detailed provisions of the local Acts and Orders relating to statutory water undertakers:—

**Public Health Act 1936** — The parts of this Act dealing with water supply, and still in force, largely concern the powers of local authorities acting in the interests of public health. All the other water supply provisions have been repealed by later Acts.

**Water Act 1945** — This Act, although substantially amended, still contains the main provisions of the law on water supply. In particular the 3rd Schedule contains, in detail, the basic legal rules for the operation of a water supply undertaking (the "Waterworks Code").

**Water Act 1948** — This is a short Act, largely concerned with amendments to the 1945 Act.

**Water Act 1973** — This Act set up the Regional Water Authorities, and made them responsible for water supply, amongst their other duties. It contains a number of amendments to earlier legislation.

The 1973 Act (Section 12) provided for the continuance of the (privately owned) statutory water companies, which account for about 22 per cent of the total water supplied in England and Wales; but required them to act on behalf of the water authorities to supply water within their limits of supply under the provisions of an agreement.

The main section in the Water Act 1973 concerned with water supply is Section 11 which provides:—

(1) Each water authority will have a general duty to supply water within their area (sub-section (1)).

(2) Water authorities will operate under the enactments in force in each locality (sub-section (6) and Schedule 6 Part II). These enactments will also continue to apply to statutory water companies and to any joint water boards or committees which continued to exist after 1st April 1974.

(3) A water authority will be under a duty to supply water for domestic purposes within the limits of supply of any of the former statutory water undertakings (sub-section (7)):
    *(a)*   under Part VII of Schedule 3 of the Water Act 1945 whether or not these sections have previously been applied to the area in question;
    *(b)*   under section 37 of the Water Act 1945.

(4) A water authority will be under a duty under certain conditions to supply water for non-domestic purposes under section 27 of the Water Act 1945 within the limits of supply of any of the former statutory water undertakings (sub-section (7)).

(5) Where the conditions relating to water charges under the Water Act 1945 for demanding a supply of water for either domestic or non-domestic purposes are not satisfied, the local authority may undertake, under section 36 of that Act, to make good that deficiency in water charges, and it will be the duty of the water authority to accept such undertaking (sub-section (7)).

(6) It will be the duty under Part IX of Schedule 3 of the Water Act 1945 to maintain a constant supply and pressure in all pipes to which fire hydrants are fixed or which are used for giving supplies for domestic purposes whether or not Part IX has previously been applied in the area concerned (sub-section (7)).

(7) Each local authority will have the duty of checking the sufficiency and purity of water supplies in their district and of notifying the water authority of any deficiency (sub-section (2)).

(8) If the local authority notify the water authority that the supply of water to specified premises is such as to endanger health, and it is not practicable to provide a piped supply at reasonable cost, it will be the duty of the water authority to provide some other means of supply within a reasonable distance if that can be done at a reasonable cost (sub-section (3)).

The Secretary of State is to determine:
- (*a*) any dispute between a local authority and the water authority as to insufficiency or unwholesomeness of supply and whether it endangers health (sub-section 4);
- (*b*) on the requisition of a local authority, parish or community council, or of ten local government electors, whether a supply of water can be provided at reasonable cost (sub-sections (4) and (5)).

(9) Local authorities will also retain a number of powers under Part IV of the Public Health Act 1936 (sub-section (9)).

The Drought Act 1976 contains special provisions whereby, in times of water shortage due to drought or excessive use resulting from hot weather, the Secretary of State may make an Order at the request of a water authority or statutory water company modifying the rights and duties of the water authority or company for a maximum period of six months (section 1).

Where he is also satisfied that the shortage is likely to impair the economic or social well-being of persons in the locality concerned, he may also order the use of standpipes or water tanks, and that use of water be restricted in general or in particular. This type of Order has a maximum life of three months (section 2).

### SUPPLY OF WATER FOR DOMESTIC PURPOSES

The duty of water undertakers in respect of a supply for domestic purposes is to be found in Part VII (comprising Sections 29 to 31) of the Third Schedule to the Water Act 1945.

By Section 29(1) of the Third Schedule, the undertakers are obliged to lay any necessary mains and to bring water to any area within their limits of supply if they are required to do so by such number of owners and occupiers of premises in that area who require a supply of water for domestic purposes that the aggregate amount of that proportion of the water charge payable annually by those owners and occupiers in respect of those premises as is stated by the water undertakers to be payable for the supply of domestic water will not be less than one-eighth of the expense of providing and laying the necessary mains, and if those owners and occupiers agree severally with the undertakers to take a supply of water for three years at least.

Where owners or occupiers of premises in any area are prevented from making a valid requisition because of an insufficiency of the aggregate amount of the relevant part of the water charge, Section 36 of the Act enables a local authority to guarantee the deficit for a period not exceeding 12 years and requires the statutory undertakers concerned to accept such guarantee. Thereupon the undertakers must lay the necessary mains and bring water to the area.

The duty of undertakers as regards sufficiency and purity of the supply is to be found in Section 31 of the Third Schedule, which enacts that they shall provide in their mains and communication pipes a supply of wholesome water sufficient for the domestic purposes of all owners and occupiers of premises within the limits of supply who, under the Act, incorporating the Schedule, are entitled to demand a supply for those purposes.

There is no definition in the Water Act 1945 of the word "wholesome". The question as to what constitutes wholesome water would appear to be a medical one. Parliament has so far refrained from attempting to lay down a standard by which water may be judged, although there are special Act provisions which lay down that a water must be treated so as to comply with a standard of purity laid down by the Minister. There is, however, an EEC Directive which governs now the standard of quality of treated water supplied to the public, and this could be the standard applicable in the future.

The obligation to provide wholesome water is not an absolute one, but is limited to the exercise of all reasonable care and skill to ensure that the water supplied is wholesome (*Read* v. *Croydon Corporation* (1938)).

The extent of the *statutory* duty was considered by the House of Lords in *Milnes* v. *Huddersfield Corporation* (1886). The appellant suffered lead poisoning as a result of drinking water which, although admittedly pure and wholesome in the mains of the corporation, became contaminated in its passage through the lead pipes of the appellant. It was held that the corporation's statutory obligation was limited to providing and keeping in the pipes laid down by them a supply of wholesome water and accordingly the appellant's case, based on breach of statutory duty, failed. However, there is also a *common law* duty in addition to and apart from the statutory obligation, and in the later case of *Barnes* v. *Irwell Valley Water Board* (1939), negligence was pleaded as well as breach of statutory duty. The Court of Appeal held that the breach of statutory duty failed because of the decision in the *Huddersfield* case but that the allegation of negligence succeeded.

In carrying out their responsibilities in relation to the purity of the supply, undertakers should carefully consider the recommendations of the government entitled "Safeguards to be Adopted in the Operation and Management of Waterworks" (1967, HMSO) and any further recommendations made, e.g. the National Water Council Technical Paper No. 2 (1979) on "Water Supply Hygiene".

The right to demand a supply for domestic purposes is to be found in Section 30(1) of the Third Schedule and this section provides that an owner or occupier of any premises within the limits of supply who has complied, in respect of those premises, with the provision of Part X of the Schedule with respect to the laying of a supply pipe and the payment or tender of the water charge, shall be entitled to demand and receive from the undertakers a supply of water sufficient for domestic purposes for those premises. However, a person is not entitled to demand a supply from a trunk main, nor are the undertakers required to afford a supply for any premises in which any of the water fittings do not comply with their bye-laws.

For the purposes of the Third Schedule to the Water Act, "a supply of water for domestic purposes" means a sufficient supply for drinking, washing, cooking, and sanitary purposes, but not for any bath having a capacity (measured to the centre line of the overflow pipe, or in such other manner as the Minister (now the Secretary of State for the Environment) may by regulations prescribe) in excess of 227 litres; and includes:—

(*a*) a supply for the purposes of a profession carried on in any premises the greater part whereof is used as a house, and

(*b*) where the water is drawn from a tap inside a house and no hosepipe or similar apparatus is used, a supply for watering a garden, and for horses kept for private use and for washing vehicles so kept.

It does not include a supply of water for the business of a laundry or a business of preparing food or beverages for consumption otherwise than on the premises. It will be observed that this definition follows broadly the test suggested in *Metropolitan Water Board* v. *Avery* (1914), when it was suggested that "the test is not whether the water is consumed or used in the course of a trade, but whether the use of the water is in its nature domestic". In these days of widespread ownership of the motor car, it is pleasing to note that water supplied for washing a car used for business purposes (*Harrogate Corporation* v. *Mackay* (1907)) or of a vehicle for private use

(*Busby* v. *Chesterfield Waterworks and Gaslight Co* (1858)—there a carriage), is water used for domestic purposes.

## Constancy and Pressure of Supply

By Section 39 of the Third Schedule to the Water Act 1945, the undertakers are under an obligation to cause the water in all pipes on which hydrants are fixed, or which are used for giving supplies for domestic purposes, to be laid on constantly and at such a pressure as will cause the water to reach the top of the top-most storey of every building within their limits of supply, subject to the proviso that they cannot be required to deliver water at a height greater than that to which it will flow by gravitation through their mains from the service reservoir or tank from which the supply in question is taken. They are themselves entitled to determine the service reservoir or tank from which any supply is to be taken. The undertakers are liable, without prejudice to their civil liability, to a fine if they fail to comply with these requirements except when prevented by frost, drought, unavoidable accident or other unavoidable cause, or during the execution of necessary works.

In connection with the obligations as to pressure of supply, it may here be mentioned that some undertakers operate under statutory powers which, in practice, are substantially different from Section 39 of the Third Schedule. For example, some local Acts specify heights above street level beyond which the undertakers are not bound to afford a supply. By Section 11(7) of the 1973 Act, Section 39 does now apply to all water authorities.

## Domestic Supply for New Buildings

Section 37 of the Water Act 1945, as amended by the Housing Act 1949, enables an owner of land, who proposes to erect thereon buildings for which a supply of water for domestic purposes will be needed, to require any water authority within whose limits of supply that land is situated to construct any necessary service reservoirs, to lay the necessary mains to such a point or points as will enable the buildings to be connected thereto at a reasonable cost, and to bring water to that point or those points. Any question arising as to the point or points to which mains must be taken in order to enable buildings to be connected thereto at a reasonable cost is, in default of agreement, to be determined by the Secretary of State, though "necessary mains" does not include trunk mains (*Cherwell District Council* v. *Thames Water Authority* (1975)).

Before complying with a requisition under this section the undertakers may require the owner to undertake to pay in respect of each year a sum amounting to one-eighth of the expense of constructing the necessary service reservoirs and providing and laying the necessary mains, less any amounts received for the supply of water from those mains, until the aggregate amount of charges for the supply of water for domestic purposes in respect of the new buildings and any other premises connected with the mains equals or exceeds the prescribed sum, or until the expiration of a period of 12 years, whichever first occurs.

Except where the owner is a local or public authority, water undertakers may also require him to deposit with them, as security for payment of the above-mentioned sums, such sum as the undertakers may require, not exceeding the total expense of constructing the service reservoirs and providing and laying the mains. The owner may require that any annual sums due under the guarantee shall be taken from the deposit. Interest is pabale on the deposit by the water undertakers at a rate prescribed from time to time by Regulations made by the Secretary of State.

## SUPPLY OF WATER FOR NON-DOMESTIC PURPOSES

Section 27 of the Water Act 1945 imposes upon water authorities supplying water, otherwise than in bulk, an obligation to give a supply of water on reasonable terms and conditions for purposes other than domestic to an owner or occupier of any premises within their limits of supply who requests them to give such a supply to those premises. This obligation, however, is subject to the proviso that the undertakers shall not be required to give such a supply if their ability to meet existing obligations to supply water for any purposes or probable future requirements to supply water for domestic purposes, without having to incur unreasonable expenditure in constructing new waterworks for the purpose, would be endangered thereby.

Any question arising under this section as to the terms and conditions on which water is to be supplied and any question whether the undertakers are justified in refusing to give a supply, is, in default of agreement, to be referred to the Secretary of State; and he may determine it himself or, if he thinks fit, refer it for determination by an arbitrator appointed by him.

## SUPPLY OF WATER FOR PUBLIC PURPOSES

### Fire Supplies

By Sections 32-34 of the Third Schedule to the Water Act 1945 (which have been applied to all statutory undertakers by the Fire Services Act 1947, Section 14(3)), all undertakers are under an obligation, at the request of the fire authority concerned, to fix fire hydrants on their mains (other than trunk mains) at such places as may be most convenient for affording a supply of water for extinguishing any fire which may break out within their limits of supply, and to keep in good order, and from time to time renew, every such hydrant. Any difference as to the number or proper position of such hydrants is to be referred to and determined by the Secretary of State (Section 32). As soon as any such hydrant is installed the undertakers must, if required by the fire authority, deposit a key thereof at each place within their limits of supply where any public fire engine is kept, and in such other places as may be appointed by the fire authority (Section 33). The cost of such hydrants and of fixing, maintaining and renewing them, and of providing keys, is to be defrayed by the fire authority (Section 34).

The undertakers must allow all persons to take water for extinguishing fires from any pipe upon which a hydrant is fixed, without payment (Section 36).

Section 35 puts upon the undertakers an obligation to fix and maintain hydrants near factories, etc., at the request and expense of the owners or occupiers of the premises.

Section 39 prescribes the pressure at which water is to be kept in any pipe to which a hydrant is affixed; these provisions are the same as those relating to pressure for domestic supply.

Sections 13 to 16 of the Fire Services Act 1947 also contain provisions with respect to a supply of water for fire fighting. The fire authority is under an obligation to take all reasonable measures for ensuring an adequate supply of water and for securing that it will be available for use in case of fire, and for this purpose the authority may enter into an agreement with water undertakers for the taking by the undertakers, on such terms as to payment or otherwise as may be specified in the agreement, of such measures as may be so specified for securing that an adequate supply of water will be available in case of fire. Water undertakers must not unreasonably refuse to enter into any such agreement proposed by a fire authority, and any question whether the undertakers have unreasonably refused to enter into an agreement is to be determined by the Secretary of State.

By Section 16 notice is to be given by the undertakers to the fire authority of proposed works affecting the water supply to fire hydrants.

### Supply of Water for Cleansing Sewers, etc., and for Other Public Purposes

By Section 37 of the Third Schedule to the Water Act 1945 the undertakers are under an obligation in the case of every pipe on which a hydrant is fixed to provide a supply of water for cleansing sewers and drains, for cleansing and watering highways, and for supplying any public pumps, baths, or washhouses. The supply is to be provided at such rates, in such quantities, and upon such terms and conditions as may be agreed between the local authority, highway authority, or sewerage authority concerned and the undertakers, or as, in default of agreement, may be determined by the Secretary of State.

### SUPPLY OF WATER IN BULK

Section 12 of the Water Act 1945 (as replaced within the Water Act 1973, Schedule 4, Part I), contains provisions with respect to a supply of water in bulk by agreement or compulsorily; by Section 59(1) of the 1945 Act a "supply of water in bulk" means a supply of water for distribution by the undertakers taking the supply. However, this power is now of less importance, since the reduction in the number of water undertakers in 1974.

An agreement may be made between any water undertakers and any other persons, whether water undertakers or not, for the giving by those other persons, and the taking by the water undertakers, of a supply of water in bulk for any period and on any terms and conditions. Where the supply is to be given by persons who are themselves water undertakers, either within or outside the limits of supply of those undertakers, an agreement to which a statutory water company is a party requires the agreement of the water authority for whom they are supplying water. The authority must withhold approval if it appears to them that the giving of the supply would be likely to interfere with the supply of water for any purpose within the authority's limits of supply.

Where the Secretary of State thinks it is expedient that a bulk supply should be given and taken between statutory undertakers and he is satisfied that the giving and taking of such a supply cannot be secured by agreement, he may bring it into effect by order upon such terms and conditions as may be provided in the Order.

For the purposes of giving or taking bulk supplies under Section 12, water undertakers are entitled to exercise the mainlaying, etc., powers contained in Parts V and VI of the Third Schedule to the Act.

### MAINS, SERVICES AND STOPCOCKS

### Definitions

*Main.*—is a pipe *laid by undertakers* for the purposes of giving a *general* supply of water as distinct from a supply to individual consumers (Third Schedule, Section 1). This definition applies whatever the size or material of the pipe, and wherever it is lain—a main may be under a highway, a street, in private land, or even up in the air.

*Service Pipe.*—is so much of any pipe for supplying water from a main to any premises as is subject to water pressure from that main, or would be but for the closing of a tap (Third Schedule, Section 1). In domestic terms this means that the whole of the pipework from the main up to taps or cistern ballcocks is a service pipe.

From the next two definitions it will be seen that a service pipe comprises the communication pipe and the supply pipe.

*Communication pipe.*—in most cases is that part of a service pipe between the main and the boundary of the street in which the main is laid; although, if there is a stopcock in the premises supplied and as near as reasonably practical to the boundary of the street, then the communication pipe extends up to (and includes) that stopcock. This is the usual rule, but included in the definition are special provisions (see section 1(1) of the Third Schedule as amended by Section 10(1) of the Water Act 1948).

*Supply Pipe.*—is much simpler—it is so much of any service pipe that is not a communication pipe (Third Schedule, Section 1).

*Street.*—includes any highway and any road lane footway square court alley or passage, whether a thoroughfare or not (Water Act 1945, Section 59). There is an exception in that a private street within the curtilage of a factory is not a "street" in which a main can be laid without notice to the owners and occupiers (Third Schedule, Section 19(5)), and there are exceptions in the case of public walkways such as in shopping centres (Regulation 4 of the Walkways Regulations 1973).

The boundary of the street in which the main is laid (not necessarily the street abutting upon premises actually supplied with water) defines the communication pipe, and hence the supply pipe. It has no influence at all upon the definition of a main.

Service pipes, like mains, can be any size. It will be seen from the definitions that there is really no such thing as a private main—such a pipe is usually a supply pipe.

## Ownership and Responsibility

Mains are pipes laid by the undertakers, who must keep them in repair, particularly with regard to their duty to maintain constancy and pressure of supply (Third Schedule, Sections 31 and 39).

All communication pipes vest in the undertakers who, at their own expense, shall carry out any necessary works of maintenance repair or renewal of such pipes and any work on their mains incidental thereto (Third Schedule, Section 44(1)). Subject to certain conditions, the undertakers must lay a new communication pipe to connect to the supply pipe laid by the owner of premises to be supplied (Third Schedule, Section 41(1)); they must also lay any part of the supply pipe which is in a highway (not a "street"—see above) (Third Schedule, Section 41(1)). The expenses reasonably incurred by the undertakers in doing this are repayable by the person giving notice that the communication pipe is required (Third Schedule, Section 41(3)), although the pipe vests in the undertakers, and not in the person paying for it to be laid. The water authority may, if they think fit, themselves bear the whole or any part of the costs of laying a communication pipe (Third Schedule, Section 41(3), but amended by the Local Government (Miscellaneous Provisions) Act 1953, Section 12(3), and again by the Water Act 1973, Eighth Schedule, Section 66).

Supply pipes belong to the owner(s) of the property supplied, who are responsible for their repair. However:—

(i) the undertakers must themselves carry out any necessary work of maintenance repair or renewal on any supply pipe laid in a highway, and may recover the costs from the *owner* of the premises supplied by the pipe (Third Schedule, Section 44(2));

(ii) if the undertakers have reason to think that a supply pipe is causing or likely to cause waste of water or injury, they may repair it themselves and recover the expenses from the owner of the premises supplied (Third Schedule, Section 63(1)); in the case of a common supply pipe the cost may be recovered from the *owners or occupiers* in such proportions as, in case of dispute, may be settled by the court (Third Schedule, Section 63(2), as amended by the Water Act 1948, Section 11(3)).

## Laying Mains and Service Pipes

The undertakers may lay a main in any street (see above) subject to the Public Utilities Street Works Act 1950, and in on or over any land not forming part of a street after giving reasonable notice to every owner and occupier (Third Schedule, Section 19(1), as amended by the Local Authorities (Miscellaneous Provisions) Order 1977). In the latter case the consent of a highway authority and/or electricity or gas board may also be required.

The undertakers may also in any street lay such service pipes as they deem necessary for supplying water to premises (Third Schedule, Section 21(1)). (This gives power to the undertakers to carry out the duties laid upon them in respect of communication and supply pipes.) Both provisions include powers to inspect repair renew or alter any of the pipes.

## Rights and Easements

The undertakers have a general right to inspect repair or alter or renew any main laid down by them, whether laid in any street or not (Third Schedule, Section 19(1) as amended). They have similar powers in respect of service pipes (Third Schedule, Section 21).

The form of protection (e.g. from interference, level alterations) depends upon whether the pipe is in a "street" or not. The wide definition of street (p. 000) means that most mains in urban areas are in "streets", even when they are in private land. These pipes are covered by the protection to undertaker's apparatus in the Public Utilities Street Works Act 1950, which contains a definition of "street" (Public Utilities Street Works Act 1950, Section 1(3)) very similar to that in the Water Act 1945.

Any pipes to be laid in a street are subject to the procedures of the Public Utilities Street Works Act 1950—even (in theory) when the street is a very minor private passage. That Act refers to "street managers" in relation to a street which is not a maintainable highway, and this expression includes any body or person having the management or control of the street (Public Utilities Street Works Act, 1950, Section 2(5)). In relation to any alley or passage around the back of old property), it may frequently be impossible to determine who this is.

In the case of land not forming part of a street, there is a general power to lay mains on giving of notice (see above). In such cases the owners or occupiers of land must not do anything to interfere materially with the undertaker's rights in the main. This protection is very vague, and there are benefits to be gained from entering into formal easement agreement with the owners, specifying each party's rights and duties. Even where such negotiated agreements are to be sought, delays are avoided by serving statutory notices (that the water undertakers are entering to lay the main) at the outset.

Undertakers have no rights to lay service pipes other than in a street (there are some unusual cases where the main is apparently outside the street, but the definition of "street" is extended (Third Schedule, Section 1; Water Act 1948, Section 10). Where a service pipe has been lawfully laid in land not forming part of a street, the undertakers may enter on that land to inspect repair or alter renew, etc., but must pay compensation (Third Schedule, Section 21(2)).

Undertakers would appear to have no title, legal or equitable, in the soil in which their pipes are laid. They merely have the exclusive right of occupation of the space in the soil taken up by their pipes (*Newcastle-under-Lyme Corporation* v. *Wolstanton* (1947)).

Where the undertakers, in the exercise of their powers, lay a main in on or over any land not forming part of a street, or inspect, repair, alter, renew, or remove a main laid in, on or over any such land, they are liable from time to time to pay compensation to every person interested in that land for any damage done.

## Valve and Hydrant Plates

The undertakers may erect and maintain in any street notice indicating the position of underground water fittings used for controlling the flow of water through their mains, whether laid by virtue of this section or otherwise, and may affix such a notice to any house or other building, wall or fence (Water Act 1945, Third Schedule, Section 19(4)).

## Mains Outside the Limits of Supply

Section 20 of the Water Act 1945 imposes conditions as to the laying of mains outside the limits of supply of the undertakers. Under this section undertakers desiring to lay mains outside the limits of supply must, in addition to complying with the conditions of Section 19, advertise the proposals in a newspaper circulating in the area in which the main is to be laid, specifying the land affected and naming a place where a plan of the proposals may be inspected. The undertakers must also serve notice on the local authority and (if any part of the main is to be laid in a highway), the highway authority. If an objection is received from such authority and not withdrawn, the matter must be referred to the Secretary of State and a Local Inquiry held. If the whole of the main is to be laid in a highway maintainable at the public expense and the consent of the local authority and (where separate) the highway authority is given, the foregoing provisions as to notices and advertisements do not apply. Under Section 13 of the Water Act 1973, statutory water undertakers have power to make agreements with other statutory water undertakers to supply water outside their limits of supply subject to such conditions as may be specified in the agreement.

## Separate Service Pipes

Section 42 enables undertakers to require the provision of a separate service pipe for each house or other building supplied, or to be supplied, by them with water. The requirement does not apply, however, to existing buildings unless (1) an existing supply pipe becomes defective or insufficient to meet the requirements of the house; (2) water charges are not paid; or (3) houses are converted, by structural alterations, into a larger number of houses. Nor does it apply where the owner of a group or block of houses is liable by law, or undertakes in writing, to pay the water charges in respect of all those houses, provided he punctually pays those charges and the supply pipe of those houses is sufficient to meet the requirements thereof.

## Stopcocks

Part XI (Section 45) of the Third Schedule contains provisions as to the position, etc., of stopcocks. The section provides that on every service pipe laid after the coming into force of this section the undertakers must, and on every service pipe laid before that date the undertakers may, fit a stopcock enclosed in a covered box, or pit, of such size as may be reasonably necessary. Every stopcock fitted on a service pipe after the coming into force of this section must be placed in such position as the undertakers deem most convenient, provided that.-

(*a*)  a stopcock in private premises must be placed as near as is reasonably practicable to the street from which the service pipe enters those premises; and

(*b*)  a stopcock in a street must, after consultation with the highway authority concerned, be placed as near to the boundary thereof as is reasonably practicable.

## BREAKING OPEN STREETS

Water undertakers' power to break open streets is contained in Section 22 of the Third Schedule of the Water Act 1945. This forms part of Part VI of that Schedule; most of the remainder of this Part has been repealed, and the provisions replaced by the Public Utilities Street Works Act 1950, which forms a separate section of this Chapter.

## THE THIRD SCHEDULE OF THE WATER ACT 1945

Much of the detailed law set out in the last few pages comes directly from the Third Schedule to the Water Act 1945. This is known as the "Waterworks Code", and was intended to replace the old Waterworks Code in the Waterworks Clauses Act 1847. In view of the difficulties which immediate implementation would have caused to the many water undertakings then in existence, the 1945 Act (Section 32) gave to the Minister (then the Minister of Health) the power to apply the new code to any water undertaking by Order as appeared to him appropriate, and subject to such modifications and adaptations as may be specified in the Order. ·

It will thus be readily appreciated that the law applicable to some water companies, some water authorities, or some parts of the areas of either, may well differ from that set out in this chapter. It may depend on old local Acts, the old Code in the 1847 Act as amended, or whether immediately before the creation of water authorities under the Water Act 1973 the new Code under the 1945 Act had been adopted in its original form, or itself modified.

The following parts of the Third Schedule have already been referred to:—

Part V        Sections 19-21—power to lay mains, etc;
Part VI       Sections 22-28—breaking open streets, etc., (dealt with in conjunction with Public Utilities Street Works Act 1950);
Part VII      Sections 29-31—supply of water for domestic purposes;
Part VIII     Sections 32-38—supply of water for public purposes;
Part IX       Section 39—constancy and pressure of supply;
Part X        Sections 40-44—laying and maintenance of supply pipes and communication pipes;
Part XI       Section 45—stopcocks.

Certain of the definitions in Part I (Section 1) have also been mentioned.

## Works and Lands

Part II of the Schedule, Sections 2-9, gives very necessary powers in this behalf. By Section 2, in the construction of any authorized works, the undertakers may deviate laterally to any extent not exceeding the limits of deviation shown on the plans submitted to the Secretary of State and, where in a street no such limits are shown, the boundaries of the street (including any verge or roadside waste adjoining it) are the limits of deviation. They may deviate vertically from the levels shown on the plans to any extent provided that no pipe, etc., shall be raised above ground except as shown on the plans or crossing a river, stream, canal, dyke, watercourse or railway, or the consent of all persons having a legal estate in the land has been obtained. The section also sets down a deviation limit upon embankments for reservoirs, but this would be subject to the provisions of the Reservoirs Act 1975. It is interesting to note, however, that Section 2 was frequently excepted from incorporation with the Special Act incorporating the Third Schedule.

Section 3 prevents undertakers from constructing works for intercepting water from lands acquired by them unless the works are properly authorized. Subject to this, however, Section 4 gives power to do subsidiary works in connection with the supply of water as the undertakers deem necessary.

Section 5 gives undertakers powers for certain purposes to lay or erect on, above, or below ground, telephone wires or cables. Certain consents are necessary.

By Section 7, as amended by Section 11 of the Water Act 1948 where undertakers are authorized compulsorily to purchase land for the purpose of executing underground works, they may, instead of purchasing the land, purchase only such easements and rights over or in the land as may be sufficient for such purpose. They shall not be entitled to fence the land in respect of which such easements or rights have been obtained except by agreement, nor required to do so. The landowner's rights of cultivation of the land are to remain unimpaired. Section 8 refers to persons under disability being able to grant easements.

Private rights of way over land which the undertakers are authorized to acquire compulsorily may (Section 9) be extinguished. Compensation is payable.

By Section 6, it is an offence for any person wilfully to obstruct a person engaged or authorized by an undertaker in setting out a site for construction works, or to pull out deface or destroy pegs or other thing made or erected for that purpose.

Part IV, Sections 11 to 18, deals with minerals beneath waterworks. As mentioned elsewhere in this Chapter, land purchased by undertakers is deemed to exclude mines and minerals except those which it is necessary for them to dig, carry away, or use in the construction of their works.

**Prevention of the Waste of Water and Water Meters**

The provisions for preventing waste, etc., of water and as to meters and other fittings are to be found in Part XIII (Sections 60-70) of the Third Schedule.

The following is a summary of the provisions:—

*Cisterns.*—Section 60 enables the undertakers to require the provision of a cistern, together with a ball and stop-cock, on the pipe conveying water to it in the case of:—

(i) any building the supply of water to which need not under the special Act be constantly laid on under pressure (as to which see Section 39 of the Third Schedule to the Water Act 1945, or any other special provisions which apply); and
(ii) any house the erection of which was not commenced before the coming into force of the Section and to which water is required to be delivered at a height greater than 10.7 m below the draw-off level of the service reservoir.

In the case of (ii), the undertakers may require a cistern capable of holding one day's supply. It is to be noted that under Section 39 of the Third Schedule the appropriate service reservoir is in the discretion of the undertakers. If the consumer fails to provide the cistern, etc., or fails to keep it in repair, the undertakers may provide it or do repairs to prevent waste of water and charge the cost to the owner of the building.

*Testing Water Fittings.*—By Section 61 the undertakers are given power to test any water fittings.

*Entry of Premises.*—Section 62 gives an authorized officer of the undertakers power to enter premises supplied by the undertakers to detect waste or misuse of water.

*Penalty of Waste, etc.*—Section 64 provides for a penalty where the owner or occupier of any premises wilfully or negligently causes or suffers any water fitting which he is liable to maintain to be out of order or repair or to be or remain so constructed or adapted or used that the water supplied to the premises is or is likely to be wasted, misused or unduly consumed, or contaminated before use, or that foul air or any impure matter is likely to return into any pipe belonging to or connected with a pipe belonging to the undertakers. If any water fitting which any person is liable to maintain is in such a condition or so constructed or adapted the undertakers may require that person to carry out necessary repairs or alterations, and if he fails to do so within 48 hours the undertakers may themselves carry out the work and recover from him their reasonable expenses. It may in some cases be a matter of much practical difficulty to discover who is liable to maintain fittings. *A modified Section 64 has been applied to water authorities by the Local Government (Miscellaneous Provisions) Act 1953, as itself amended by the Water Act 1973, though the practical effect of the original and the current form of the section is similar.*

*Penalty for Fraudulent Use of Water.*—By Section 66 persons who fraudulently alter the index of a meter or prevent it registering correctly are subject to a penalty as well as those who fraudulently abstract or use water of the undertakers (e.g. by abstracting water before it has passed the meter). The onus is upon the consumer to prove absence of fraud. Where a meter has been fraudulently interfered with the undertakers are enabled to put it in order at the expense of the offender. See also Section 115 of the Water Resources Act 1963, and the Theft Act 1968.

*Penalty for Interference with Valves and Apparatus.*—Section 67 subjects to a penalty anyone who wilfully and without the consent of the undertakers or negligently turns on, opens, closes, shuts off or otherwise interferes with any valve, cock or other work or apparatus belonging to the undertakers. This and the next section have been amended by Schedule 9 to the Water Resources Act 1963.

*Penalty for Extension or Alteration of Pipes, etc.*—Section 68 provides for a penalty where any person, without consent, attaches any pipe or apparatus to a pipe of the undertakers, or who uses any pipe or apparatus so attached or altered. This Section is directed, for example, to cases where, without consent, stop taps, hosepipes, etc., are fixed or a pipe is wrongfully attached to the service pipe of one house for the supply of another house.

*Meters.*—By Section 69 a consumer must not, without consent, connect or disconnect a meter. He must give 24 hours notice to the undertakers and they must carry out the work and are enabled to recover the expenses involved from the consumer.

Section 70 enables the undertakers to break open streets to affix and maintain meters on their mains and service pipes for the purpose of measuring the quantity of water supplied or preventing and detecting waste. They may insert in the street (but as near as is reasonably practicable to the boundary of it) the necessary covers or boxes. Protection is given to telegraphic lines of the Post Office and apparatus of electricity and gas undertakers.

Under Section 32 of the Water Act 1973, provision is made for the installation of meters. This section provides for the making of regulations by the Secretary of State in respect of the installation of meters, but these have not yet been made.

## 5. PUBLIC UTILITIES STREET WORKS ACT, 1950

GENERAL

This Act has three main purposes. Firstly, it contains a uniform code for the protection of highway and transport, etc., authorities where a street or controlled land is broken up by statutory undertakers in exercise of statutory powers. Secondly, it contains a code of protection for statutory undertakers where road or bridge alterations or transport works are likely to affect apparatus of the undertakers in a street or controlled land. Thirdly, it contains provisions for the mutual protection of undertakers having apparatus in the same street or controlled land. The provisions of the Act are complicated and detailed, and, although they are of importance in the day-to-day administration of water and other statutory undertakings, space permits of reference here only to the general scope of the Act.

PART I: THE STREET WORKS CODE

This part provides a uniform code (in the Act referred to as "the street works code") regulating the exercise of any statutory power to carry out *undertakers' works in streets*, whether that power is derived from a public general Act or from a special enactment. The code supersedes previous legislation and overrides future legislation on the matter (unless the contrary intention appears therein) and also agreements (other than reinstatement agreements) inconsistent with the code.

Those protected by the code include street (including private street), bridge, public sewer, and transport authorities and managers (called "authorities and managers concerned").

The code applies to:—

(1) placing, inspecting, maintaining, adjusting, repairing, altering or renewing, changing the position of, or removing apparatus, and

(2) breaking-up or opening a street or controlled land for the purposes mentioned in (1), and tunnelling or boring under a street or controlled land for those purposes or breaking up or opening a sewer, drain or tunnel for those purposes or purposes incidental thereto.

"Street" is defined in the Act and means any length of a highway (other than a waterway), road, lane, footway, alley or passage, any square or court, and any length of land laid out as a way, whether it is for the time being formed as a way or not, irrespective of whether the highway road or other thing in question is a thoroughfare or not.

"Controlled land" may broadly be said to be land in the control of the highway authority which adjoins a street and which is to be used for the eventual widening of that street.

Highway authorities are enabled to obtain on behalf of undertakers an authorization for them to place and maintain their apparatus in controlled land. Indeed, a highway authority may disapprove (subject to arbitration in case of dispute) the plan and section of the work (referred to in the next paragraph) on the grounds that the work should be carried out in controlled land.

The general scheme of protection is as follows. Before commencing major works (i.e. works other than inspection, maintenance, adjustment or repair of apparatus or, in certain circumstances, laying or maintenance of service pipes) the undertakers, except in the case of emergency works, must submit to and settle with the authorities and managers concerned a plan and section of the proposed works. Arbitration is provided for in the event of dispute. Where an arbitrator is satisfied that the execution of works in a bridge would be likely to affect injuriously the structure or stability thereof and it is not practicable to meet the objection on that ground to the plan and section he must so declare and disapprove them. In the case of emergency works, a plan and section must be submitted subsequently and the authorities and managers concerned may insist on reasonable alterations to the works being carried out at the undertakers' expense.

Except in the case of emergency (where notice must be served as soon as reasonably practicable after commencement), the prescribed notice of commencement must be served on the authorities and managers concerned before commencing not only major works but also all other code-regulated works, with the expection of surface works.

In the execution of the works undertakers must comply with the plan and section as settled and with the reasonable requirements of the authorities and managers concerned as to the execution of incidental works. The code also imposes upon the undertakers requirements as to fencing, guarding and lighting, traffic signals, length and width of openings, etc.

Undertakers are responsible for reinstating the street or controlled land broken up. Although the primary responsibility for reinstatement is upon the undertakers, the code enables highway, etc., authorities to elect (generally or in a particular case) to carry out, at upper levels, the necessary reinstatement after major works, at the undertakers' expense. Reinstatement agreements made since the coming into operation of the code frequently provide that the highway authority shall carry out reinstatement after other than major works as the agents of the undertakers. In London the highway authorities can elect to carry out reinstatement after both major and other works. Undertakers must afford to authorities and managers concerned facilities for, and are liable for their reasonable expenses of, supervising reinstatement and the undertakers must comply with their reasonable requirements as to the execution of the work.

The undertakers are made liable for subsidence and deterioration (in so far as such deterioration is due to defective workmanship or use of defective materials by the undertakers) for six months after the completion of reinstatement. Where, however, the highway, etc., authority have done the reinstatement at upper levels, the undertakers are not liable if the subsidence is due to the defective workmanship or the use of defective materials by that authority.

The code contains important compensation provisions so far as transport and street and bridge authorities and managers are concerned. Where undertakers carry out works in streets which cross or are crossed by transport property, they must compensate the transport authority for damage done to such property in the execution of the works and for damage done to such property by the bursting, etc., of their pipes. Equally, undertakers must compensate street and bridge authorities or managers for damage done in the execution of street works and they are also made liable at law, *irrespective of negligence*, for damage done to the property of these authorities and managers by the bursting, etc., of mains in streets.

Transport authorities are further favoured by the code inasmuch as they may elect to carry out, at the undertakers' expense, works of the undertakers (except the placing of apparatus or other principal operation in question) and certain reinstatement in streets which cross or are crossed by transport property. Further, they may do such additional works, at the expense of the undertakers, as may be necessary (subject to arbitration in the case of dispute) for the protection of their property. The undertakers must also secure that their apparatus laid in these circumstances is maintained to the reasonable satisfaction of the transport authority.

## PART II: CODE WHERE APPARATUS IS AFFECTED BY ROAD, BRIDGE OR TRANSPORT WORKS

The code in this part is complementary to the code in Part I, and applies for the protection of undertakers where their apparatus in a street or controlled land is affected by highway or bridge alterations or transport works. The code supersedes previously existing protective provisions, whether derived from statute or otherwise; and, unless the contrary intention appears therein, no future corresponding provisions in statutes are to have effect, nor are any general agreements inconsistent with the code.

The general principle of the protection is that a promoting authority must pay to undertakers concerned the cost of any necessary alterations and protective works to their apparatus or to their consumers' apparatus. As to "necessary" alterations, reference may be made to *Paisley Magistrates* v. *South of Scotland Electricity Board* (1956) S.C.502, a case concerning cables in footpaths, where it was held that measures taken by that board to restore and maintain the state of efficiency in their system, which common practice in the industry recognized and which the street reconstruction would otherwise have impaired, were "necessary" measures. Except in emergency, a specification of any such alterations and protective works must be settled before the promoting authority's works are begun. The general rule as to the payment by the promoting authority of the cost of protective works is subject to the following qualifications.

No payment is to be made where roadworks are done to make good subsidence unless the undertakers prove that such subsidence was caused by the road authority; and no payment is to be made where apparatus has been placed after prescribed notice has been given to undertakers of road, etc., works and certain conditions have been complied with by the promoting authority.

The undertakers must themselves bear the additional expense involved where, for their own purposes, they substitute apparatus of better type, greater dimensions (other than length), or greater capacity or lay apparatus at a greater depth than that provided for in the agreed or settled specification of works. Again, where the undertakers lay a new pipe in place of an existing pipe more than 7½ years old, the financial benefit to the undertakers of deferment of the time for renewal of the pipe in the ordinary course is to be set off.

## PART III: UNDERTAKERS WORK LIKELY TO AFFECT APPARATUS OF OTHER UNDERTAKERS

This part contains, *inter alia*, a mutual code of protection for undertakers who have apparatus in the same street or controlled land. The code does not apply to railway works or to works relating to service pipes, service lines, or overhead telegraphic lines.

The code, unlike the street works code and the code in Part II, is in addition to any other previously existing or subsequently obtained protective provisions, statutory or otherwise.

The undertakers carrying out works must give to other undertakers concerned three days' notice (except in emergency, when notice must be given as soon as possible after commencement), and afford reasonable facilities for supervision. They must comply with certain requirements as to support, etc., and, in the case of electric line works, must effectively insulate, etc., such works. They must, in addition, comply with the reasonable requirements of the other undertakers. In emergency works they are to be treated as having complied with these requirements if they have done everything reasonably practicable in the circumstances. They must in any event pay compensation for damage done.

## HIGHWAYS STOPPED UP OR DIVERTED

There are various powers under which highways may be stopped up or diverted—e.g. under Highways, Town and Country Planning, and Housing Acts.

All these enactments contain provisions concerning the rights of the undertakers who have apparatus in the highways so stopped up or diverted. In most cases the rights of the undertakers to use, repair, etc., that apparatus are protected, but with provision for the authority who applied for the stopping up or diversion to require the removal and relocation of that apparatus, should they so choose, at their cost (the latter being usually subject to diminution if there is betterment).

## 6. SEWERAGE

### INTRODUCTION

By Section 14(1) of the Water Act 1973, the water authority has the duty to provide, either inside or outside their area, such public sewers as may be necessary for effectually draining their area, and to make such provision, whether inside or outside their area, by means of sewage disposal works or otherwise as may be necessary for effectually dealing with the contents of their sewers. This provision substantially re-enacts the provisions of the former Section 14 of the Public Health Act 1936 and accordingly that section and section 14 of that Act ceased to have effect.

In addition, by Section 14(2) of the Water Act 1973, the functions conferred on the former local authorities by the following enactments were transferred to the water authority:—

(a) Sections 15 to 24, 27 to 31, 33 to 36, and 42 of the Public Health Act 1936, and so much of Part (XII) of that Act as relates to those Sections (general powers, etc., concerning sewerage and sewage disposal);
(b) the Public Health (Drainage of Trade Premises) Act 1937;
(c) Section 13 of the Local Government (Miscellaneous Provisions) Act 1953 (power to waive certain sewerage charges); and
(d) Sections 12 to 14 and Part (V) of and Schedule 2 to the Public Health Act 1961 (contribution to costs of sewers).

Further, by virtue of paragraphs 38, 39 and 40 of Schedule 8 to the Water Act 1973, functions under Sections 40(4), 48(1), and 50(1) of the Public Health Act 1936 were also conferred on the water authority, in these cases along with the local authority.

However, within the area of each water authority, there is a duty imposed by Section 15 of the Water Act 1973 on the water authority and local authorities or new town development corporations to endeavour to make arrangements for such local authorities or new town development corporations to discharge in their area the functions of the water authority under those provisions of the Public Health Act 1936, mentioned above, other than any functions relating to sewage disposal or to the maintenance or operation of any sewer which, immediately before 1st April 1974, was vested in a joint sewerage board or the Greater London Council.

Section 15 provides for the matters to be covered in such arrangements, and for the variation or ending of such arrangements which, in default of agreement between the parties, may be varied or ended by direction of the Secretary of State.

These Section 15 arrangements are often called "Sewerage Agency Agreements", although the local authorities and new town development corporations are not strictly "agents" of the water authorities in this matter.

## DEFINITIONS

It is necessary to understand the scope of three definitions, namely, those of *"drain"*, *"sewer"* and *"public sewer"* in order to appreciate the extent and limits of the powers and duties of a water authority.

These definitions are contained in Section 20 and Section 343 of the Public Health Act 1936, as amended and re-enacted, and are as follows:—

*Drain.*—means a drain used for the drainage of one building or of any buildings or yards appurtenant to buildings within the same curtilage;

*Sewer.*—does *not* include a drain as defined above but, save as aforesaid, includes all sewers and drains used for the drainage of buildings and yards appurtenant to buildings;

*Public sewer.*—means:
(i)   All sewers vested in a water authority upon reorganization by virtue of Section 254 or Section 68 of the Local Government Act 1972;
(ii)  all sewers constructed by the water authority at their expense or vested in the water authority in pursuance of arrangements under Section 15 of the Water Act 1973 or otherwise acquired by the authority;
(iii) all sewers constructed under Part IX of the Highways Act 1959, except sewers belonging to a road maintained by a highway authority;
(iv)  all sewers with respect to which a Declaration of Vesting under Section 17 of the Public Health Act 1936 has taken place.

*Note.*—(Section 20 of the Public Health Act 1936 appears in re-enacted form at paragraph 33 of Schedule 8 to the Water Act 1973.)

It should be noted that, by virtue of (i) above, there vested in a water authority at 1st April 1974 all sewers considered to be public sewers and vested in local authorities under previous legislation, notably Section 20 of the Public Health Act 1936 as originally enacted, irrespective of whether the pipe or sewer in question would fall within the present definition of sewer for the purposes of the Public Health Act 1936 and the Water Act 1973. Thus, all sewers vested in the former local authority by virtue of the provisions of the Public Health Act 1875 will continue to be vested in the water authority as public sewers. In order to determine, therefore, the status of a particular pipe at law, it will be necessary, according to its age and origin, to understand the various procedures which could give rise to the status of a public sewer at any particular time. It should be noted that the term "public sewer" was not in common usage prior to the Act of 1936, the relevant question being at that time whether a sewer was vested in a local authority. The next two paragraphs summarize the manner in which a pipe or conduit could come to be regarded as a sewer or public sewer under the Public Health Act 1875 and the Public Health Act 1936, respectively.

## Public Health Act 1936 (Operative 1st October 1937)

There should be little difficulty in identifying which of the sewers provided since the 1936 Act came into effect are public sewers; since to be public they must have been one of the following:—

(1) provided by the local authority (or joint sewerage board) at their expense, except for those sewers draining only property belonging to them and not the subject of a vesting declaration;

(2) constructed as part of private street works except highway drains;

(3) subject to a declaration of vesting (Section 17);

(4) considered to be an existing "sewer" on the date prior to the commencement of the Act (i.e. upon 30th September 1937) and these are considered in two sub-groups:

(a) all sewers within the meaning of the Public Health Act 1875 which were by virtue of that Act vested in a local authority prior to 1st October 1937 which should continue to vest in the local authority, and

(b) all combined drains constructed before 1st October 1937 which by virtue of the 1875 Act would have been vested in a local authority before that date, had it not been for the provision of some enactment, statutory scheme or order.

The combined drain was of course within the definition of "sewer" in the 1875 Act, since it drained more than one property not within the same curtilage, but various local Acts and statutory schemes contrived to relieve local authorities of obligations in respect of combined drains. The provision in Section 20 of the Public Health Act 1936 (as originally enacted) made it clear that combined drains were public sewers within the meaning of the Act, irrespective of the provisions of any previous enactment or statutory scheme. The special status of combined drains was however to some extent retained by the provisions of Section 24 of the Public Health Act 1936, which imposed liabilities for maintenance on persons using the "sewer". These combined drains are referred to as "Section 24 sewers". The term "public sewer" as distinct from private sewer was not in regular use in this context before the Public Health Act 1936, but as will be seen it was still the case prior to 1st October 1937, that not all sewers were vested in the local authority.

### Sewer Maps

The map of public sewers, which the local authority has to keep under Section 32 of the Public Health Act 1936, is not conclusive at law as to the status of a sewer shown as public on that map; but in practice it is likely to be difficult to show that any sewer marked on the map as public does not have that status unless it is specified as something else. In any event the map is not normally a complete record of the public sewers in the area, in view of the limitation on the local authority's duty contained in Section 32(3) whereby the local authority need not show on the map any public sewer which was vested in it before 1st October 1937, unless the sewer was reserved for foul water only or for surface water only. It is desirable to mark all public sewers on the map even if no duty to do so exists.

### Public Health Act 1875 (Operative 15th August 1876)

The definition of sewer in the 1875 Act was wider than in the 1936 Act, and included at Section 4 *sewers and drains of every description*, except:—

(i) drains which drained one building only or premises within the same curtilage and made merely for the purpose of communicating therefrom with a cesspool or with a sewer serving two or more buildings or premises, and

(ii) drains vested in or under the control of any authority having the management of roads not being a local authority under the 1875 Act.

The definition of sewer was thus not precise, and in particular no specific limitation was imposed requiring the drainage involved to be drainage only from yards and buildings. This lack of a precise definition caused a good deal of difficulty of interpretation, but certain guidelines can be drawn. A sewer it has been said "must be in some form a line of flow by which sewage or water of some kind should be taken from a point to another point and then discharged".

It was thus important that there should be some form of outfall, whether from a pipe or from a septic tank. As will be seen below, not all sewers within the definition were in fact vested in the local authority in any event.

The following were *not* within the definition of "sewer" under the 1875 Act:—

(1) a cesspool and the conduit leading to it or a conduit linking two cesspools unless there is an overflow from the cesspool to a sewer so that the cesspool acts only as a catchpit;

(2) any natural watercourse not receiving the sewage from houses prior to 15th August 1876; it should be particularly noted here that no discharge of sewage after this date into a watercourse can at law affect the status of a watercourse and render it a sewer.

The status of a watercourse receiving such sewage prior to 1876 would depend upon the degree of usage for that purpose so that the mere discharge of sewage from a small number of properties would not necessarily render the watercourse a sewer, depending on the nature of the discharge and the size of the watercourse. The culverting of a watercourse did not *per se* affect its status in any way. On the other hand, a pipe taking the drainage from more than one building was clearly a sewer within the 1875 Act unless the buildings were all within the same curtilage. In certain cases it was held that an artificially constructed land or agricultural drain or pipe could be within the definition of sewer, although for reasons explained below it did not vest in the local authority. It was also accepted that the collection of surface water drainage from a number of premises into a main drain (i.e. not sewage in the normal sense) could constitute that main drain a sewer within the meaning of the 1875 Act thus establishing the concept of a surface water sewer.

Having considered whether or not a pipe or drain in question is within the definition of a sewer under the 1875 Act, there are many cases where this is a difficult decision in view of the lapse of time and the lack of evidence. It is then necessary to consider whether it vested in the local authority at the time. This was determined by the provisions of Section 13 of the 1875 Act which are as follows:—

"all existing and future sewers within the district of a local authority together with all buildings, works, materials, and things belonging thereto, except:—

(i) sewers made by any person for his own profit, or by any company for the profit of the shareholders and

(ii) sewers made and used for the purpose of draining, preserving or improving land under any local or private Act of Parliament, or for the purpose of irrigating land and

(iii) sewers under the authority of any commissioners of sewers appointed by the Crown shall vest in and be under the control of such local authority".

Exceptions (ii) and (iii) do not call for lengthy comment. Sewers for the purpose of irrigating land need not have been made and used under a local or private Act of Parliament in order to get the benefit of the exception, nor is the exception lost by a land drainage sewer because it receives drainage from a small number of houses. The principal problem in interpreting the Section arises from the concept of sewers made for profit. This is purely a question of fact and instances of an intention to profit from the making of the sewer would be of selling or utilizing the sewage for manure or the surface water collected in the sewer for drinking water for cattle or for irrigation purposes as the case may be.

The fact that a sewer was made by a person developing a building estate in order to provide sanitation for the houses does not itself constitute sufficient evidence that the sewer was made for profit. On the other hand, if a sewer was made by a person, other than the developer of the estate, who has purchased the right to construct it with the object of turning the right to account by demanding payment for connection, the sewer would be held to have been made by him for profit. At this distance in time, it will clearly in most cases be difficult or impossible to establish this sort of factual evidence.

## CONSTRUCTION OF PUBLIC SEWERS

The water authority which proposes to construct a new public sewer must first obtain the necessary rights to lay the pipes, manholes, etc., through and in the land which it requires. The water authority may obtain the necessary rights to do this either by agreement or by the service of Notice under Section 15 of the Public Health Act 1936, which gives, in effect, a compulsory power. By virtue of Section 15, a water authority may, *inter alia*, construct a public sewer:—

(i) in, under or over any street or under any cellar or vault below any street, subject, however, to the provisions of Part XII of the 1936 Act with respect to the breaking open of streets; or

(ii) in, on or over any land not forming part of the street, after giving reasonable notice to owner and occupier of that land.

The right to break open the street in order to construct the sewer under (i) above is now contained in Section 279(1) of the Public Health Act 1936, which incorporates the provisions of Part VI of the Third Schedule to the Water Act 1945 and the Street Works Code contained in the Public Utilities Street Works Act 1950 relating to the breaking open of streets, as applied to the 1936 Act.

"Street" is defined for the purposes of the 1936 Act as including (and therefore the definition is not necessarily exclusive) any highway, including over any bridge, and any road, lane, footway, square, court, alley or passage, whether a thoroughfare or not (Section 343(1)). The definitions of "street" are even wider in the Third Schedule to the Water Act 1945 and the Public Utilities Street Works Act 1950.

The Section seems to give the water authority an absolute discretion in selecting the route for the sewer, the sole requirement being to give reasonable notice to every owner and occupier of the land. It was held, for instance, in *Hutton* v. *Esher U.D.C.* (1973) that the power given by Section 15 was wide enough to justify the demolition of a building where this was required for the chosen route. Any person who has sustained damage by reason of the exercise by the water authority of their powers under Section 15 can, of course, claim full compensation under Section 278 of the 1936 Act, subject to any question of betterment which arises under Section 278(4). In addition, if a person is affected by the negligent construction or design of a sewer, he will have his normal remedies at law in that respect.

By virtue of Section 15(1) (iii) the water authority retain the right by agreement to acquire, whether by way of purchase, lease or otherwise, any sewer or the right to use any sewer.

## ADOPTION OF SEWERS

Under Section 17 of the Public Health Act 1936, a water authority may, by way of vesting declaration, adopt any sewer or sewage disposal works within their district after giving the appropriate notice to the owner or owners of the sewer or works in question. Conversely, the owner of a sewer or sewage disposal works may apply to the water authority for such a declaration to be made. If such an application is refused, or if the owner wishes to resist a proposal by the water authority to vest his sewer in them, the owner may appeal to the Secretary of State for the Environment who may then allow or disallow the proposal of the water authority or, as the case may be, make any declaration which the water authority might have made and may in addition satisfy conditions including conditions as to the payment of compensation by the water authority.

By virtue of Section 18 of the 1936 Act, the water authority may agree in advance with any person constructing or proposing to construct a sewer or sewage disposal works that, provided that such sewer or works is constructed in accordance with the terms of the agreement, they will in due course declare that sewer or works to be vested in them.

## MAINTENANCE OF SEWERS

By virtue of Section 23 of the Public Health Act 1936, the water authority has the duty to maintain, cleanse and empty all public sewers vested in them, subject to the right under Section 24 of the Act to recover in certain cases the expenses or a part thereof incurred by them in maintaining a length of public sewer to which that Section applies. Section 24 applies to two different types of length of sewer constructed before 1st October 1937, being either

(1) a length of sewer for the maintenance of which persons other than the local authority were responsible immediately prior to that date, or
(2) a length which was not constructed at the expense of the local authority but was vested in the local authority prior to that date.

## RIGHT OF CONNECTION

By virtue of Section 34 of the Public Health Act 1936, as amended by Section 14(4) of the Water Act 1973, the owner or occupier of any premises or the owner of any private sewer shall be entitled to have his drains or sewer made to communicate with the public sewers of any water authority and thereby to discharge foul water and surface water from those premises or that private sewer subject to the restrictions that nothing would entitle that person:—

(a) to discharge directly or indirectly into any public sewer
  (i) any liquid from a factory other than domestic sewage or surface or storm water, or any liquid from a manufacturing process; or
  (ii) any liquid or other matter, the discharge of which into public sewers is prohibited by or under any enactment (including any enactment such as Section 27 of the Public Health Act itself); or
(b) where separate public sewers are provided for foul water and for surface water to discharge directly or indirectly
  (i) foul water into a sewer provided for surface water; or
  (ii) except with the approval of the water authority, surface water into a sewer provided for foul water; or
(c) to have his drains or sewer made to communicate directly with a storm water overflow sewer.

A person wishing to take advantage of this Section must nevertheless comply with the provisions of the Section which require the service of notice of the proposals on the water authority, who may at any time within 21 days after receipt of the notice give notice of refusal to permit the communication to be made if it appears to them that the mode of construction or condition of the drain or sewer is such that the making of the communication would be prejudicial to their sewerage system, and, for the purpose of examining the mode of construction and condition of the drain or sewer, the water authority may, if necessary, require it to be laid open for inspection. Any question as to the reasonableness of the requirement of the local authority to lay open for inspection any works, or of their refusal to permit a new communication to be made, may be determined by a Court of Summary Jurisdiction. The water authority may also, under Section 36 of the 1936 Act, elect to carry out the making of the communication themselves and may, under that Section, require the deposit in advance of the cost of the work involved.

### REQUISITIONING OF NEW SEWERS

Under Section 16 of the Water Act 1973, it is the duty of a water authority to provide a public sewer to be used for domestic purposes for the drainage of premises in their area in three sets of circumstances.

The *first set* of circumstances is if the owners or occupiers of existing premises require such a sewer, the reckonable charges payable in respect of the drainage of the premises will be not less than the qualifying amount (being one-eighth of the expense of providing the sewer and any other sewer which it is necessary or appropriate to provide in consequence), and the persons making the request agree severally to pay the reckonable charges in respect of the premises for at least three years from the completion of the sewer.

The *second set* of circumstances is if the owners of the premises require a public sewer for the drainage of new buildings, they provide a private sewer which communicates with the requisitioned sewer in such manner and in such place as the water authority consider appropriate and the owners undertake to meet any relevant deficit arising from the requisition for a period of 12 years from the completion of the sewer, the relevant deficit being the difference in any year between the qualifying amount and the reckonable charges received by the water authority.

The *third set* of circumstances is if a local authority, within whose area the premises are situated, undertake to meet any relevant deficit in a case where the reckonable charges payable in respect of the premises will be less than the qualifying amount.

Section 16(12) provides that a sewer shall be treated as used for domestic purposes if it is used for removing the contents of a lavatory or for removing water used for cooking or washing other than water used for the business of a laundry or for the business of preparing food or beverages for consumption otherwise than on the premises. A water authority may require a landowner (other than a public authority) to deposit with them as security a sum not exceeding the total expense of laying the sewer. The water authority must pay interest at a rate prescribed on the deposit, and must appropriate out of the deposit upon the request of the landowner any amount due under his undertaking, any balance being finally repaid to him when the undertaking is finally discharged (subsections (6) and (7)).

Alternatively, a water authority may agree to the payment of a capital sum in satisfaction of any liability entered into under the Section, in respect of the expense of providing a sewer (subsection (8)). The sanction on the water authority for failure to provide the required sewer within six months, or such longer period as may be agreed or determined by a referee, is a fine not exceeding £400 unless the water authority can show that the failure was due to unavoidable accident or other unavoidable cause.

### HIGHWAYS DRAINS

A highway drain may be defined as any conduit or ditch, whether artificial or natural, which removes or conveys surface water from a highway maintainable at the public expense. Thus, drains which take surface water from a highway and which have no other function will normally be vested in the highway authority as highway drains.

A pipe which drains the highway, together with other premises, constructed subsequent to 1st October 1937 by the highway authority, will be a public sewer if it has been constructed under an enactment relating to the sewering of private streets (Section 20(1)(c) as originally enacted) or if it was a pipe constructed before 1st April 1974 by a highway authority who were at that time also the local sanitary authority, provided that the pipe also drains other premises not belonging to the local authority. Otherwise, if the pipe drains the highway alone, it would not be a public sewer unless and until the water authority, or its predecessor local authority, have made a declaration of vesting under Section 17 of the 1936 Act.

The fact that surface water flows from a highway into a public sewer would not affect the status of that sewer, and Section 21 of the Public Health Act 1936 provides for a county council as highway authority and the sewerage authority to enter into an agreement in any particular case whereby the one may use the drain or sewer vested in the other for the purpose of conveying away surface water which is its responsibility. There is provision for the resolution by the Secretary of State of any dispute arising from unreasonable refusal or the imposition of unreasonable terms at subsection 3.

A highway authority has the power under Section 103 of the Highways Act 1959 as amended by Section 22 of the Highways Act 1971 for the purpose of draining the highway or of otherwise preventing surface water from flowing onto it, to scour, cleanse and keep open all drains situated in the highway or in land adjoining or lying near to the highway, and the highway authority may construct or lay open drains as they consider necessary and divert surface water into or through any existing drain. It would seem that, following the removal of the defence of non-feasance, the highway authority is now also under a duty to maintain at the public expense any highway drains which are part of the highway.

## DRAINAGE OF TRADE PREMISES

The drainage of trade premises is controlled by the provisions of the Public Health (Drainage of Trade Premises) Act 1937, as amended by the Public Health Act 1961, and the Control of Pollution Act 1974. Section 1 of the 1937 Act as amended provides that, notwithstanding the restrictions imposed by Section 34 of the Public Health Act 1936, the occupier of any trade premises may, with the consent of the water authority, discharge into the public sewers any trade effluent proceeding from those premises. Such consent may be subject to conditions with respect to various matters specified in Section 2 of the 1937 Act and Section 59 of the Public Health Act 1961. Any refusal of consent or the imposition of conditions which the occupier considers unreasonable may be the subject of an appeal under Section 3 of the 1937 Act.

"Trade premises" are defined in Section 14 of the 1937 Act as any premises used or intended to be used for carrying on any trade or industry. This definition has been extended by Section 63 of the Public Health Act 1961 to include any premises used or intended to be used (whether for profit or not) for agicultural or horticultural purposes or for scientific research or experiments. "Trade effluent" is also defined by Section 14 to mean any liquid, either with or without particles of matter in suspension therein, which is wholly or in part produced in the course of any trade or industry carried on at trade premises, but excluding domestic sewage. Liquid produced solely in the course of laundering articles used to be excluded from trade effluent control by Section 4(4) of the 1937 Act, but this exemption has been terminated by Schedule 8 to the Water Act 1973.

No trade effluent can, by virtue of Section 2 of the 1937 Act, be discharged to the public sewer otherwise than in accordance with a Trade Effluent Notice served on the water authority by the owner or occupier of the premises from which discharge is required. The Trade Effluent Notice must state the nature and composition of the trade effluent, the maximum quantity of the trade effluent which it is proposed to discharge on any one day, and the highest rate at which it is proposed to discharge the trade effluent. No trade effluent may then be discharged until two months have expired unless the water authority agree otherwise and this period of two months may be extended by direction of the water authority that no trade effluent shall be discharged until a specified date thereafter. Any contravention of these provisions may give rise to a fine of £200 plus £50 for every day the offence continues.

Where a trade effluent consent already exists, whether subject to conditions or not, the terms of that consent may be varied by the water authority giving a direction under Section 60 of the Public Health Act 1961, provided that two years have expired since the date of the original consent or the making of a previous direction. Section 45 of the Control of Pollution Act 1974, when brought into force, will allow the water authority to give a direction within the two year period without the consent of the owner or occupier of the trade premises if the water authority considers it necessary to do so in order to provide proper protection for persons likely to be affected by discharge which could lawfully be made apart from the giving of the direction. In such a case, compensation may be payable to the owner and occupier of the premises concerned. The owner and occupier of the trade premises may, however, consent to a direction being given within such two-year period if they so wish. The conditions imposed by any direction must be such as may be imposed on an original consent and the owner or occupier of the trade premises has a right of appeal within two months of the giving of the notice of direction to him, although the water authority may agree to extend that period.

## 7. SEWAGE PURIFICATION

### SEWAGE DISPOSAL WORKS

Under Section 14 of the Water Act 1973, the water authority has a duty to make such provision, whether inside or outside their area, by means of sewage disposal works or otherwise as may be necessary for effectually dealing with the contents of their sewers. The water authority has power under Section 15 of the Public Health Act 1936 to construct sewage disposal works on any land acquired or lawfully appropriated for the purpose (sub-section (1)(ii)) or by Agreement to Acquire, whether by way of purchase, lease or otherwise, any sewage disposal works or the right to use any such works (sub-section (1)(iii)). "Sewage disposal works" is defined by Section 90(4) of the 1936 Act to include the machinery and equipment of those works and any necessary pumping stations and outfall pipes.

In addition, a water authority may, by vesting declaration under Section 17 of the 1936 Act, adopt private sewage disposal works, subject to the provisions of that Section, or may agree under Section 18 of that Act to adopt, by vesting declaration, a sewage disposal works constructed in accordance with the terms of the agreement. There are thus vested in a water authority:—

(i)   all sewage disposal works which vested in a local authority under Section 13 of the Public Health Act 1875 as "buildings, works, materials and things belonging to sewers". In *Clark* v. *Epsom R.D.C.* (1929) a septic tank filter and outfall privately constructed were held to fall within this definition and to vest in the local authority together with the sewers draining them. These works become vested in the Water Authority by

virtue of the re-enacted Section 20 of the 1936 Act which is contained in paragraph 33 of
Schedule 8 to the Water Act 1973;

(ii) all sewage disposal works constructed by the water authority or any predecessor local
authority or acquired by them (see again the re-enacted Section 20 as referred to in (i)
above);

(iii) all sewage disposal works in respect of which a vesting declaration has been made by the
water authority or a predecessor local authority under Section 17 of the 1936 Act (see
again the re-enacted Section 20).

## MAINTENANCE OF SEWAGE DISPOSAL WORKS

The water authority has the duty under Section 31 of the Public Health Act 1936
to carry out its functions so as not to create a nuisance, but there is no express
statutory duty relating to the cleansing or maintenance of sewage disposal works
equivalent to Section 23 of the 1936 Act relating to the cleansing of public sewers.
Section 30 of the 1936 Act makes it clear that nothing in that Act authorizes a water
authority to construct or use any sewer, drain or outfall for the purpose of conveying
foul water to any natural or artificial stream, watercourse, canal, pond or lake until
the water has been so treated as not to affect prejudicially the purity and quality of
the water therein. The requirement to maintain standards of the effluent discharged
from sewage disposal works is dealt with in the section on pollution control.

In the leading case of *Price of Derby* v. *British Celanese Limited and Derby
Corporation* (1953) it was held that nothing in the Derby Corporation Act 1901,
which had authorized the Corporation to construct and maintain their sewage
disposal works, authorized the commission of a nuisance and, indeed, that Act on
similar lines to the 1936 Act contained an express prohibition against the
Corporation operating the works so as to cause nuisance. Derby Council therefore
had no statutory defence to the plaintiff's action for nuisance, and the question of
non-feasance, as distinct from mis-feasance, was irrelevant; the question being
whether the thing complained of as a nuisance was expressly or impliedly authorized
by the Act under which the works in question were constructed.

## 8. LAND DRAINAGE

### LAND DRAINAGE POWERS

The law on land drainage was consolidated in the Land Drainage Act 1976, which
repealed most of the previous legislation. The Act lays few duties on authorities since
the powers it provides are permissive. For the purposes of the Act, water authorities
and internal drainage boards are "drainage authorities", local authorities, and
others with land drainage interests (together with "drainage authorities") are
"drainage bodies".

The system of administration for land drainage provided by the 1976 Act is based
on Water Authority areas and comprises:—

**The Water Authority**, who must exercise supervision over all land drainage matters and must
delegate all land drainage functions except charges, precepts, borrowing, and charges option
orders, to:

**The Regional Land Drainage Committee**, who may delegate functions to:

**Local Land Drainage Committees** (usually based on the areas of former river authorities),
within whose area there may be:

**Internal Drainage Boards (IDBs)**, who are the drainage authorities for internal drainage
districts (IDDs) that "derive benefit or avoid danger" as a result of drainage operations; and

**Local Authorities** (and other drainage bodies such as conservators, commissioners, etc), who
may exercise certain land drainage functions mainly in respect of watercourses which are the
responsibility of neither a water authority nor an internal drainage board.

The powers, etc., of these various bodies are:—

## Water Authorities and their Regional Land Drainage Committees

The basic duty of a water authority is now set out in Section 1 of the Land Drainage Act 1976:—

"1 (1)—A Water Authority shall exercise a general supervision over all matters relating to drainage in their area but shall arrange for the discharge by their regional land drainage committee . . . of all their land drainage functions except the raising of drainage charges, the levying of precepts, the borrowing of money and the making of an application for a water charges option order".

Each water authority should have set up under the Water Act 1973 a Regional Land Drainage Committee (RLDC). The 1976 Act required their continuance, and specified their constitution (Section 2). Members are appointed by the Minister (i.e. Minister of Agriculture, Fisheries and Food), the water authority, and county (or London Borough) councils for the water authority's area. (There are special provisions regarding the Thames Water Authority's Committee).

The water authority may direct its RLDC as to the exercise of its functions (except those defined as "internal drainage functions" within the section) but *only* so far as the exercise of such functions appears likely to affect materially the authority's management of water for purposes other than land drainage (Section 1(2)). It will be seen that RLDCs enjoy, under the Acts, a considerable degree of freedom of action.

The powers of water authorities are described below under "Drainage Authorities".

## Land Drainage Committees

A RLDC may submit to the water authority a "local land drainage scheme". This is a scheme for the setting up of a "local land drainage district" and "local land drainage committee" (LLDC). The water authority must send such a scheme received from the RLDC to the Minister; he may approve it with or without modification. Any scheme so approved by him will come into effect on a date fixed by him (Section 4). The constitution of an LLDC is dealt with in Section 5 and Schedule 1.

RLDC and LLDC meetings are open to the public under the Public Bodies (Admission to Meetings) Act 1960. The RLDC and LLDC manage the affairs of their own meetings; the water authority has no right to endeavour to control them in this.

## Internal Drainage Boards

In some places, which fall within the definition of "such area as will derive benefit or avoid danger as a result of drainage operations", there are established Internal Drainage Boards (IDBs), each having its own "internal drainage district". IDBs consist of directly elected members and are corporate bodies; their purpose is to "exercise a general supervision over all matters relating to the drainage of land within their district". Their powers and duties, which include power to levy drainage rates, are defined in the Land Drainage Act 1976, and are described below under "Drainage Authorities".

## Local Authorities

Local Authorities have certain powers by way of the 1976 Act as follows:—

(1) District Councils (and also London Borough Councils and the Common Council for the City of London) have most of the powers of an IDB for execution of drainage works (Section 98). Schedule 5 contains special provisions relating to London:

(2) The Greater London Council has power to operate a flood warning system for a certain area (Section 101), and necessary incidental powers:

(3) They may contribute to such degree as seems to them proper in view of the benefits to be derived from drainage works, towards the costs of drainage works by a drainage body (Section 102):

(4) Council Councils have certain powers:—

    (a) the powers of an IDB under Section 18 (as to requiring the removal of certain obstructions to watercourses) but before exercising these powers the council shall, if the watercourse or part of it is in an internal drainage district, notify the IDB or otherwise, the water authority. (This power also applies to district councils (Section 97).);

    (b) similar powers to do works for other persons as are set out in Section 22 for drainage authorities, save that they can only be done within the council's own area (Section 99);

    (c) Section 30 powers (schemes for drainage of small areas) apply, though with somewhat different formalities. Before exercising these powers, the water authority must be consulted. The council has, in respect of these works, the powers of an IDB under Section 17 and Section 33 (disposal of spoil) (Section 100). These powers also apply to London Boroughs with special provisions.

It should be noted that the drainage situation of London and particularly the "London excluded area" differ from that elsewhere. Schedule 5 should be consulted on all questions affecting these areas.

## Other People

Nothing in the 1976 Act releases any person from obligations by reason of tenure, custom, prescription or otherwise to do any work by way of repair, maintenance or otherwise to any watercourse, bridge or drainage work. He can be required at seven days' notice to do such works after which time the drainage authority can do whatever is necessary and recover the expenses from him (Section 24).

However, where there is such a duty to do work in connection with the drainage of land (and here the section specifies the repairing of banks, or walls, maintaining watercourses or otherwise) then, subject to certain formalities, this obligation may be commuted by the relevant drainage authority to a capital sum or terminable annuity (Section 26). Awards under public or local Acts containing like obligations may be dealt with under Section 25.

## MAIN RIVER

This term requires definition. It is not limited to major watercourses but includes any watercourse designated upon a "main river map" as a "main river". For this purpose, "main rivers" are intended to be the more important watercourses in an area. There is no firm line of division of function, size, or operation between main or non-main river; a main river may even be susceptible of drying up in times of drought.

Powers as to main rivers, their banks or (prima facie) any structure or appliance on the bank or in the channel for regulating or controlling the flow of water into or out of main river, are solely exercisable by a water authority (Section 8).

A "main river map" (Section 9) is a map of the water authority's area relating to the land drainage functions of the authority, "main river" being marked in a distinctive colour.

The map may be varied under the following circumstances:—

(a)   the water authority's area is altered in such a way as to affect the map;

(b)   the Minister confirms a scheme under Section 50—such watercourses are to be treated as "main river";

(c)   the water authority apply for a variation of the map as to the extent to which any watercourse is to be treated as main river.

After appropriate notices, etc., the Minister may either make further alteration of the map, prepare a new map following a water authority's application, or refuse any variation. The main river map is conclusive for all purposes as to what is "main river".

## DRAINAGE AUTHORITIES

A "drainage authority" is a water authority or internal drainage board (Section 17(7)).

It is noteworthy that the Land Drainage Act 1976 does not, by and large, impose duties, but merely confers powers. For example, Section 17 opens with the words "Every drainage authority acting within their area shall have power . . .". A drainage authority will accordingly not be liable if it does not do works and flooding occurs, but if it negligently exercises its powers, liability can follow by way of the negligence.

The general powers of a drainage authority within its own area are:—

(i)   to cleanse repair or otherwise maintain in a due state of efficiency any existing watercourse or drainage work;

(ii)   to deepen, widen, straighten or otherwise improve any existing watercourses or remove or alter mill dams, weirs or other obstructions to watercourses, or raise, widen, or otherwise improve any existing drainage works;

(iii)   to make any new watercourse or drainage work or erect any machinery or do any other act (except as above) required for the drainage of their area.

In their exercise of the above functions, the powers of a water authority are limited to work on a "main river", except in respect of defence against sea water or tidal water. A water authority's power to maintain, improve, or construct drainage works for defence against sea water or tidal water may be exercised other than on "main river", including beyond low water mark. Where its area abuts the sea or an estuary, the water authority may do all such things in the sea or estuary as they believe to be necessary to secure adequate outfall for the "main river". IDB powers do not extend to "main rivers" (Section 8).

Only the maintenance of existing works carries with it powers of entry under this section (Section 17(6)), but this is remedied by Sections 111 and 112 of the Water Resources Act 1963, which give general powers of entry. Compensation is payable to any person sustaining injury as a result of the exercise of powers under this section.

## INTERNAL DRAINAGE BOARDS

The land drainage powers and duties of IDBs are similar to those of a water authority, except that they cannot execute works on main rivers and only apply within their area.

An IDB has specific powers of land acquisition (Section 37), including the creation or acquisition of new interests or rights (easements)—this is unlike water authorities. It has a general power to borrow money to defray the cost of exercising its functions, but this is usually subject to Ministerial consent (Section 87). As to impeded (Section

18) or obstructed (Section 28) watercourses, disposal of spoil (Section 33) and private works (Section 22), the powers of the IDB are similar to those of the water authority, but only for other than main rivers.

Section 34 and Schedule 4 apply for byelaws, but since Section 29 relating to structures in, over or under watercourses only applies to a water authority and main river and not an IDB, such matters in internal drainage districts can only be controlled by byelaws.

Section 15 gives a water authority "for the purpose of securing the efficient working and maintenance of existing drainage works within the water authority area and the construction of such new drainage works as may be necessary" power to give general or special directions to an IDB for their guidance as to the exercise and performance by their boards of their powers. Such a board shall not, without the consent of the water authority, construct or alter any drainage works (maintenance excepted) if by so doing the interest of, or working of another IDB is affected; nor shall it construct or alter any works for the discharge of water from its district into main river except on terms agreed with the water authority. If certain IDB powers are not adequately exercised, the water authority may itself exercise them, or may direct the appropriate county council so to do (Section 16).

## OBSTRUCTIONS IN WATERCOURSES

Under Section 18 where any watercourse is in such condition that the proper flow of water is impeded, a notice may be served requiring that the condition be remedied. From this is excluded an impeded flow being the result of mining or brine-pumping. The notice will be served by the water authority in the case of main river, otherwise by the IDB.

Normally, the notice will not require works to be done on land not owned or occupied by the recipient of the notice without the consent of the owner and occupier of the land concerned. The notice shall indicate:—

(1) the nature of the works to be executed, and the time in which they are to be done;
(2) the right of appeal to a magistrate's court under Section 19.

Failure to comply with a notice is a summary offence.

The drainage authority's powers under this section do not apply in certain cases of non-main river under the control of a local authority, harbour or navigation authority (or certain other authorities).

Section 19 contains details as to rights of appeal.

By Section 28, no person shall, without the written consent (not to be unreasonably withheld) of the drainage authority, erect any mill, dam, weir or like obstruction to the flow of a watercourse or alter any such existing obstruction; or erect a culvert or alter an existing culvert, in either case in such a way as to be likely to affect the flow of the watercourse. The authority have two months within which to reply to an application for consent. If they do not reply in that time, they are deemed to have consented. In cases of dispute, arbitration is available. This Section contains notice provisions, though apparently without the right of an appeal. Again a wrongful erection or culvert, or wrongful alteration of either is a summary offence.

By Section 29, no person shall (except with the consent of the water authority which shall not be unreasonably withheld and in accordance with plans and sections approved by the water authority):—

(a) erect any structure in, over or under a watercourse which is main river;
(b) alter or repair any such structure if the work is likely to affect the flow of water in the watercourse (again, main river), or impede any drainage work;

(c)   erect or alter any structure designed to contain or divert the floodwater of any part of the main river.

Consent may be conditional, and if not given or refused within two months is deemed to be given. If unauthorized works are removed by the water authority, the authority may recover the expenses incurred from the person who carried out the works.

### DISPOSAL OF SPOIL

Spoil is an inescapable by-product of drainage works on watercourses. Section 33 provides that a drainage authority may, without making any payment for it, appropriate and dispose of any matter removed in the course of work for widening, deepening or dredging any watercourse. Matter so removed may be deposited on the banks of the watercourse on such width of land as is sufficient to enable it to be removed from the watercourse and deposited in one mechanical operation unless it would constitute a nuisance under Part III of the Public Health Act 1936. Compensation is discretionary, unless the damage could have been avoided by reasonable care.

### FLOOD WARNING SYSTEMS

Reference has already been made to the power of the Greater London Council to operate a flood warning system by virtue of Section 101. By Section 32, a water authority has power to provide and operate a flood warning system for its own area. Powers of maintenance are included, as are the collection and provision of information concerning rainfall, flow or water levels, or other matters seeming relevant.

### BYELAWS

Section 34 empowers a drainage authority to make such byelaws as it considers necessary for securing the efficient working of the drainage system in its area. Purposes include (but are not limited to):—

(i)    regulating the use, and preventing improper use of watercourses, banks or works, or preserving the same from damage or destruction;
(ii)   regulating the opening of sluices and floodgates;
(iii)  preventing the obstruction of watercourses by the discharge flowing or falling into them of any solid or liquid matter;
(iv)   compelling the cutting and removal of vegetable growths in or on the banks of watercourses;
(v)    —(water authorities only)—for securing the proper defence against sea or tidal water of any part of their area.

Schedule 4 deals with the procedure necessary to obtain Ministerial confirmation; no drainage authority byelaw may conflict with any byelaw of a navigation authority, harbour authority, or conservancy authority.

### POWERS OF THE MINISTER

Central government, through the Ministry of Agriculture Fisheries and Food, has a much closer and more detailed involvement in land drainage than in the other activities of a water authority. References to the powers of the Minister appear in various places in this Chapter. In addition, he has powers to:

(1)    make grants towards the expenditure incurred by a water authority on the improvement of existing works, or construction of new works. The plans and sections must have been first approved, and the work properly carried out;

(2)  to make grants to IDBs and other drainage bodies;
(3)  to make grants towards the cost of flood warning systems;
(4)  to authorize landowners to execute drainage works in certain circumstances where land belonging to others would be affected by the works;
(6)  to make various regulations;
(6)  to hold inquiries.

## 9. FISHERIES

### DUTY OF WATER AUTHORITIES

The law relating to fisheries goes back many centuries. Earliest statutory references were in the thirteenth century (Magna Carta, 1215, and the Statute of Westminster II, 1285), but alongside the growth of statute law emerged rights to take fish (piscary) under common law. The Water Act 1973 transferred to water authorities duties relating to fisheries contained in the Salmon and Freshwater Acts 1923 to 1972. The law was consolidated by the Salmon and Freshwater Fisheries Act 1975; Section 28 provides:—

"It shall be the duty of every water authority—
(a)  to maintain, improve and develop the salmon fisheries, trout fisheries, freshwater fisheries and eel fisheries in the area for which they exercise functions under this Act."

It is also the duty of a water authority to establish a Regional Advisory Committee for the whole of its area, and such Local Advisory Committees, dealing with specific parts of the authority's area, as the authority shall consider necessary. The Committees are to be composed of persons who appear to the authority "to be interested in" fisheries in the authority's area, and the authority must consult such Committees as to the manner in which the authority is to discharge their fisheries duty.

### FISHING LICENCES

A water authority has the duty "by means of a system of licences to regulate fishing for salmon and trout in their area and, except so far as excused by the Minister, shall by such means regulate fishing for freshwater fish of any description or eels in their area" (section 25(1)). A fishing licence entitles the person to whom it was granted to use the instrument specified in the licence to catch the type of fish specified. It does not confer any right to fish at a place or a time at which the licencee is not otherwise entitled to fish.

By section 27 a person is guilty of any offence if, in a place where fishing for fish of any description is regulated by licences, he:

(a)  fishes for or takes fish of that description otherwise than by means of an instrument which he is entitled to use for that purpose by virtue of a fishing licence or otherwise than in accordance with the conditions of the licence; or
(b)  has in his possession with intent to use it for that purpose an instrument other than one which he is authorized to use for that purpose by virtue of such a licence.

### BYELAWS

Byelaws may be made for the whole or any part of the water authority's area. The purposes for which byelaws may be made include:—

(i)   Close seasons for various types of fish.
(ii)  Provisions as to use, carrying, marking of nets or other instruments for fishing, and of boats, coracles or other vessels for fishing.

(iii) Prohibitions as to taking certain fish, alive or dead, from specified waters at certain times, or at any time.
(iv) Specifying minimum sizes of different species of fish which may be taken;
(v) Regulation of the deposit or discharge in waters containing fish any material which is detrimental to fish.
(vi) Types of bait when fishing with rod and line.

## WATER BAILIFFS

A water authority may appoint water bailiffs, and the Minister may appoint persons who, though not officially designated as such, enjoy most of the powers of a water bailiff, which include wide powers of search and examination, and in certain instances the entry onto land. Such bailiff may stop and search any boat, vessel or vehicle which he reasonably suspects to contain illegally caught fish or a wrongful instrument, bait, or container. He may seize any fish, instrument, vessel or vehicle or other thing liable to be forfeited under the Act. A Justice of the Peace may authorize a water bailiff to enter premises to detect persons committing an offence. A water bailiff is deemed to be a constable when in the exercise of his duties.

## OWNERSHIP OF FISHING RIGHTS

The basic rule is that the ownership of the bed of non-tidal waters carries with it the right to fish there. Usually the owner of land adjoining a stream owns the bed to the centre of the stream, and thereby has a right to fish. However, ownerships may become severed, or rights granted to other people which exclude the right of the riparian owner to fish. There is legally no general right for the public to fish in non-tidal waters, though a practice of doing so may go unmolested by the true owner of the right. In tidal waters the public can, in general, fish as of right.

Fishing in non-tidal waters without the consent of the owner of the fishing rights is "poaching". This is a matter to be dealt with under the Theft Act 1968, not the Salmon and Freshwater Fisheries Act 1975, though the water bailiff can, in his role as a constable, arrest a poacher without warrant for fishing at night.

## 10. AMENITY AND RECREATION

The Water Act 1973 created new powers and duties in relation to amenity and recreation. It achieved this in three main ways.

(1) Under Section 20, it gave *permission* to water authorities and all other statutory water undertakers (such as water companies), to take steps to secure the use of water and land associated with water for the purpose of recreation, and in addition, it imposed an *obligation* on such bodies to "take such steps as are reasonably practicable for putting their rights to the use of water and of any land associated with water to the best use for those purposes". Further, a water authority may, with the consent of the owner, use land or water it does not own for the purposes of recreation.

(2) Under Section 22, water authorities must, in the formulation or consideration of any proposals relating to the discharge of any of their functions, have regard to the desirability of preserving natural beauty, of conserving flora, fauna and geological or physiographical features of special interest, and of protecting buildings and other objects of architectural, archeological or historic interest. In addition, they must take into account any effect that the proposals would have on the beauty of, or amenity in, any rural or urban area. The authority also has to consider the desirability of preserving public rights of access to the countryside.

(3) Under Section 23, a Water Space Amenity Commission (WSAC) was set up with duties which include advising the Government on the formulation, promotion and execution of the national policy for water, so far as it relates to recreation and amenity, and to advise water authorities on the discharge of their recreation and amenity functions. WSAC also have to "encourage and assist" water authorities in the preparations of plans and programmes made under Section 24 of the Act for the discharge of their functions so far as relating to recreation and amenity in England. (The Commission's responsibilities do not extend to Wales.)

The provision of facilities for recreation and amenity are subject to the general rules in Section 30 of the Act, which require that in fixing charges for services and facilities, a water authority shall have regard to the cost of performing those services or providing those facilities, and that their charges shall be such as not to show undue preference to, or discriminate unduly against, any class of persons.

## 11. POLLUTION CONTROL

### THE RIVERS (PREVENTION OF POLLUTION) ACTS

Section 9 of the Water Act 1973 transferred to the water authorities the functions of the former river authorities, including those relating to control of pollution of inland watercourses under the Rivers (Prevention of Pollution) Acts 1951 to 1961.

These statutes are due to be wholly repealed and replaced by the Control of Pollution Act 1974, Part II which was passed on 31st July 1974 but which will not become operative until such date or dates as the Secretary of State for the Environment may appoint. Until then, the Rivers (Prevention of Pollution) Acts 1951 to 1961 remain on the Statute Book and provide a water authority with basic powers in respect of pollution control.

The Acts aim to control pollution of inland watercourses in two ways; firstly by creating criminal *offences* punishable by fines, and secondly, by creating the administrative framework of a *consent* system whereby water authority consent is required for polluting discharges of trade and sewage effluent to inland watercourses.

### OFFENCES

The basic offence is in Section 2(1) of the 1951 Act which provides that a person (a) who *causes* or *knowingly permits* to enter a stream any poisonous, noxious or polluting matter, or (b) who *causes* or *knowingly permits* to enter a stream any matter so as to tend, either directly or indirectly or in combination with similar acts (whether his own or another's), to impede the proper flow of the water of the stream in a manner leading, or likely to lead, to a substantial aggravation of pollution due to other causes or of its consequences, commits an offence. Since the coming into force of the Criminal Law Act 1977, the maximum fine which can be imposed on summary conviction is now £1 000 in respect of offences committed after 17th July 1978. (Section 2 is to be replaced by Section 31 of the Control of Pollution Act 1974.)

On a charge of "causing" pollution, it is not necessary for the prosecution to prove that the defendant knew of the pollution, or that he was intentional or negligent in any way (*Alphacell Ltd.* v. *Woodward* (1972)). A defendant will have a defence, however, to a charge of causing pollution if he can show that the pollution was due to the intervening act of a trespasser or other unauthorized person (*Impress (Worcester) Ltd.* v. *Rees* (1971)).

For the purposes of the Acts, "stream" is defined by Section 11(1) of the 1951 Act as including any river, stream, watercourse or inland water (whether natural or artificial) except that it does not include either (i) any lake or pond which does not discharge to a stream, or (ii) any sewer vested in a water authority or any tidal waters. Any reference to a stream includes a reference to the channel or bed of a stream which is for the time being dry.

"Poisonous, noxious or polluting"—No definition is given by the Act, but Section 11 does state that matter is not to be deemed to be poisonous, noxious or polluting by reason of any effect it may have in discolouring a stream, if the discolouration is innocuous.

## Matter Discharged Through Sewers

Section 2 of the Act further provides that for the purposes of paragraph (a) of the subsection—i.e. causing or knowingly permitting polluting matter to enter a stream—a water authority, harbour authority, or development authority shall be deemed to cause or knowingly permit to enter a stream any poisonous noxious or polluting matter which passes into the stream from *any sewer or sewage disposal works* vested in them in any case where they were bound to receive the matter into the sewer or sewage disposal works, or they consented to do so unconditionally, or subject to conditions which were observed.

This provision is of little importance so far as a water authority is concerned in view of the provisions of Section 11 of the 1961 Act which restricts the institution of legal proceedings in respect of offences under the Acts to a water authority or subject to the consent of the Attorney General. It should be noted, however, that the Control of Pollution Act 1974, which re-enacts and extends the basic offence of Section 2(1)(a), removes this restriction on the institution of proceedings, and this provision may thus become of practical importance when the 1974 Act comes into force.

## Waste from Mines

Section 2(4) provides that Section 2(1)(a) (the basic offence) is not to penalize the discharge of water raised or drained from any underground part of a mine into a stream in the same condition in which it is raised or drained from underground, though the Minister may by Order direct that this protection is not to apply to discharges into any specified stream or part thereof.

Equally, Section 2(1)(a) is not to penalize the deposit with the consent of the water authority (not to be unreasonably withheld) of solid refuse from a mine or quarry on any land so that it falls or is carried into a stream, if no other site for the deposit is reasonably practicable and all reasonably practicable steps are taken to prevent the refuse entering the stream.

Any question whether a water authority's consent has or has not been unreasonably withheld is to be determined by the Secretary of State for the Environment.

## Prevention and Making Good of Defaults

Section 3 of the 1951 Act provides that where a water authority apprehends that a contravention of Section 2 is likely to occur by reason of any use or proposed use of the stream, or of any land for the disposal or storage of any matter, or by reason of any use or proposed use of a vessel in a defective state of repair for the carriage of cargoes from which poisonous, noxious, or polluting matter may enter the stream they may apply to the Court for an Order prohibiting or restricting the use complained of.

The Court may on such an application make an additional order directing the removal of polluting matter from a stream or from land and authorizing the water authority, if the direction is not complied with, to undertake the removal, and to dispose of the matter removed in any manner which may be authorized by the Court. In addition, a water authority has power to take emergency action in cases of pollution of water under Section 76 of the Water Resources Act 1973.

## Byelaws

Section 5 of the 1951 Act enables water authorities to make byelaws prohibiting or regulating the washing or cleansing in the streams to which the byelaws relate of things of any class or description, or the putting into the stream of litter or other objectionable matter, whether poisonous, noxious or polluting or not.

A water authority may also by byelaw prohibit or regulate the keeping or using on a stream of vessels provided with sanitary appliances from which polluting matter passes or can pass into the stream.

In exercising its powers under this section, a water authority must have regard to the character and flow of the stream, and to the extent to which the stream is or may in the future be used for industrial purposes, fisheries, water supply, agriculture, transport, or navigation.

## CONSENTS—CONTROL OF DISCHARGES OF TRADE AND SEWAGE EFFLUENT

Section 7 of the 1951 Act enables water authorities to control the making of *new* discharges of trade and sewage effluent to watercourses or the bringing into use of a new or altered outlet for the discharge of such effluent, by requiring the prior *consent* of the authority to the discharge or outlet, such consent not to be unreasonably withheld.

A new or altered outlet means any outlet which is wholly or partly constructed on or after 1st October 1951, or which (whether so constructed or not) is substantially altered after that date.

A new discharge means a discharge which is not as respects the nature and composition, temperature, volume, and rate of discharge of the effluent, substantially a continuation of a previous discharge made within the preceding 12 months (whether by the same or a different outlet), so however, that a discharge which is in other respects a continuation of a previous discharge made as aforesaid shall not be deemed to be a new discharge by reason of any reduction of the temperature or volume or rate of discharge of the effluent, as compared with the previous discharge—Section 7(8)(b) 1951 Act.

Ten years later, a similar system of control was extended to pre-1951 discharges by Sections 1-3 of the 1961 Act. The powers are now exerciseable by water authorities who have full control in respect of *all discharges* to watercourses of trade and sewage effluent and outlets for such discharges.

A water authority is required to keep a register containing the prescribed particulars of conditions which have been imposed in relation to outlets or discharges in their area, and which are for the time being in force. Such a register is to be open to inspection at all reasonable hours by any person appearing to the authority to be interested in the outlet or in the land or premises to which the consent relates as the case may be.

Generally, the Act provides protection for persons complying with conditions imposed under the 1951 and 1961 Acts who are not to be held guilty of an offence under Section 2(1) of the 1951 Act in respect of polluting discharges in so far as the discharge is consented and any conditions imposed have been observed. Water authorities have a duty to review conditions from time to time, and may revoke them or make any reasonable variation thereof.

### Discharges by a Water Authority

Section 17 of the Water Act 1973 provides that the Rivers (Prevention of Pollution) Acts are to have effect in relation to new or altered outlets or discharges of a water authority, subject to such exceptions and modifications as may be prescribed by regulations and such regulations may provide for securing that:—

(1) consent to the bringing into use of a new or altered outlet, or the making of a new discharge shall be granted or be deemed to be granted by the Secretary of State,

(2) in such cases and subject to such conditions as may be prescribed, any necessary consent shall be deemed to be granted by the Secretary of State, unless he required an application for it to be made to him by the water authority, and

(3) where a consent is deemed to be granted, the water authority shall give such notice of that fact as may be prescribed.

### POLLUTION OF UNDERGROUND STRATA

The Water Resources Act 1963 confers powers on water authorities in respect of pollution prevention:—

(a) enabling them to control polluting discharges into underground strata, and

(b) enabling them to take certain emergency measures to remedy or mitigate the effects of a polluting incident.

Section 72 of the 1963 Act states that it is unlawful, by means of any well, borehole or pipe to discharge into any underground strata within a water authority area any trade or sewage effluent, or any other poisonous noxious or polluting matter except with the consent of the water authority, such consent not to be unreasonably refused.

The water authority on application to them may grant consent, subject to such conditions as they may reasonably impose as to:—

(i) the nature, composition and volume of the effluent or other matter to be discharged;

(ii) the strata into which it may be discharged;

(iii) measures to be taken for protecting water contained in other underground strata through which any well, borehole or pipe containing the effluent or other matter will pass;

(iv) the provision of facilities for inspection including the provision, maintenance and use of observation wells and boreholes.

There is provision for appeal to the Secretary of State against the decision of the authority.

### EMERGENCY MEASURES TO FORESTALL POLLUTION OF WATERS

Section 76 of the 1963 Act provides that where it appears to a water authority that any poisonous, noxious or polluting matter is present in any inland water in its area, and has entered that water in consequence of an accident or other unforeseen act or event, the water authority may carry out such operations as it considers necessary or expedient for removing that matter from the inland water and disposing of it in such a matter as the authority considers appropriate and for remedying or mitigating any pollution caused by its presence in the inland water.

The Section does not however enable the Authority to construct any works other than works of a temporary character which are removed on or before the completion of the operations.

## POWERS OF ENTRY AND SAMPLING

Sections 111-113 of the Water Resources Act 1963 deal with powers of entry, and empower any person duly authorized in writing by a water authority at any reasonable time to enter upon any land or vessel for the purpose of performing any functions of the authority, whether in relation to that land or not or for the purpose of determining whether and if so in what manner, any functions of the authority are to be performed.

Section 112 provides that a person so authorized must produce evidence of his authority before entering if he is required to do so, and may take with him on to the land or vessel such other persons and such equipment as may be necessary.

However, it should be noted that admission to any land used for residential purposes, and admission with heavy equipment to any other land, shall not, except in an emergency, be demanded as of right unless seven days' notice in writing of the intended entry has been given to the occupier.

A person, who in the exercise of these powers enters premises which are unoccupied or of which the occupier is temporarily absent, is required to leave the premises as effectually secured against trespassers as he found them.

Section 112(8) deals with compensation, and provides that where as a result of the exercise of powers of entry conferred by the Act, any damage is caused to land or to chattels any person interested in the land or chattels shall be entitled to compensation in respect of that damage from the water authority on whose behalf the power was exercised, and where in consequence of the exercise of any such power any person is disturbed in his enjoyment of any land or chattels, he is entitled to compensation in respect of the disturbance.

Any disputes or questions arising are to be determined by the Lands Tribunal.

Section 113 deals with powers of sampling and gives a water authority power to obtain and to take away samples of any effluent which is passing from any land or vessel into any inland water or underground strata within its area, or into tidal waters adjoining its area.

For the results of analysis of a sample so obtained to be admissible in legal proceedings, the following requirements must be complied with:—

(1) the person taking the sample must forthwith notify to the occupier of the land, or the owner or master of the vessel, his intention to have it analysed;

(2) the sample must there and then be divided into three parts and each placed into a container which is sealed and marked;

(3) one part must be delivered to the occupier of the land or the owner or master of the vessel, one part retained for future comparison, and one submitted for analysis if the person taking the sample thinks fit to have an analysis made.

Note in this connection the case of *Trent River Board* v. *Wardle Ltd* (1957), which decided that it is open to the prosecution to prove pollution in any way they choose—they are not obliged to have samples analysed.

## CONTROL OF POLLUTION ACT 1974

The Control of Pollution Act 1974 did not come into force as soon as it was passed, but contained provisions for it to be brought into force, section by section, by Order of the Secretary of State. **It is therefore important to check which sections of the Act are effective at any given time,** and which Regulations have been made.

Part II of the Act, when applied, repeals the 1951 and 1961 Acts but re-enacts the basic offence of Section 2(1)(a) of the 1951 Act which is extended to a new species of water known as "controlled waters". Thus, Section 31(1) of the Act provides that a person is guilty of an offence if he causes or knowingly permits:—

(a) any poisonous, noxious or polluting matter to enter a stream or controlled water, or any specified underground water; or

(b) any matter to enter a stream so as to tend (either directly or in combination with other matter which he or another person causes or permits to enter the stream) to impede the proper flow of the stream in a manner leading or likely to lead to a substantial aggravation of pollution due to other causes or of the consequences of such pollution; or

(c) any solid waste matter to enter a stream or restricted waters.

"Stream" has the same meaning as in the 1951 Act, though Regulations may be made whereby "stream" includes a "lake, loch or pond which does not discharge into a stream". Specific lakes, lochs or streams may be prescribed, or those of particular descriptions (Section 56(4) of the 1974 Act).

"Controlled waters" means the sea within three nautical miles from any point on the coast measured from low-water mark of ordinary spring tides, such other parts of the territorial sea adjacent to Great Britain as may be prescribed by regulations, and any other tidal waters in Great Britain.

"Specified underground water" means underground water in a water authority area specified as water which is used or is expected by the authority to be used for any purpose, in a document in a form prescribed by regulations for the purposes of this definition, and contains prescribed particulars and of which a copy is kept available, and has for not less than one month been kept available, at the principal office of the authority for inspection by the public free of charge during office hours.

Other Sections of the 1974 Act, which will be of importance when they are brought into operation, are:—

(i) *Section 32*, which is a considerable extension in the controls contained in the earlier legislation and, in particular, prohibits the discharge of sewage and trade effluent into rivers, estuaries or coastal waters except in accordance with a consent under this Part of the Act from either the water authority or the Secretary of State.

(ii) *Section 33* will control the discharge of polluting matter from a vessel into the water. Where water authorities consider it necessary to collect waste from vessels in their area as a consequence of the provisions of this section, they will have a duty to do so under Section 47. Water authorities may exclude unregistered vessels from their area by bye-laws made under Section 48.

(iii) *Section 34* will regulate the making of discharges of effluent into controlled waters and will replace the licensing system under the 1951 and 1961 Acts. While a consent given under this Section will be a defence to proceedings taken under Section 31, it will *not* be a defence to a civil action for an injunction or damages brought by a riparian owner against the person responsible for the discharge. Section 35-40 deal with other aspects of consents to discharges.

(iv) *Section 41* provides that it shall be the duty of a water authority to maintain registers which are to be open to inspection by the public free of charge at all reasonable hours and to afford the public reasonable facilities for obtaining copies. These registers have to be maintained in accordance with regulations and to contain prescribed particulars specified in the Section including:—

(a) application for consent to discharge under Part II,

(b) consents given under Part II and the conditions to which the consents are subject,

(c) samples of effluent taken by the water authorities, information produced by analyses of the samples, and the steps taken in consequence of the information.

The practical effect of this will be that water authorities will have to show in the registers details of consents imposed on their sewage works effluents and the results of samples, and these will be available for public inspection.

(v) *Section 46* enables water authorities to take precautionary or salvage action where injurious pollution of a stream is feared or has actually occurred, and they may carry out operations to remedy or mitigate the pollution. The Section enables them to take action to prevent polluting matter entering relevant waters and recover their costs thereby incurred. This will be a considerable extension of powers granted under the Water Resources Act 1963 or, to certain water authorities (or their predecessors) under local Act powers.

(vi) *Section 49* provides that a person commits an offence if other than in the exercise of statutory land drainage, flood prevention or navigation powers, without the consent of the relevant water authority (which is not to be unreasonably withheld) he "removes from any part of the channel or bed of a stream a deposit accumulated by reason of any dam weir or sluice holding back the water of the stream and does so by causing the deposit to be carried away in suspension in the water of the stream"; or if by his wilful default "any substantial amount of vegetation cut or uprooted in a stream or so near to the stream that it falls into it, is allowed to remain in the stream".

## Exemptions from Offences

A person is not guilty of an offence under Section 31(1) of the 1974 Act if:—

(1) the entry in question is authorized by, or is a consequence of an act authorized by, a disposal licence (defined in the Act), or a consent given by the Secretary of State, or a water authority in pursuance of the Act, and the entry or act is in accordance with any conditions to which the licence or consent is subject; or

(2) the entry in question is authorized by, or is a consequence of an act authorized by
   (a) Section 34 of the Water Act 1945 (which relates to temporary discharges by water undertakers, or any enactment prescribed by regulations or
   (b) any provision of a Local Act or Statutory Order which expressly confers power to discharge effluent into water, or
   (c) a licence granted under the Dumping at Sea Act 1974; or

(3) the entry in question is attributable to an act or omission in accordance with good agricultural practice other than an act or omission which
   (i) is of a kind specified in a notice which is in force when the entry occurred and which was served under Section 53(3)(a) of the Act (relating to notices to abstain from certain agricultural practices) on the occupier or a previous occupier of the place where the act or omission occurs, and
   (ii) occurs after 28 days from the date entered in the register maintained under Section 51(4) as the date of service of the notice; or

(4) the entry in question is caused or permitted in an emergency in order to avoid danger to the public and as soon as reasonably practicable after the entry occurs, particulars of the entry are furnished to the water authority in whose area it occurs; or

(5) the matter in question is trade or sewage effluent discharged in accordance with a consent granted under the Act and the entry in question is not from a vessel.

## WASTE DISPOSAL

Waste disposal procedures are governed by various statutes from the Public Health Act 1936 to the Control of Pollution Act 1974, so far as disposal on land is concerned.

Under the 1936 Act local authorities have powers to abate statutory nuisances caused by waste. Refuse and litter are dealt with by the provisions of the Litter Act 1958, the Public Health Act 1961, the Civic Amenities Act 1967, and the Dangerous Litter Act 1971.

The Control of Pollution Act 1974 deals extensively with waste disposal in Part I. Sections 1 to 30 of this Act deal with very many aspects of waste disposal, including arrangements for disposing of controlled wastes, street cleaning, and refuse collection and reclamation.

"Controlled waste" is defined as "household, industrial and commercial waste or any such waste". "Disposal authorities" (the County Councils in England and District Councils in Wales and Greater London) are required to make plans for disposal of such waste. In preparing this plan, they must consult, amongst others, the water authorities in their area.

Section 3 of the 1974 Act places a prohibition on the unlicensed disposal of waste and, if the waste is poisonous or polluting, contravention of the Section may lead to a fine.

The disposal authority may licence sites for disposal of controlled waste. Before they grant such licence, they are required to ascertain whether or not the application should be rejected for the purpose of preventing pollution of water or danger to public health, and to ascertain this the water authority must be consulted.

Part I of the Control of Pollution Act 1974 (which is in operation) controls the deposit and disposal of waste on land by substituting a licensing system for the deposit of controlled waste for the somewhat unsatisfactory notification system of the Deposit of Poisonous Wastes Act 1972. While the provisions have to be applied by the local authority, the water authority has to be consulted in the preparation of the waste disposal plan of the disposal authority and before a disposal licence can be issued, the disposal authority must refer the proposal to the water authority.

## 12. ACQUISITION OF LANDS AND RIGHTS

### GENERAL POWERS

Although the Water Act 1973 does not itself endow water authorities with any specific powers in relation to the acquisition of lands or associated rights, it does provide (see paragraph 2 of the Third Schedule) them with a general power to acquire any property or rights which they may consider "is calculated to facilitate or is conducive or incidental to, the discharge of any of their functions".

Water authorities have, however, inherited certain specific powers of acquisition formerly enjoyed by their predecessors in connection with the various statutory functions which became the responsibility of water authorities under the 1973 Act and, in the main, it is on the basis of these specific powers that acquisitions of land by water authorities proceed.

One of the factors which the several enabling Acts have in common is that they afford to water authorities the power to acquire land in the first place by agreement with the owner of the land concerned and compulsorily in the absence of agreement. There is similar uniformity in the Acts as to the interpretation of the word "land" which is to be taken as including *any* interest in land and *any* easement or right in, to or over land and, in the case of the Water Resources Act 1963, including land covered by water.

### WATER SUPPLY

In relation to water supply, the main enabling powers are to be found in the Water Act 1945 (Section 24) under which statutory water undertakers (which includes water companies) may acquire land by agreement whether by way of purchase, lease or exchange for any of the purposes of their undertakings, including the provision of houses for employees and also for the protection of water against pollution. Ministerial consent is not required unless the land is not immediately required for the purpose for which it is being acquired and it is outside the relevant area of supply. Under the same Section undertakers may apply to the Secretary of State for authority to purchase land compulsorily, the procedure being regulated by the Second Schedule to the 1945 Act and the Schedule to the Water Act 1948.

Two other points in relation to water supply land are perhaps of some interest. Firstly, contrary to normal conveyancing practice, mines and minerals other than those which require to be excavated in connection with the particular works of construction do not pass with the land unless there is specific mention to the contrary in the acquiring deed. Secondly, the Secretary of State may authorize undertakers proposing to acquire land to carry out preliminary surveys, including experimental boring, of that land (Water Act 1948—Section 8).

## SEWERAGE AND SEWAGE DISPOSAL

With regard to the responsibilities of water authorities in relation to sewerage and sewage disposal, specific powers are to be found in relation to acquisition by agreement in Section 15, and in relation to compulsory acquisition in Section 306, both of the Public Health Act 1936. The more general powers relating to acquisition by agreement previously afforded to local authorities under the Local Government Act 1933, and for which similar provision is now contained in the Local Government Act 1972, do not appear to be available to water authorities who must, it seems, rely upon the general powers in the Water Act 1973 to meet any deficiencies there may be in specific powers. The procedure in respect of compulsory purchase is contained in the Acquisition of Land (Authorization Procedure) Act 1946.

## RIVER AUTHORITY FUNCTIONS

Water authorities' powers to acquire land and interests and rights over land for their "river authority functions" (i.e. water resources, pollution prevention, land drainage and fisheries) are to be found in the Water Resources Act 1963 (Sections 65 and 66) and cover acquisitions, whether by agreement or compulsorily, of land and existing or new rights in connection with it. The same limitations as to ministerial consent apply as for water supply, and the Acquisition of Land Act 1946 applies to compulsory acquisitions.

## FISHERIES

It is provided by the Salmon and Freshwater Fisheries Act 1975 (paragraph 37 of Schedule 3) that the acquisitive powers contained in the Water Resources Act 1963 are to be available to water authorities in relation to their functions under that Act.

## WATER MAINS

Water supply undertakers enjoy a general power, under Section 19 of the Third Schedule to the Water Act 1945, to lay a water main in any street. This right is subject to the provisions of the Public Utilities Street Works Act 1950. (See also p. 80).

Under the same Section, as amended by Article 9 of the Water Authorities etc. (Miscellaneous Provisions) Order 1974, they may also lay a water main in, on or over any land not forming part of a street, after giving reasonable notice to every owner and occupier of that land, and with the consent of:—

(a) the highway authority concerned, if the main will be laid within 220 ft of any highway, and (*b*)  the electricity or gas board concerned, if the main will be laid in, on or over any land of that board being operational land.

Having laid such a main, they may from time to time inspect, repair, alter or renew it. There are minor restrictions on this right where mains will cross or interfere with any watercourse under the control of a land drainage authority.

Section 11 of the Water Act 1948 provides that where the undertakers are authorized by a local enactment to acquire any land compulsorily for the purpose of executing underground works, they may instead of purchasing the land purchase only such easements and rights as may be sufficient for their purpose.

Compensation is payable in all cases where water mains are laid in private land.

## SEWERS

Under powers in Section 15 of the Public Health Act 1936, as amended by Schedule 8 to the Water Act 1973, a water authority may construct a public sewer in, under or over any street or under any cellar or vault below any street. The Public Utilities Street Works Act 1950 applies, as to water mains. (In practice the work may actually be undertaken by a district council acting for the water authority pursuant to arrangements made under Section 15(1) of the Water Act 1973.)

A water authority may also construct a public sewer in, on or over any land not forming part of a street, after giving reasonable notice to every owner and occupier of that land. This is a slightly wider power than that to lay water mains in land not forming part of a street, and appears to give a water authority an absolute discretion as to the course the sewer is to follow.

Compensation is payable, as in the case of water mains.

## 13. TOWN PLANNING

### DEVELOPMENT

*Planning permission* is required if *development* is to take place. "Development" is defined in the Town and Country Planning Act 1971 as "the carrying out of building, engineering, mining or other operations in, on, over or under land, or the making of any material change in the use of any buildings or other land."

The Act also specifies that "development" does not generally include works of maintenance on the inside of buildings, or of roads, and it also excludes works for the purpose of inspecting repairing or renewing any sewers, mains pipes cables or other apparatus, and the use of any land for the purposes of agriculture or forestry.

### PERMITTED DEVELOPMENT

Normally an application for planning permission must be made to the local planning authority if development is to take place. However, certain classes are listed as *permitted development*, and can take place without specific planning permission. The lists of permitted development are determined by the Secretary of State, and are contained in the Town and Country Planning General Development Order 1977. At the time of writing (March 1979) there have been proposals to amend this Order and the lists of permitted development, but at present they include the following:—

|  |  |
|---|---|
| *Class I* | — Limited enlargements improvements or other alterations to a dwelling house. |
| *Class IV* | — Temporary buildings and uses to enable operations to be carried out for which planning permission has been granted or for which planning permission is not required. |

*Class X* — Inspecting repairing or renewing sewers mains pipes cables or other apparatus, including the breaking open of any land for that purpose.

*Class XV* — Development by a drainage authority in on or under any watercourse or drainage works in connection with the improvement or maintenance of such watercourse or drainage works.

*Class XVI* — Development of any of the following descriptions by a water authority:-
   (*a*) The laying underground of mains, pipes or other apparatus.
   (*b*) The improvement, maintenance or repair of watercourses or land drainage works.
   (*c*) Erection, etc., of buildings or apparatus or the carrying out of engineering operations for the purpose of surveys or investigations.

*Class XVII* — Any development by or on behalf of a water authority or a development corporation to exercise powers relating to sewerage or sewage disposal, being development not above ground level required in connection with the provision improvement or maintenance of sewers.

*Class XVIIIC* — Water or hydraulic power undertakers:—
   (i) The laying underground of mains, pipes or other apparatus.
   (ii) The improvement, maintenance or repair of watercourses or land drainage works.
   (iii) The maintenance or repair of works for measuring the flow in any watercourse or channel or the improvement of any such works (other than by the erection of structures of the nature of buildings, or of any plant or machinery).
   (iv) The installation in a water distribution system of booster stations, meter or switchgear houses, not exceeding (except where constructed underground elsewhere than under a highway) 29 m³ in capacity.
   (v) The erection, construction, etc., of buildings plant or apparatus on land, or the carrying out of engineering operations, for the purpose of surveys or investigations.
   (vi) Any other development carried out in, or over or under the operational land of the undertaking except:—
      (*a*) The erection, or the reconstruction or alterations so as materially to affect the design or external appearance thereof, of buildings.
      (*b*) the installation or erection by way of addition or replacement of any plant or machinery or structure exceeding 15 m in height or the height of the item replaced, whichever is the greater.

This list is not exhaustive, and the Order imposes conditions on some of the Classes. In addition, there is provision for the Secretary of State, or for a local planning authority with his permission, to direct that arrangements for "permitted development" shall not apply to all or any development of all or any of those Classes in any particular area, or any particular development, specified in the direction, falling within any of those Classes.

## PLANNING PERMISSION

If development is not "permitted", then an application for planning permission must be made to the local planning authority. The forms of that authority must be used for the application, and the procedure requires the applicant to give appropriate notices to tenants or owners of the land concerned, and to certify that he has done so. In certain cases it is also necessary to publish notice in the local press that an application is being made. These cases include proposals for the construction of buildings or other operations (other than the laying of sewers and minor works), or use of land for the purpose of attention, treatment or disposal of sewage, trade waste or sludge. Advertisement is also required if it is proposed to construct buildings to a height exceeding 20 m.

Applications may be for "outline permission", in which case the acceptability of the development may be established in principle, but a further application will be required giving full details of the proposal, before full permission can be obtained and work started. Alternatively, an application for full planning permission may be made in the first place, although this may be expensive if full details have to be prepared before it has been established that the proposal is acceptable in principle to the planning authority.

Applications will be considered and determined by the planning authority, usually acting by one of its committees, who may arrange for consultation with other authorities before coming to a decision. The applicant has no right to be heard by the committee making the determination, but it is becoming increasingly common to give applicants the chance to appear and to answer questions and explain their proposals; there is also a trend for planning authorities to involve local residents in consultations about planning applications, and the applicant may find that he has to explain his proposals in some way to these residents, either by a public meeting or letter or some other means.

## APPEALS

In theory, a planning application must be determined within two months. If the applicant has received no reply by the end of that period he may assume that permission has been refused, and may appeal accordingly (see below). However, there are provisions for this period of two months to be extended (even indefinitely) by mutual agreement between the applicant and local planning authority, and this is frequently done.

If an application for planning permission is refused, the applicant may appeal to the Secretary of State. The appeal will then be decided either by the Secretary of State himself or one of his inspectors under delegated powers. This will be done either on the basis of written representations, or after the holding of a Public Enquiry; the choice is initially that of the applicant.

Planning permissions may be, and often are, granted subject to conditions, and the applicant may appeal against these conditions in the same way that he may appeal against a refusal of planning permission. Conditions to a planning permission must be planning ones and cannot, for instance, be for public health purposes (although if the development would harm public health this might contribute to a refusal of planning permission).

## PLANNING AGREEMENTS

Local planning authorities may enter into Agreements with developers to obtain the carrying out of various requirements supplemental to the planning permission. Such requirements may include provision of infrastructure or drainage works prior to development.

## PLANNING LIAISON

Section 24 of the Water Act 1973 requires each water authority to carry out surveys and reviews and to make plans and programmes. Subsection (8) says that in carrying out these duties water authorities shall consult local authorities and have regard to structure plans, local plans, and development plans prepared under the Town and Country Planning Act 1971. In that Act these plans are described as follows:—

(i) *Structure Plan (Section 7).*—The structure plan for any area shall be a written statement formulating the local planning authority's policy and general proposals in respect of the development, etc., in that area and stating the relationship of those proposals to general proposals for the development and other use of land in neighbouring areas; it shall contain such other matters as may be prescribed or directed by the Secretary of State.

(ii) *Local Plan (Section 11).*—In certain cases a local planning authority may, if they think it desirable, prepare a local plan, which shall consist of a map and a written statement and shall formulate such detail as the local planning authority think appropriate to their proposals for the development and other use of land in that area, and shall contain such matters as may be prescribed or directed by the Secretary of State.

(iii) *Development Plan (Schedule 5).*—(The reference to development plans in the Water Act 1973 is confined to those which are within the meaning of Schedule 5 of the 1971 Act, which are the nature of interim arrangements holding good only until the full provisions of 1971 Act have been applied. This is done by Order, area by area.)

In the other direction, planning authorities consult water authorities during the preparation and amendment of their major plans and in connection with specific applications for planning permission, the grant of which might affect or be affected by the water authority's activities.

This places two duties upon the water authorities. The first of these is the need to co-ordinate their own planning with that of the planning authorities, so that each may properly reflect the contents of the other. For example, so that the water authority may make preparations for capital works required to serve planned development, and so that the planning authority may not propose development to which it would be unusually difficult or expensive to afford water services. The second duty is to examine the detailed applications for planning permission, to secure that the authority's interests are protected (e.g. from possible pollution that would arise from the proposed development), to avoid land drainage or flooding problems such as would arise from development in flood plains, and to advise in cases where water services would be unusually difficult or expensive to provide. Obviously, the water authority might wish to oppose development which would place an added strain on sewage purification works, and might therefore advise permission be refused for development until those works could be extended. On the other hand, the water authority has no power in this matter, and the planning authority is free to reject the advice offered.

## 14. BYE-LAWS AND BUILDING REGULATIONS

### BYE-LAWS

Under Section 17 of the Water Act 1945 statutory water undertakers (which include water companies) are empowered to make Bye-laws for preventing *waste undue consumption, misuse or contamination* of water supplied by them. Such Bye-laws may prescribe the size, nature, materials, strength and workmanship and the mode of arrangement, connection, disconnection, alteration and repair of the water fittings to be used. They may also forbid the use of any water fittings likely to cause or permit waste, undue consumption, misuse, erroneous measurement or contamination of water.

Procedures relating to the making of Bye-laws are now contained in Schedule 7 of the Water Act 1973.

Bye-laws made by former water supply undertakers within their areas have been inherited by the water authorities. Most of them followed the form of Model Bye-laws published by the former Ministry of Housing and Local Government, but there were some variations which therefore continued to apply within the areas of the former undertakers.

Where Bye-laws apply, it is the duty of the water supply undertaking to enforce them. Enforcement is by way of summary proceedings as a result of which a fine of up to £200 can be imposed.

Water authorities may also make Bye-laws concerning pollution of streams. The power to make such Bye-laws is described in the section of this Chapter on Pollution Control.

At one time water supply undertakers had the power to make Bye-laws for the purpose of protecting against pollution any water which belonged to them or which for the time being they were authorized to take. This power, however, has now been repealed, and protection of sources is applied through the Control of Pollution Act 1974.

Other powers for water authorities to make Bye-laws concerning land drainage and fisheries are described in those Sections of this Chapter.

### BUILDING REGULATIONS

Systems of local authorities' Building Bye-laws have been in existence for more than 100 years. Their purpose was to ensure that buildings were constructed so that they were safe and not a danger to the health of those who occupied them, nor to the neighbours and public generally.

Although Building Bye-laws were made by individual local authorities, they usually followed a government model in the same way as the water Bye-laws. This system ended in 1965, when Building Bye-laws were superseded by Building Regulations made by the Secretary of State for the Environment under powers in Section 61 and 62 of the Public Health Act 1936, and Sections 4 to 9 of the Public Health Act 1961.

Building regulations apply not only to the construction of new buildings and the installation of fittings in them, but also to the alteration and extension of existing buildings and the replacement of fittings. Part N of the 1976 Building Regulations deals with drainage, private sewers and cesspools; and Part P with sanitary conveniences. Enforcement is by local authorities.

### FUTURE CHANGES

It is apparently intended that a new form of Building Regulations should replace Water Bye-laws as, since the coming into force of the Health and Safety at Work etc. Act 1974, building regulations and include provisions for the prevention of waste, undue consumption, misuse or contamination of water.

## 15. CONTRACTS

### REQUIREMENTS FOR A CONTRACT

A *contract* requires several elements. In the case of verbal contracts, these tend to be imprecisely defined and, in view of the lack of formalities and precision, unless the requirements are very simple, verbal contracts are not recommended.

(1) **Offer**
    To form a contract, there must be an offer and an acceptance of that offer. In works contracts, the offer is usually made by tender.

## (2) Acceptance

If there is to be a formal contract, i.e. under hand or under seal, then the acceptance is usually conditional upon the contractor agreeing to complete a formal contract embodying the provisions of the tender documents, conditions of contract and any other points raised in correspondence, all of which documents are bound or incorporated into the actual formal contract. A contract does not come into existence until there is a firm offer and an unconditional acceptance.*

## (3) Consideration

"Consideration" is usually the price to be paid for the work carried out, whatever may be the method of payment agreed between the parties.

## (4) Certainty

A further element is certainty, and one should always strive to make sure that the terms and conditions of contracts are clear and unambiguous and that both parties know what is expected of them. Further, that the objects, terms and conditions of the contract mean the same thing to both parties. If one party is under a misapprehension, the contract may be voidable, or there may be grounds for submission of the dispute to an arbitrator. In most contracts, there is a clause specifying that in the event of a dispute the Arbitration Act 1950 can be invoked. A dispute not on the actual terms and conditions of contract, i.e. negligence or faulty workmanship causing damage, may be settled by the Courts.

## (5) Fairness

Under common law, an oppressive or unduly harsh contract could, in certain circumstances, be set aside by the Courts. This does not, however, give an escape route to someone who entered a contract without doing his initial preparation work or doing it inadequately, or where the other party had simply secured "a good deal".

Now, by the Unfair Contract Terms Act 1977, which has been operative since 1st February 1978, the law is substantially modified. The exclusion of liability for negligence is greatly reduced, especially where that negligence results in serious bodily injury or death. For example, this would greatly reduce the effect of documents which occupiers of land require visitors to sign excluding liability for damage or injury to health by whatever cause. So-called "guarantees", unreasonable indemnity clauses, and exclusion clauses receive attention. The rights of a person supplying goods or a service particularly on his own written standard terms of business, e.g. contract for maintenance of a lift, to exclude his own liability for breach or render performance substantially different from what was envisaged by the contract are drastically reduced.

Under English Law, contracts under seal are actionable for up to 12 years after the date of the contract, whereas contracts under hand are actionable for six years only from such date. Scottish Law, however, differs in that whether contracts are under hand or under seal, they are only capable of being acted upon for six years from the date of the contract, so that, should a contract be contemplated with a contractor

---

*Note It is not considered desirable to allow contractors to qualify tenders. Where the contractor wishes to qualify his tender, the original tender should be completed with a separate additional tender or offer embodying the qualification. Proper comparison of tenders will then be possible.

whose registered office is in Scotland, for the protection of the employer, a clause should be inserted that the contract will be completed under English Law.

Most contracts will provide for an element of "liquidated damages" to be applied on a weekly basis should the contractor not complete the works in the time specified by the contract. Liquidated damages are not meant to be a penal condition, they should be a genuine pre-estimate of the loss that the employer would suffer each week from the time the works should be completed until the time that they actually are completed.

In some instances, a contractor, whose tender is the most favourable in respect of price and workmanship, etc., could be less well financed than other competing contractors. It may be felt by the employer that a bond or guarantee should be completed. The contractor may then be asked to provide a bond or guarantor suitable to the employer. A bond is usually for 10 per cent of the whole of the total cost of the works (though the proportion will vary from one type of industry or work to another). The guarantor will guarantee to provide finance and/or carry out the work should the actual contractor go into liquidation or otherwise not be able to complete the contract. Forms of bonds and guarantees can be found in the various text books and in the standard forms of Conditions of Contract.

## INSURANCES

Contractors should be asked to provide evidence of their insurance position, and the employer should make sure that the insurance cover for the works and the contractors' liabilities to the employer matches that which is required in the appendix to the tender; usually not less than £250 000. This is usually done before acceptance of the contract, and will relate to the requirement regarding bonds and guarantees. Public liability insurance should also always be required, the cover to be provided by an insurance company of repute.

## SUB-CONTRACTORS

If sub-contractors are employed, they will be liable to the main contractor while the main contractor remains fully liable to the employer throughout the period of the contract. Sub-contracting is the letting of a part of the works only, but there is no assignment of liability for the works on behalf of the main contractor. If works are delayed or disrupted, the employer will claim against the main contractor and the main contractor will have a remedy against the sub-contractor.

If sub-contractors are used by main contractors, it will usually be necessary for the terms and conditions of the main contract to be applied to the sub-contract with the main contractors. The sub-contractor will be liable to the main contractor in the event of breach of the sub-contract; conversely, the main contractor will be liable to the sub-contractor if the main contract is forfeited or there are delays to the sub-contractors working caused by the main contractor.

## NOMINATED SUB-CONTRACTORS

Sub-contractors may be nominated by the employer for specialist type of work. The main contractor has a right to object to a nomination, where for instance the nominated sub-contractor declines to enter into a sub-contract with the main contractor or give an undertaking such as will enable the main contractor to carry out the works as required by the main contract. It should also follow that there should be provision in the sub-contract for the main contractor to recover from the nominated sub-contractor any liabilities imposed on the main contractor by the employer through delays, disruption, etc., caused by the nominated sub-contractor.

Generally, the main contractor is liable for delay, defects, etc., in the works to the employer and will recover any loss or damage from the sub-contractor or nominated sub-contractor provided that the chain of responsibility embodied in the main contract and sub-contract is not broken. It will be appreciated, of course, that this is an area which can become very involved and to try to forestall disruption or litigation, it will be in the employer's interest to make sure from the outset, at the tender stage or at any contract conference, that all points are clarified and agreed in writing and embodied in the main contract and that the main contractor is made aware that the same care should be taken with sub-contracts.

## ASSIGNMENT OF CONTRACT

Assignment of a contract is not normally allowed without the written consent of the employer. In most contracts there is a clause specifically prohibiting assignment. If the contractor attempts to assign without the necessary written consent, then the employer has a right to forfeit the contract. Should Assignment be allowed, however, and the contractor has provided a bond, then of course the bond will have to be amended.

## FIXED-PRICE CONTRACTS

The principal types of civil engineering and building contracts now in use are fixed-price contracts.

(a) *Contracts based on bills of quantities which are priced by the contractor.*—The total of all the bills of quantities, generally with certain additions, e.g. for contingencies, fixes the contract sum. It is usual to provide that the total payment is made according to measurement of the actual work done, the price for such work being fixed according to the bills of quantities. The contractor is therefore not responsible for the accuracy of the quantities set out in such bills, but only for the accuracy of the rates therein appearing.

(b) *Lump sum.*—No bills of quantities are prepared, but the contractor quotes a lump sum based on drawings and specifications.

(c) *Schedule contracts.*—A priced schedule is usually sent to the contractor and he quotes a percentage above or below the prices in the schedule, or occasionally his price will be approximately the same. This type of contract is usually adopted in cases where a close estimate of the quanities required is not possible.

Although the above types of contract are termed fixed-price contracts, it is frequently impossible to obtain a tender for a firm price without the inclusion of a "rise and fall' clause, i.e. a clause providing for an adjustment, up or down, of the contract price following any change in the cost of specified materials or labour during the term of the contract.

## CONTRACT DOCUMENTS

The documents which usually constitute an engineering contract are:—

(i) The *contract drawings*, which are a diagrammatic description of the works which are to be carried out under the contract. The general conditions of contract referred to in (iv) below usually provide that the contract drawings may be varied or modified as the engineer thinks necessary to deal with circumstances which arise during the construction of the works and which are not ascertainable at the time of going to tender.

(ii) A *specification* based upon the work shown upon the contract drawings and which particularizes the materials to be used and the manner in which the work is to be carried out, and sets out the obligations of the contractors to do or refrain from doing that which, in the opinion of the engineer, is respectively desirable or undesirable for the successful carrying out of the work.

(iii) *Bills of quantities* or a *schedule of prices* (except in the case of lump sum contracts) or both, prepared by the engineer or by a quantity surveyor and priced by the contractor. The bill of quantities, when priced and totalled (generally with the addition of a sum for contingencies), should give the total price (the "contract price ") at which the contractor has made an offer and at which an offer has been accepted by the employer.

(iv) *General conditions of contract.*—these are usually standard forms of conditions and commonly deal *(inter alia)* with the following matters:—

Interpretations and definitions; restrictions against assignment and sub-letting; extent and scope of contract; drawings; general obligations of contractor; labour; work; materials and plant; commencement, time and delays; maintenance and defects; alterations, additions and omissions; property in materials and plant; insurance, responsibility for accidents and damage, claims-measurement and valuation of works; prime costs and provisional sums; certificates and payment; penalties; remedies and powers; determination of disputes.

## DISPUTES AND BREACH OF CONTRACT

It is usual to include in the conditions of contract an arbitration clause providing for disputes between the contractor and the employer to be referred to the award and decision of some person to be mutually agreed upon, and the provisions of the Arbitration Act 1950 are made to apply to this clause.

It is also usual to provide that, for certain specific breaches of the contract by the contractor, the employer shall be at liberty to determine the contract and take possession of the contract works, but without prejudice to any liability of the contractor for breach of contract already incurred. In this case the employer may re-let the contract to another contractor, and the original contractor will be liable for any losses to the employer thereby incurred.

Examples of eventualities in which an employer may be entitled to take this course are want of due diligence on the contractor's part, malpractices such as bribery, assignment of the contract without the employer's permission, or failure to observe the fair wages clause.

## WATER AUTHORITY CONTRACTS

By the Corporate Bodies' Contracts Act 1960, a contract may be made on behalf of a corporation (such as a water authority) by any person acting under its express or implied authority with no more formality than is required in the case of contracts between private persons. This dispenses with the necessity of a seal, except where a seal is required by law in the case of contracts made by a private person. A contract not otherwise requiring a seal may still be made under seal if the corporation so desire.

Section 111 of the Local Government Act 1972, authorizes local authorities to do anything which is calculated to facilitate, or is conducive or incidental to, any of their functions. They thus have power to enter into contracts necessary for the discharge of any of their functions. By the Local Authorities (Goods and Services) Act 1970, local authorities may make contracts one with another for the supply of goods or services. By Section 7 of Water Act 1973, a water authority is brought within the definition of a "public body" within the Act of 1970. The provisions of Paragraph 2 of the Third Schedule to the Water Act 1973 are similar to Section 111 of the Local Government Act 1972, and so the contractual position of water authorities is similar to that of local authorities.

## 16. LIABILITY FOR INJURY OR DAMAGE

### DAMAGE

Actions for damages against statutory water undertakers in respect of alleged loss or injury have usually been brought either on the ground of *negligence* or *nuisance*, or both. "Negligence", to be actionable, is conduct constituting a breach of a duty to take reasonable care imposed by law upon some person or persons towards some other person or persons and resulting in injury or damage to the latter.

"Nuisance" is confined to injuries which primarily affect the use or enjoyment of land and has been said to be "an inconvenience materially interfering with the ordinary comfort physically of human existence, not merely according to elegant or dainty modes and habits of living, but according to plain and sober simple notions among the English people". A person is liable for a nuisance constituted by the state of his property:

(1) if he causes it;
(2) if, by some neglect of some duty, he allows it to arise;
(3) if, when it has arisen without his own act or default, he omits to remedy it within a reasonable time after he became, or ought to have become, aware of it.

There is also the rule in *Rylands* v. *Fletcher* (1868). This rule makes a person prima facie answerable for all the damage which is the natural consequence of the escape of a thing which, for his own purposes, he brings on his land and collects and keeps there and which is likely to do mischief if it escapes. Such "things" can include water.

In the case of water undertakers operating under statutory powers, however, it is well settled that no action for *nuisance* will lie unless there has been *negligence* by the undertakers in the exercise of those powers. The principle was expressed in the case of *Geddis* v. *The Proprietors of Bann Reservoir* (1878) by Lord Blackburn, who stated "It is now thoroughly well established that no action will lie for doing that which the legislature has authorized if it be done without negligence, although it does occasion damage to anyone, but an action does lie for doing that which the legislature has authorized if it be done negligently". No action will therefore lie against statutory water undertakers, either in nuisance of *ex hypothesi* in negligence in respect of injury arising from something done under, and in accordance with, their statutory powers, unless negligence on the undertaker's part in exercising those powers is established. There are some exceptions to this rule, e.g. in the case of reservoirs (see below and p. 71).

When Parliament has authorized a certain thing to be made or done in a certain place, there can be no action for nuisance caused by the making or doing of that thing if the nuisance is the inevitable consequence of the making or doing so authorized. The onus of proving that the result is inevitable is on those who wish to escape liability for nuisance, but the criterion of inevitability is not what is theoretically possible but what is possible according to the state of scientific knowledge at the time, having also in view a certain commonsense appreciation, which cannot be rigidly defined, or practical feasibility in view of situation and of expense (*Manchester Corporation* v. *Farnworth* (1930)); also see *Pride of Derby and Derbyshire Angling Association Ltd. & Anor.* v. *British Celanese Ltd., Derby Corporation and the British Electricity Authority* (1952).

Many cases have been brought against water undertakers when damage is caused by water escaping from their pipes and mains. It was established in *Green* v. *The Chelsea Waterworks Company* (1894) that there is no liability upon the undertakers unless they are shown to have been negligent either in the way the pipes were laid or in their maintenance or in some other manner, and thereby to have caused the damage. If a main suddenly bursts without any circumstance which would have led the undertakers to suppose that such a burst was likely, there is no liability, but if, for example, the undertakers knew that a main was liable to burst and took no steps to relay it, or if a burst occurred and there was unreasonable delay in shutting down the main, liability would ensue.

The case of *Manchester Corporation* v. *Markland* (1936) illustrates this point, and confirms that, even though the escape of water may have occurred without any negligence on the part of the undertakers, they have a duty to take all reasonable precautions to secure that leaks in their system should be brought to their knowledge and be repaired with promptitude. In *Markland's* case, a leak occurred in a service pipe and water escaped on to the highway, where it formed a pool. Three days later, the water having frozen in the meantime, a motorist skidded on the ice and an accident ensued. The corporation, who were the water undertakers, had no knowledge of the leak. Their practice was to check pipes every nine days, and rely on the public for the rest. It was held that they were liable in negligence as they had no proper or sufficient system of acquainting themselves within a reasonable time when a burst or a leak had occurred in one of their mains or pipes.

Undertakers also have certain common law duties which extend to other persons besides their customers. For example, in *Read* v. *Croydon Corporation* (1938) where, owing to the negligence of the corporation, the water delivered to some of their customers contained typhoid germs, persons who became ill through drinking the water were held to be entitled to recover damages from the corporation. This right of action accrued, not only to the consumers but their households, and other persons too. It was held that it must have been within the contemplation of all concerned that the water supplied would be drunk by persons other than the strictly limited class of the consumers to whom it was supplied and to whom a statutory duty was owed, and that the undertakers were under a common law duty to such other persons to take reasonable care to safeguard the purity of the supply.

If works constructed under statutory powers are negligently or improperly constructed, and injury ensues as a result thereof, an action for damages will lie. However, if a claim arises from the negligence of the contractor carrying out the work, the general rule of law is that no action will lie against the person employing the contractor if he retained no authority or control over the contractor during the carrying out of the work. There are, however, some limitations to this rule in the case of public authorities contracting for the construction of works. For instance, if the work is of such a nature as to be likely to cause damage to others, even if lawful and done in pursuance of statutory powers, there is a duty on the authority employing the contractor to take all reasonable precautions against such damage.

There are certain exceptions which have been created by various statutes to the general rule that negligence must be proved before an action will lie. In the case of reservoirs, Section 7 of the Reservoirs (Safety Provisions) Act 1930, lays down that, where damage or injury is caused by an escape of water from a reservoir constructed after the commencement of the Act under statutory powers granted after the passing thereof, the fact that the reservoir was constructed under statutory powers shall not exonerate the undertakers from any indictment, action or other proceedings to which they would otherwise have been liable. This section is specifically retained by the Reservoirs Act 1975 which, when it becomes operative, will replace the 1930 Act.

It has been believed that Section 18 of the Public Utilities Street Works Act 1950, in favour of street and bridge authorities and managers where undertakers' pipes, in a street, burst, etc., is another like exception. However, there is a school of thought that, in the absence of negligence, liability only extends to such damage to the highway as would be necessarily involved in locating and repairing the burst. Only a case decided upon this specific point will clarify the matter.

In some cases the statute conferring the powers on the undertakers, contains a clause expressly retaining the liability of the undertakers for nuisance. It appears, however, from the decision of the Court of Appeal in *Dunne* v. *North Western Gas Board* (1963) that where there is a mandatory obligation, then even though there is a saving clause for nuisance, there is no liability if what is done is that which is expressly required by statute to be done or is reasonably incidental to that requirement and is done without negligence. The facts were that a water main belonging to the second defendants, Liverpool City Corporation, burst. Although the water ran harmlessly into a sewer and away, it washed away earth round a gas pipe of the first defendants. The gas pipe burst, and an explosion resulted.

As to the liability of the two defendants:—

  (a) Gas Board—though the Gas Act retained liability for nuisance, they acted under a statutory obligation, and were not liable under *Rylands* v. *Fletcher* or in nuisance because—

      (i) what they had done, without being negligent, was what statute required of them; and

      (ii) the effective cause of the accident was the burst water main.

  (b) Water undertaker—they acted under a permissive statutory power. Lord Justice Sellers said:—

> "The Corporation did not intentionally discharge the water in the manner in which it entered the sewer, it was an escape. It is clear that water may escape without negligence and as an incident of its provision in pipes, for example by reason of frost or at joints. In our opinion the cases establish that in such circumstances a water authority is not liable under the strict rule in *Rylands* v. *Fletcher* or in nuisance".

The basic duties placed upon a water authority in respect of sewerage and sewage disposal by Section 14 of the Water Act 1973, may be found in Sections 15 to 30 of the Public Health Act 1936. As to the mode of their discharge, Section 31 requires that the water authority ". . . shall so discharge their functions under the foregoing provisions of this Act as not to create a nuisance".

Irrespective of this, case law holds that, where there is no negligence, there is no liability. In *Stretton's Derby Brewery Co.* v. *Derby Corporation* (1894), Derby Corporation had constructed a sewer in 1855. It was properly constructed and properly maintained, there being no negligence in either respect. The brewery was built later, their cellars were flooded from the sewer in 1892 and 1893, this due to extra properties being connected to it. The Public Health Act 1875, provided that "every local authority shall cause sewers belonging to them to be constructed and kept so as not to be a nuisance". It was held that as there was no negligence there was no liability.

A more recent case, decided under Section 31 of the 1936 Act, is *Smeaton* v. *Ilford Corporation* (1954). A small sewer ran into a larger, and in times of heavy rains, the larger sewer overloaded, and flooding was caused by sewage issuing from a manhole in the small sewer due to the inability of the larger one to accept it.

The decision was on two points:—

  (i) the flooding was caused by overloading; this was due to the duty under Section 34(1) of the 1936 Act to permit occupiers to discharge sewage into the sewers; the authority had neither created nor continued the nuisance and so were not liable;

(ii) the authority could not claim exemption from the principle in *Rylands* v. *Fletcher* on the ground that the use of land for sewage collection was for the general benefit of the community or that such collection was a natural user of the land, but the proper construction of Section 31 was that, in the absence of negligence, it excluded liability for the escape of sewage and so excluded the application of *Rylands* v. *Fletcher*.

The corollary of this is that, where negligence exists, there can be liability in nuisance or under *Rylands* v. *Fletcher*. In this case it was found, as a fact, that the sewers concerned were properly cleansed and maintained. Thus, there will only be liability where it can be shown that there was negligence in the way in which the sewer was managed.

The recent case of *Anns* v. *London Borough of Merton* (1977) shows another way in which the authority can be liable in respect of sewers. Though the case concerned foundations to a building which were found to be inadequate and which inadequacy would have been seen had the local authority inspected them properly, the like principle based upon negligence would apply in respect of new sewers. Before entering into an agreement under Section 18 of the 1936 Act, the water authority must be satisfied that the sewer is properly designed, of adequate size, and will be fit for its purpose if built according to the agreed plan and specification. It should inspect the sewer as construction proceeds—the *Anns* case shows that whether the authority has a duty to inspect, or merely a power to do so, does not matter. If a water authority permits a sewer which it will be adopting to be constructed incorrectly, or to inadequate specification, then it will be liable in the event of overflow by virtue of its initial negligence. The right of action would accrue from the time when the damage occurred resulting from the negligence, i.e. the date of the first overflow.

While on the question of sewage disposal, there is a further sanction upon the authority under Section 322 of the Public Health Act 1936. In general terms, if a person suffers loss of injury through the failure of the authority to carry out their obligations (e.g. adequately to sewer a district), his only remedy is to complain to the Minister under Section 322. If he is satisfied that the authority has failed to discharge their functions, he may declare them to be in default and direct them to remedy matters. He has further powers if the authority does not then comply.

## LIABILITY TO PENALTIES

There are a considerable number of instances in the various Acts relating to the supply of water where penalties are imposed upon the undertakers for breaches of some one or more duties laid upon them by the statutes and, where undertakers can be shown to have failed to fulfil such duties, they will be liable in each case to the prescribed penalties. It has frequently been held that, where undertakers have thus incurred penalties, they cannot be sued for damages by any person injured through their breach of a statutory duty, but that the only remedy is to recover the penalties. Thus, in *Atkinson* v. *Newcastle and Gateshead Water Co.* (1877) owing to the failure of the undertakers to keep their pipes charged at the required pressure, a proper firefighting supply could not be furnished and the plaintiff's premises were destroyed by fire. It was held that no action for damages lay to the plaintiff against the undertakers, as the Act itself provided a remedy by way of a penalty and this was the only remedy available.

This and similar decisions have given rise to a good deal of difficulty and the cases on this subject are not always easy to reconcile. For example, in *Read* v. *Croydon Corporation* noted above, one of the plaintiffs was the consumer himself, and as against him this defence was set up, but it was held that, whilst for breach of some statutory duties, the prescribed penalties were an exclusive remedy, it was impossible to hold that the legislature intended that there should be one remedy and one remedy only, equally applicable to so trivial a breach as the failure to maintain a certain pressure behind a fire plug, and (to take a hypothetical case) to a deliberate dereliction of duty resulting in the destruction of a large community by the supply of poisonous water. Damages were therefore awarded to the consumer. From this and other cases on the point, the general principle has now emerged that the statute concerned must be looked at and the Court must determine in each case the intention of the legislature in that particular case with regard to exclusive or alternative remedies. Sometimes, of course, the position is made clear by the section under consideration itself; for example, Section 27(4) of the Water Act 1945 provides penalties for failure to afford a non-domestic supply in accordance with the terms of the section, but enacts that these penalties shall be without prejudice to any civil liability. This is also the case under Section 39 of the Third Schedule to the Water Act 1945.

## COMPENSATION

It is usual to provide, in Acts of Parliament giving undertakers the right to exercise statutory powers over private property, that full compensation must be paid to persons injuriously affected thereby. This liability to compensation is quite different in principle from the liability to damages considered above. It does not depend in any way upon a wrongful act or some neglect or breach of duty by the undertakers, and is merely a reimbursement to the owner in respect of his loss through an infringement of his private rights by statutory undertakers, authorized in that behalf by Parliament for the public good, and is payable even though the statutory powers have been in every way properly exercised. (Where such powers have been improperly exercised, the remedy of an aggrieved party is by way of action for damages or penalties and not by way of compensation.)

An example of the duty to pay compensation may be found in Section 17 of the Land Drainage Act 1976. After setting out the general drainage powers of a water authority, Subsection 5 states:—

"Where injury is sustained by any person by reason of the exercise by a drainage authority of any of their powers under this section, the authority shall be liable to make full compensation".

Then, as in the case of many statutory provisions where the parties cannot agree on terms where land or rights allied to land are concerned:—

"and in case of dispute the amount of the compensation shall be determined by the Lands Tribunal".

The water authority's power to cancel licences during the period of their currency often carries with it the duty to pay compensation. Examples include the revocation under Section 44 of the Water Resources Act 1963 or a licence to abstract water (Water Resources Act 1963, Section 46), or of a licence to permit effluent to be discharged into a watercourse (Control of Pollution Act 1974, Section 38).

Compensation may also be payable where a water authority does not exercise its statutory duties in the usual way because, for instance, such duty has been temporarily modified by a ministerial Order under Section 1 or Section 2 of the Drought Act 1976. Schedule 2 to that Act deals with compensation, and again the Lands Tribunal may be required to assess the compensation.

## 17. HEALTH AND SAFETY AT WORK

### THE 1974 ACT

The Health and Safety at Work etc Act 1974 extends the protection given by previous Acts, such as the Factories Acts and the Offices, Shops and Railway Premises Act 1963, to *all persons at work* whatever the nature of the work or the premises at which it is carried on. Protection is also provided for persons not at work who may be affected by an employer's undertaking.

"Premises" is defined by Section 53 to include any place and, in particular, to include:—

(1)  any vehicle, vessel, aircraft or hovercraft;
(2)  any installation on land (including the foreshore and other land intermittently covered by water), offshore installations, or other installation whether floating or resting on the seabed;
(3)  a tent or moveable structure.

Though not specifically set down in the Act, "place" would also include open land, a construction site, or any other location at which people work.

The aims of the Act will gradually be achieved by the making of Regulations and the issue of non-statutory Codes of Practice which will eventually replace existing legislation. Therefore, apart from the Act itself, reference must be made to Regulations and Codes issued by the Health and Safety Commission or Committees for particular industries, e.g. The National Joint Health and Safety Committee for the Water Service.

The purposes of Part 1 of the Act are:—

(a)  to secure the health, safety, and welfare of persons at work;
(b)  to protect persons other than persons at work against risk to health or safety arising out of the activities of persons at work;
(c)  to control the keeping and use of explosive, highly flammable or otherwise dangerous substances, and to prevent their unlawful use or possession;
(d)  to control the emission into the atmosphere of noxious or offensive substances.

### GENERAL DUTIES

Section 2 places a general duty on an employer to secure, so far as is reasonably practicable, the health, safety, and welfare at work of all his employees. In particularly, this includes the provision and maintenance of:—

(i)    safe and healthy plant, machinery, equipment and appliances;
(ii)   safe and healthy premises and working environment;
(iii)  a safe and healthy system of work, including safe handling, storage, and removal of materials;
(iv)   information to, instruction and training for, and supervision of employees as are necessary to ensure their health and safety at work;
(v)    adequate means of safe access to and egress from the place of work;
(vi)   a written safety policy; this to be kept updated and revised;
(vii)  consultation with employee safety representatives appointed by a recognized trade union, and if required, to form a safety committee.

Section 3 extends the duty to conduct an undertaking in a safe way to the extent that employers must not place at risk persons *not* employed by them. Section 4 places duties upon those who control premises where people work but who are not their own employees. The premises, and plant or machinery used there and which is supplied by the person controlling the premises, must be safe. So must means of access and egress.

Those who design, manufacture, import or supply an article for use at work must ensure, so far as they can, that it is safe when properly used. They must carry out tests, examinations and research, give necessary information, and ensure that such items are properly installed (Section 6). The term "supplier" is widely interpreted in the Section.

An employer may not charge his employees for anything done, or for equipment provided for health and safety purposes under a statutory requirement (Section 9).

Most duties under Sections 2, 3, 4, 5, and 6 embody the concept of "reasonableness", so far as the execution of the employer's duties are concerned.

An employee too has duties. He is obliged while at work (Section 7):

(1) to take reasonable care for the health and safety of himself and others who may be affected by his acts or defaults; and

(2) to co-operate with his employer and any other person so far as necessary to ensure that duties or statutory requirements are complied with.

No person (this would cover employer, employee or an outsider) shall intentionally or recklessly interfere with or misuse anything provided in pursuance of any statutory provisions as to health, safety or welfare (Section 8).

## HEALTH AND SAFETY COMMISSION, AND HEALTH AND SAFETY EXECUTIVE

These two bodies corporate are set up under Section 10. Broadly, the Commission's duties involve assisting and encouraging in respect of health and safety at work, research, information, training, and preparing and submitting proposals for regulations. The Commission is under the control of the Secretary of State for the Environment. The Executive undertakes for the Commission such of the Commission's duties as the Commission may direct. On the Commission's behalf it may investigate situations or incidents and issue reports on them.

So as to provide practical guidance to the provisions of Sections 2-7, the Health and Safety Regulations, or any existing statutory provisions, the Commission may issue Codes of Practice prepared by itself or by others (Section 16). While it is not an offence to act contrary to a Code of Practice, the failure to comply with the Code may be used as evidence in a prosecution for breach of duty (Section 17). The Executive has the duty of making arrangements for the enforcement of the statutory provisions (including Regulations) either itself, or by other "enforcing authorities" (Section 18). Inspectors may be appointed (Section 19) having wide powers (Section 20) including the service of "improvement notices", or "prohibition notices" (Sections 21-23). There is a right of appeal against such notices (Section 24).

An inspector may serve an *improvement notice* if he is of the opinion that a person is contravening the statutory provisions, or has done so and is likely to do so again. The notice must include details of that opinion, and requires the person in question to remedy the contravention within a stated period. A *prohibition notice* may be served when the inspector is of the opinion that the activities involve or will involve a risk of "serious personal injury". The notice must contain details, and a direction that the activities concerned shall not be carried on unless the matters which create the risk have been remedied.

## OFFENCES

Section 33 contains a list of offences under the Act. These include:—

(a) failure to discharge a duty under Sections 2 to 7;

(*b*)   contravening Sections 8 or 9; or a requirement of Regulations;
(*c*)   various offences concerning requirements imposed by inspectors, or under improvement notices or prohibition notices.

There are varous provisions as to evidence, what is "reasonable", and powers of the Court to make orders requiring situations to be remedied or items forfeited. Section 37 is of particular interest and importance. This provides that where an offence under the Act committed by a body corporate is proved to have been committed with the consent or connivance of or is attributable to any neglect on the part of "any director, manager, secretary or similar officer" of the body corporate or a person who was purporting to act in any such capacity, he (as well as the body corporate) shall be guilty of the offence and liable to be proceeded against and punished accordingly.

## SAFETY REPRESENTATIVES AND SAFETY COMMITTEES

The Regulations on Safety Representatives and Safety Committees became operative on 1st October 1978; and the Commission have issued a Code of Practice on Safety Representatives, and a Guidance Note on the subject.

Regulation 3 deals with the appointment of safety representatives, regulation 4 with their functions. As well as representing the employees in consultations with the employer concerning arrangements for co-operation between employer and employee for the promotion of health and safety at work (Section 2(6)), their functions (which are specifically stated not to be duties), are:—

(i)     to investigate potential hazards and dangerous occurrences at the place of work, and to examine the causes of accidents at the workplace;
(ii)    to investigate complaints as to health, safety or welfare of employees at work;
(iii)   to make representations to the employer on these matters;
(iv)    to make representations to the employer on general matters affecting the health, safety, or welfare at work of the employees at the workplace;
(v)     to carry out inspections;
(vi)    to represent the employees in consultations with inspectors of the Executive or other enforcing authority;
(vii)   to receive information from inspectors;
(viii)  to attend safety committee meetings in their capacity as safety representatives.

The employer is obliged to allow them to take time off with pay for the carrying out of their functions, or undergoing training as safety representatives.

Safety representatives may inspect the workplace (broadly every three months); the employer will assist and provide such reasonable facilities as may be required (Regulation 5). Further inspections may be carried out following notifiable accidents, occurrences or diseases (Regulation 6). Within certain limits, safety representatives may inspect documents and receive information which it may be the employer's duty to keep or give under statutory provisions within the Act (Regulation 7).

Where at least two safety representatives make a request in writing to the employer for the setting up of a Safety Committee, he shall, within three months from the request and after consultation with the safety representatives, set up a Safety Committee (Regulation 9). Though the Act and Regulations are largely silent as to the consititution objectives and functions of such committees, and the conduct of their meetings, the Commission's Guidance Notes should be consulted upon these matters. Much, however, depends on the situations in individual places of work.

## 18. EEC DIRECTIVES

Since the accession of the U.K. to the European Communities on 1st January 1973, an additional source of law to those of Statute Law and the Common Law has come into being, namely Community Legislation. This may take one of five forms:—

    (1)  Regulations
    (2)  Directives
    (3)  Decisions
    (4)  Recommendations
    (5)  Opinions
    (Article 189, EEC Treaty)

In essence, only the first two are of the nature of legislation. *Regulations* are binding in their entirety and are applicable in all the member states. *Directives* are binding as to the result to be achieved and apply only to those states to whom they are addressed, although generally this is all member states. In the field of water legislation, it is by directive that the Council of Ministers has chosen to act.

Those already in force include directives on detergents, on the disposal of waste oils, on the quality of surface water intended for abstraction for drinking water, on the quality of bathing water, on the disposal of polychlorinated biphenoyls, on the disposal of toxic wastes. There is also (1979) a Draft Directive for the protection of groundwater.

New domestic legislation does not always need to be passed to comply with Directives. In many cases, the existing legislation goes far enough. On the other hand, the Draft Directive mentioned above is an example of a case where quite considerable change may be necessary.

The U.K. is fully represented on the Institutions of the Community, and national interests and expert bodies are consulted in the process of the making of Directives, so that these are not alien laws but the laws of a supranational community of which the U.K. is a part.

## 19. NATIONAL VARIATIONS

So far this Chapter has dealt with water law as it applies in England and Wales, although references had been made to the organization of the water industry in Scotland and Northern Ireland. The chief differences in water legislation, as it applies to these two countries, are noted below.

## 20. THE POSITION IN SCOTLAND

GENERAL OBSERVATIONS (*see p. 65*)

In dealing with Scotland the sequence of subjects on pages 65 to 131 has, as far as possible, been followed.

The principal differences between English and Scottish water legislation are noted and, where there is no material difference, the Scottish reference is given. Some Acts apply equally in Scotland as in England and for simplicity all the principal acts which apply in Scotland have been listed.

Differences at common law are not discussed, and the foregoing sections relating to England and Wales should be read with due regard to Scots Law.

## "SECRETARY OF STATE"

In Scotland, the term "the Secretary of State" refers to the Secretary of State for Scotland unless otherwise stated.

## GENERAL BACKGROUND

In Scotland the local government system was reorganized with effect from 16th May 1975 when nine Regional, three Islands, and 53 District Councils were formed in terms of the Local Government (Scotland) Act 1973. This Act dissolved the water boards established by the Water (Scotland) Act 1967 (except the Central Scotland Water Development Board), and transferred their functions, together with the sewerage and sewage disposal functions, to the Regional and Islands Councils. Each Region was divided into a number of Districts but the District Councils have no functions in the public water supply or sewerage and sewage disposal services, although they are involved in respect of environmental health and building regulations. The Act also dissolved the nine River Purification Boards established under Part II of the Rivers (Prevention of Pollution) (Scotland) Act 1951, and transferred the responsibility for the prevention of pollution from them and 12 local authorities to seven new independent River Purification Boards and the three Islands Councils. Membership of the River Purification Boards is by nominations from the Regional Councils, the District Councils, and the Secretary of State, each providing one-third of the total membership.

The Act maintains the previous arrangement for public and domestic water rates to be levied in respect of the residual cost of the water supply service (residual after allowing for charges levied and for grants, etc.). The corresponding cost of sewerage and sewage disposal is met from the regional or general rate. This rate is paid regardless of whether or not the sewerage service is provided. The cost of the River Purification Boards is met by requisition on the regional authorities (i.e. again through the regional rate).

## PRINCIPAL STATUTORY PROVISIONS

The principal statutory provisions relating to water in Scotland are listed below:—

### Water Supply and Water Management

Reservoirs (Safety Provisions) Act 1930
Rural Water Supplies and Sewerage Act 1944
Water (Scotland) Act 1946
Water (Scotland) Act 1949
Public Utilities Street Works Act 1950
Rural Water Supplies and Sewerage Act 1955
Water Act 1958
Spray Irrigation (Scotland) Act 1964
Industrial Training Act 1964
Water (Scotland) Act 1967
Countryside (Scotland) Act 1967
Rural Water Supply and Sewerage (Scotland) Act 1970
Local Government (Scotland) Act 1973
Health and Safety at Work Act 1974
Reservoirs Act 1975
Acquisition of Land (Authorization Procedure) (Scotland) Act 1976

### Sewerage and Sewage Purification

Rural Water Supplies and Sewerage Act 1944
Rural Water Supplies and Sewerage Act 1955

Sewerage (Scotland) Act 1968
Rural Water Supply and Sewerage (Scotland) Act 1970

**Land Drainage**
Land Drainage (Scotland) Act 1958
Flood Prevention (Scotland) Act 1961

**Pollution Prevention**
Rivers (Prevention of Pollution) (Scotland) Act 1951
Rivers (Prevention of Pollution) (Scotland) Act 1965
Control of Pollution Act 1974

**Fisheries**
Salmon Fisheries (Scotland) Act 1862
Salmon Fisheries (Scotland) Act 1868
Salmon and Freshwater Fisheries (Protection) (Scotland) Act 1951
Freshwater and Salmon Fisheries (Scotland) Act 1976

In addition to the provisions listed above, some authorities have private Acts which are still in force.

## WATER RESOURCES *(see p. 67)*

Section 21 of the Act of 1946, as amended by the 1949 Act and adapted by the Acts of 1967 and 1973, empowers Regional and Islands Councils and Water Development Boards to acquire water rights by agreement or compulsorily. In the latter case by order of the Secretary of State. Acquisition of water rights by agreement requires to be approved by an Order by the Secretary of State under the procedure in the First Schedule to the 1946 Act. The Section also sets out requirements with regard to the maximum abstraction of water or, in the case of an impoundment, the provision of compensation water.

Under the Rivers (Prevention of Pollution) (Scotland) Act 1951 the river purification authorities have a duty to conserve, so far as possible, the water resources of their area.

Legislation to assist with the conservation of stream water is provided in the Spray Irrigation (Scotland) Act 1964, which enables river purification boards to control the abstraction of water for spray irrigation purposes.

## RESERVOIR SAFETY *(see p. 71)*

The Reservoirs (Safety Provisions) Act 1930 applies in Scotland, as will the Reservoirs Act 1975 when it comes into effect. In the case of the latter, the local authorities in Scotland with responsibility for the enforcement of the Act will be the Regional and Islands Councils.

## WATER SUPPLY *(see p. 72)*

Legislation relating to water supply in Scotland derives from the Water (Scotland) Acts, 1946 to 1967, together with the Local Government (Scotland) Act 1973. The Act of 1967 reorganized the administrative structure of the water supply service into 13 Regional Water Boards, while retaining most of the powers and duties contained in the earlier legislation. The Local Government (Scotland) Act 1973 dissolved the water boards, except the Central Scotland Water Development Board, and transferred responsibility for water supply to the Regional and Islands Authorities which were created by the Act. In the case of two of the Regional Authorities they have responsibilities for supplying water in areas outwith their own region. These are called "added areas", and are defined in Section 148 of the 1973 Act.

There are no water companies in Scotland and the Regional and Islands Councils between them are responsible for the supply of water within their respective areas. Five of the Regional Councils are members of the Central Scotland Water Development Board which supplies treated water, in bulk, to four of them.

The Act of 1946 lays duties and powers on the Secretary of State for Scotland in relation to the conservation of water resources and the provision of adequate water supplies comparable to those conferred on the Minister of Housing and Local Government by the Water Act 1945 as adapted. The Secretary of State is required by Section 1 of the Act to appoint an Advisory Committee to advise him on any of his functions under the Act.

The principal provisions of the Water (Scotland) Act 1949, which have no English counterpart, established a uniform system of rating and charging throughout Scotland. The Act, which was modified to some extent by the Acts of 1967 and 1973, is based broadly on the recommendations in the report of the Committee on water rating in Scotland (Cmnd. 6765).

The Rural Water Supplies and Sewerage Acts 1944 and 1955 and the Rural Water Supply and Sewerage (Scotland) Act 1970 under which grants are available in certain circumstances for supplies in rural areas apply in Scotland as does the Water Act 1958 which, as adapted by the Acts of 1967 and 1973 gives the Secretary of State powers by Order to enable water authorities to meet deficiencies in their supplies of water in time of drought.

**Supply of Water for Domestic Purposes** (*see p. 74*)

Section 8 of the Water (Scotland) Act 1946, as adapted by the Acts of 1967 and 1973, lays upon Regional and Islands Councils the duty of providing a supply of wholesome water to every part of their area where a supply is required for domestic purposes and can be provided at a reasonable cost. Pipes affording a supply of wholesome water must be taken to such points as will enable buildings for which a supply is required for domestic purposes to be connected thereto at a reasonable cost, but the authorities are not required to do anything which is not practicable at a reasonable cost. While "reasonable cost" is not defined in the Act, any question as to what is practicable at a reasonable cost may, in cases of dispute and at the request of ten local government electors, be determined by the Secretary of State. The definition of water for domestic purposes in Section 9 of the 1946 Act is similar to the English definition, but includes water for central heating and for baths up to 455 litres capacity (as compared with 227 litres in England).

In carrying out their responsibilities in relation to the purity of the supply, undertakers should carefully consider the recommendations of the Scottish Development Department as set out in Memorandum No. 13, 1979, and entitled "Water Supply Hygiene, Safeguards in the Operation and Management of Waterworks in Scotland".

**Supply of Water for Non-domestic Purposes** (*see p. 77*)

Section 11 of the Water (Scotland) Act 1946 is equivalent to Section 27 of the Water Act 1945. The Section, as amended by the Acts of 1949 and 1967, provides that a water authority may require, as a condition of giving a supply, an agreement to pay yearly sums for providing and laying mains and for payments for a specified period.

## Supply of Water for Public Purposes (*see p. 77*)

Part V of the Fourth Schedule to the Water (Scotland) Act 1946 is equivalent to Part VIII of the Third Schedule to the Water Act 1945.

## Supply of Water in Bulk (*see p. 78*)

Section 19(1) of the Water (Scotland) Act 1946, as adapted by the Acts of 1967 and 1973, empowers a Regional or Islands Council or Water Development Board to enter into an agreement to receive a supply of water in bulk from any other person whether a water authority or not. In the absence of agreement between local water authorities the Secretary of State may require the giving and taking of such a supply by such authorities by Order under Section 19(2) where it appears to him to be expedient and may in the Order fix terms and conditions of supply. In an emergency, the Secretary of State may make the necessary Order without following the normal procedure laid down in the First Schedule to the Act and, if the interests of public health so require, may modify the provisions governing laying of mains and breaking open streets in relation to any works for the purposes of the Order.

## Mains, Services and Stopcocks (*see p. 78*)

The provisions of the Water (Scotland) Act 1946, in respect of mains supply pipes, communication pipes, and stopcocks are similar to those in the Water Act 1945, but the Water (Scotland) Act 1949 amended the definition of "communication pipe", where the premises supplied do not abut on the part of the street in which the main is laid, to read "so much of the service pipe as lies between the main and the boundary *of the part* of the street in which the main is laid"—the words in italics being added by the 1949 Act. Section 28 of the 1946 Act, as amended and explained by the 1949 and 1967 Acts, is equivalent to Section 41 of the Third Schedule of the Water Act 1945. The relevant definitions are given in Section 84.

## Prevention of Waste (*see p. 83*)

Under Section 60 of the Water (Scotland) Act 1946, as adapted by the Acts of 1967 and 1973, Regional and Islands Councils and Water Development Boards are authorized to make bye-laws for the prevention of waste, undue consumption, misuse or contamination of water (Section 60 is equivalent to Section 17 of the Water Act 1945). Revised model bye-laws for this purpose were drafted by the Scottish Development Department in 1978. Under Section 30 of the 1967 Act, the Secretary of State is empowered to make regulations for any of the purposes for which bye-laws may be made under Section 60 of the 1946 Act.

The Scottish provisions, for the prevention of waste, etc., which are similar to those in Part XIII, Sections 60 to 70, of the Third Schedule to the Water Act 1945, are contained in Part VII of the Fourth Schedule to the Water (Scotland) Act 1946. Part VII is applied by Section 43 of the 1946 Act as adapted by the Acts of 1967 and 1973.

## PUBLIC UTILITIES STREET WORKS ACT 1950 (*see p. 85*)

This Act applies in Scotland.

## SEWERAGE AND SEWAGE PURIFICATION (*see pp. 85 and 96*)

The public sewerage and sewage disposal system has been governed by the Sewerage (Scotland) Act 1968 from the appointed day (16th May 1973) when the major provisions were made effective by statutory order. Broadly, this single Act covers the corresponding objectives of the legislation for England and Wales. The Act brought up to date the law governing the provisions of sewerage services by local authorities (which previously had depended in the main on statutes of the 1892 and 1897 period) and introduced a comprehensive code regulating the discharge of trade effluent to public sewers.

Provision is made in the 1968 Act for the determination of many specific matters where disputes could arise, some by the sheriff and others (the greater number) by the Secretary of State. As in water supply, one obvious difficulty is "reasonable cost" and the consequential extent of the duty to provide sewers. When intimating the date when the Act was to come into force, the Scottish Development Department issued an Explanatory Memorandum (No. 21, 1972) in which, in addition to explanations, the intentions of the Secretary of State were set out, especially with regard to the primary duty of local authorities as indicated hereunder.

Accordingly, when it is necessary to define the extent of the public sewers to be provided for premises and especially for new development in addition to a study of the Act it is necessary to have regard to the stated intention of the Secretary of State. This intention has been further clarified by the publication, from time to time, of the determinations made in a number of cases referred to the Secretary of State under the disputes procedure.

Another point of difficulty, the responsibility for maintenance of the minor sewers and drains provided by developers within new developments, has been clarified by the definitions in the Act, especially that of "drain", but so as to add to the expense of the local authority. A further novel definition, that of "surface water" may be used to diminish costs to the local authority by enabling the negotiation of a contribution for the right to discharge rainwater from streets to the public sewer.

The matters are discussed further with reference to the particular sections of the act as follows:

*Sewerage (Scotland) Act 1968*
*Part I—General Provisions as to Sewerage Duties and Powers of Local Authorities*

*Section 1.*—The explanatory memorandum quoted above states—"Section 1 makes it the duty of every county or town council to provide such public sewers as may be necessary for effectually draining their area of domestic sewage, surface water and trade effluent (which are defined in Section 59), and to make provisions, by means of sewage treatment works or otherwise, for effectually dealing with the contents of their sewers. In discharging their general obligation, a local authority must take their sewers to such point or points as will enable the owners of premises which are to be served by the sewers to connect their drains or private sewers to the public sewers at reasonable cost. In carrying out their duties under this section a local authority is not required to do anything which is not practicable at reasonable cost. Disputes about what is practicable at reasonable cost, or as to the point or points to which sewers must be taken, may be referred to the Secretary of State for determination. Without prejudice to the Secretary of State's decision in any particular case, the general intention is that local authorities should provide the main network of services within areas of new development".

*Section 2.*—requires every local authority to inspect, maintain, repair, etc., its sewers and sewage treatment works.

*Section 7.*—provides for agreements between a sewerage authority and the Secretary of State as to the provision, maintenance, and use of their respective sewers for the conveyance of water from the surface of streets or surface water from premises. (The Secretary of State was designated as a consequence of the re-organization of local government and takes the place of a highway authority contained in the original Act.) The distinction regarding water from the surface of streets and that from premises arises from the definition of surface water in Section 59 (*see below*).

*Section 8.*—enables a local authority to make an agreement with any person as to the provision, by that person or by them, of sewers and sewage treatment works to serve new premises which are to be constructed. An agreement under this section is limited to cases where the authority has no duty under Section 1 and might cover cases where the developer would meet part of the cost of the sewerage works.

*Section 10.*—empowers local authorities to resolve to empty septic tanks. The operation is to be reasonably practicable and a free service can be provided, but septic tanks which receive trade effluent are excluded from the effect of the resolution.

*Section 20.*—deals with compensation to be made by the Council for any loss, injury, or damage arising from the exercise of the powers in the Act.

## Part II—Trade Effluents

This part of the Act entitles traders to discharge trade effluent into the public sewers, subject to conditions determined by the Regional or Islands Councils, and with provision for appeals. The conditions are essentially those necessary for safety and health, protection of structures and plant and prevention of difficulties in maintenance and in the disposal of contents of the sewers and to enable costs to be recovered. The situation is basically similar to that in England and Wales.

*Section 38.*—empowers the Secretary of State (subject to statutory procedures) to apply the provisions of Part II of the Act to specified liquid or other matter, discharged to local authority sewers, which is not covered by the definition of "trade effluent" in the Act. Its purpose is that any new kind of effluent which might create difficulties can be controlled. Section 46 (in part III) prohibits anyone from discharging injurious substances, as in the earlier legislation.

## Part III—Miscellaneous and General

*Part III.*—contains miscellaneous and general provisions which are mostly consequential upon the provisions of Parts I and II. Sections give a right to sewage, authorize processing and selling, permit research and publicity, recovery of expenses, prohibit injurious discharges, restrict disclosure of information such as trade secrets, provide the procedure for appeals etc., and, most importantly, set out in Section 59 the following definitions, which are not necessarily the same as those in the legislation of England and Wales:—

*"domestic sewage"* in relation to any area or premises means sewage which is not surface water or trade effluent;

*"drain"* in relation to premises, means any pipe or drain within the curtilage of those premises used solely for or in connection with the drainage of one building or of any buildings or yards appurtenant to buildings within the same curtilage;

*"foul water"* means any water contaminated by domestic sewage or trade effluent;

*"public drain"* means any drain which is vested in a local authority;

*"public sewer"* means any sewer which is vested in a local authority;

*"Sewage"* includes domestic sewage, surface water and trade effluent;

*"sewage treatment works"* means any works, apparatus or plant used for the treatment or disposal of sewage, and includes a septic tank;

*"sewer"* does *not* include a drain as defined in this section, but, save as aforesaid, includes all sewers, pipes or drains used for the drainage of buildings and yards appurtenant to buildings;

*"surface water"* means the run-off rainwater from roofs and any paved ground surface within the curtilage of premises;

*"trade effluent"* means any liquid, either with or without particles of matter in suspension therein, which is wholly or in part produced in the course of any trade or industry carried on at trade premises, including trade waste waters or waters heated in the course of any trade or industry and, in relation to any trade premises, means any such liquid as aforesaid which is so produced in the course of any trade or industry carried on at those premises;

*"trade or industry"* for the purpose of the definition of *"trade effluent"* shall include agriculture, horticulture and scientific research or experiment and the carrying on of a hospital or a nursing home, and for the purpose of the definition of *"trade premises"* shall include premises used or intended to be used in whole or in part for carrying on agriculture, horticulture or scientific research or experiment, or as a hospital or a nursing home;

*"trade premises"* means any premises used or intended to be used for carrying on any trade or industry.

## LAND DRAINAGE (*see p. 97*)

Land drainage is a function of Central Government. The drainage of agricultural land in Scotland is covered by the Land Drainage (Scotland) Act 1958, and by certain agricultural legislation. Regional and Islands Councils are enabled to take measures for the prevention or mitigation of flooding of non-agricultural land in their areas under the Flood Prevention (Scotland) Act 1961.

## FISHERIES (*see p. 103*)

The salmon fisheries of Scotland have been the subject of legislation since 1318. Under the Salmon Fisheries (Scotland) Acts of 1862 and 1868 salmon fishing is controlled by District Salmon Fishery Boards. The Freshwater and Salmon Fisheries (Scotland) Act 1976 is mainly concerned with trout, and it enables the Secretary of State for Scotland to make a Protection Order for areas where schemes have been submitted significantly to increase the availability of fishing for freshwater fish in inland waters.

## AMENITY AND RECREATION (*see p. 104*)

Responsibility for amenity and recreation within the areas of Regional Councils is divided between the Regional and District Councils. In the Islands areas the Islands Councils have responsibility.

As far as expenditure on amenity and recreation at reservoirs, etc., is concerned, powers are contained in the Countryside (Scotland) Act 1967 which enable water authorities to spend money on the provision of facilities.

## POLLUTION CONTROL (*see p. 105*)

### The Rivers (Prevention of Pollution) Acts

The relevant Acts for pollution control in Scotland at the present time are the Rivers (Prevention of Pollution) (Scotland) Acts 1951 and 1965. These statutes are due to be almost wholly repealed and replaced by the Control of Pollution Act 1974, Part II, which was passed on 31st July 1974, but which will not become operative until such date or dates as the Secretary of State for Scotland may appoint.

The Secretary of State is required by Section I of the 1951 Act to appoint an Advisory Committee to advise him on any matters relating to the cleanliness of the rivers and other inland waters of Scotland and also in regard to the prevention of pollution of such rivers and waters.

Under the 1951 Act the river purification authorities have a duty to promote the cleanliness of rivers and other inland waters and the tidal waters in their areas. The main function of the Act is to control new outlets and new discharges of trade and sewage effluent.

The 1965 Act, which came into effect on 2nd November 1966, extended control to cover all existing discharges to inland waters and new discharges to certain areas of tidal waters and controlled waters which were specified in a schedule to the Act.

The Secretary of State has made tidal waters orders under the 1951 Act for certain areas including the main estuaries and certain sections of the coastline. These tidal waters orders enable the river purification authorities to control in these designated areas both new and existing discharges of trade and sewage effluent.

## ACQUISITION OF LANDS AND RIGHTS (*see p. 112*)

Section 20 of the Water (Scotland) Act 1946, as adapted by the Acts of 1967 and 1973, gives Regional and Islands Councils and Water Development Boards power to acquire land (other than water rights) by agreement or compulsorily. Sections 70 and 71 of the Local Government (Scotland) Act 1973 also contain powers for the acquisition of land.

The procedure for authorizing compulsory acquisition is governed by the Acquisition of Land (Authorization Procedure) (Scotland) Act 1947, and involves the making of an order by the authority and its confirmation by the Secretary of State subject to provisions for advertising and for considering objections. The Compulsory Purchase of Land (Scotland) Regulations 1976 (S.I. 1976 No. 280), set out the forms to be used in carrying out the procedure.

Section 23 of the Water (Scotland) Act 1949, as amended by the Act of 1967, modified the procedure enabling orders made by the Secretary of State under Section 21 of the 1946 Act to provide for compulsory acquisition of any land required in connection with the acquisition of water rights. The First Schedule to the 1949 Act lays down the appropriate procedure in relation to such orders.

Section 22 of the 1946 Act is equivalent to Section 25 of the Water Act 1945, on holding land, but with certain modifications calling for the consent of the Secretary of State to its disposal.

The acquisition of water rights has been referred to in the section dealing with water resources.

## TOWN PLANNING (*see p. 114*)

Although the Planning Code in England and Scotland is set out in separate legislation, there are very marked similarities. For instance, "development" is defined in the same terms but the relevant Act in Scotland is the Town and Country Planning (Scotland) Act 1972.

In relation to permitted development, the relevant legislation in Scotland is the Town and Country Planning (General Development) (Scotland) Order 1975.

Planning Liaison as described on p. 116 stemming as it does from the Water Act 1973 has no equivalent in Scotland.

## BYE—LAWS AND BUILDING REGULATIONS (*see p. 117*)

Under Section 60 of the Water (Scotland) Act 1946 local water authorities in Scotland are empowered to make bye-laws for preventing waste, undue consumption, misuse, or contamination of water supplied by them and, under Section 61 of the Water (Scotland) Act 1946, for the prevention of pollution of water whether on the surface or underground which belongs to them or which they are authorized to take.

Procedures relating to the making of Bye-laws under these Sections are contained in Part IV of the First Schedule to the Water (Scotland) Act 1946.

Regulations relating to building work were made by the Secretary of State for Scotland in 1970 (The Building Standards (Scotland) (Consolidation) Regulations 1970) and have subsequently been revised in The Building Standards (Scotland) (Consolidation) Regulations 1971.

Part M. of the Regulations deals with drainage and sanitary appliances.

## CONTRACTS (*see p. 118*)

In Scotland water and drainage and sewerage are functions of Regional and Islands local authorities and the general powers enabling them to enter into contracts necessary for the discharge of any of their functions are contained in Sections 69, 78 and 81 of the Local Government (Scotland) Act 1973.

## LIABILITY FOR INJURY OR DAMAGE (*see p. 123*)

"Nuisance" is broadly defined in Scottish law as being based on the principle that no person shall use his own property in such a way as to injure his neighbour. It should also be made clear that the rule established by the English case of *Rylands* v. *Fletcher* (1868) is not part of the law of Scotland. Whereas English law accepts the principle of absolute liability arising from non-natural use of land, in Scottish law this is not the case. Scottish law would approach the case of an escape of water from a reservoir on the basis that the person putting the reservoir on the land had to exercise a very high degree of skill or care (as opposed to the normal standard of reasonable care). This is, of course, not absolute liability although the very high degree of skill or care required probably means that the practical effect in the Scottish and English legal systems is the same although there are differing principles.

In the event of failure by an authority in their statutory duty to provide adequate sewers for a district, the remedy in England is to complain to the Minister. In Scotland, whilst there is a statutory right to complain to the Secretary of State under the Local Government (Scotland) Act 1973, there is no bar which would prevent the raising of an action in court in respect of the local authority's failure.

**HEALTH AND SAFETY AT WORK** (*see p. 128*)

The major part of the Health and Safety at Work Act 1974 applies in Scotland. Part III, except sections 75 and Schedule 7, does not however, extend to Scotland.

**EEC DIRECTIVES** (*see p. 131*)

Directives issued by the European Economic Community are applicable in Scotland.

## 21. THE POSITION IN NORTHERN IRELAND

**GENERAL**

The Water Service of the Department of the Environment for Northern Ireland (hereafter referred to as the Department) became the sole water supply authority in Northern Ireland on 1st October 1973, under the general reorganization of local government. Prior to that date some 76 local authorities and joint water boards had statutory responsibility for water supply, under the Waterworks Clauses Acts, 1847 and 1863, the Public Health (Ireland) Act 1878, and the Water Supplies and Sewerage Act (Northern Ireland) 1945.

The Waterworks Clauses Acts, 1845 and 1863, and such parts of the Public Health Act 1878 relating to the supply of water, were repealed with effect from 1st October 1973. The Water Supplies and Sewerage Act (Northern Ireland) 1945 was also repealed from 1st October 1973, with the exception of two Sections (4 and 5) relating to the sufficiency of water supply for new or occupied houses, which transferred to the new district councils.

**OPERATION AND ORGANIZATION**

The Water Service operates under a divisional structure centred on Belfast, Ballymena, Craigavon, and Londonderry, with local sub-divisional offices in most of the provincial towns. A Headquarters unit at Stormont, Belfast, is responsible for policy, co-ordination, finance, engineer planning, and capital programme control. The four water service divisions are based on the major water catchment areas.

**NORTHERN IRELAND WATER COUNCIL**

The Council was established under the Water Act (Northern Ireland) 1972 and the Water and Sewerage Services (Northern Ireland) Order 1973. It consists of 15 persons who are appointed by the head of the Department. The members are chosen to reflect a wide spectrum of opinion. Industry, commerce, agriculture, angling, and the trade unions are represented. The functions of the Water Council include the giving of advice to the Department on the exercise of its functions under the Order. It also advises the Department on all major policy matters relating to the supply of water.

**WATER APPEALS COMMISSION FOR NORTHERN IRELAND**

The Commission was established under the Water and Sewerage Services (Northern Ireland) Order 1973. Where an application or appeal is made to the Commission it may cause a local inquiry to be held to consider the application or appeal. The Commission is required to report its decision on an application or appeal to the Department and the Department is required to notify the applicant or appellant of any decision so reported. The Department is also empowered to vary a decision of the Water Appeals Commission or substitute for it a new decision. In practice this would not be done save in exceptional circumstances with ministerial approval.

## WATER SUPPLY AND WATER RESOURCES

Legislation for the supply of water is now contained in the following enactments:—

*The Water and Sewerage Services (Northern Ireland) Order 1973 [1973 No. 70 (NI 2)].*—The Order placed a duty on the Department to supply and distribute water, in addition to responsibility for sewerage and sewage disposal. The Order also requires that water supplied by the Department shall be wholesome. The Department is also empowered to *(a)* provide and maintain such works, *(b)* perform such services, and *(c)* do such things as it considers necessary or expedient for the purposes of any of its functions under the Order. The Order also sets out the rights and duties of owners and occupiers of premises in relation to the supply of water.

*The Water Charges Regulations (Northern Ireland) 1973 [SR 1973 No. 158].*—These Regulations provide for the levying on owners and occupiers of premises of charges for the supply of water, i.e. metered water supplies for industry, agriculture, and commercial undertakings.

*The Water and Sewerage Regulations (Northern Ireland) 1973 [SR 1973 No. 334].*— These Regulations provide for the proper provision and maintenance of service pipes and water fittings.

*The Water Regulations (Northern Ireland) 1974 [SR 1974 No. 143].*—These Regulations provide for standards for the provision of water fittings and pipes. They replaced the water bye-laws of the former local authorities and joint water boards.

*The Water Act (Northern Ireland) 1972 [1972 C5].*—While not directly related to the supply of water, the Act provides for the conservation and cleanliness of water resources. The Act also empowers the Department to promote water management programmes and to make regulations controlling the abstraction of water. To date, no regulations have been made.

## RESERVOIR SAFETY

The Department may make regulations with respect to the construction, inspection, maintenance, and repair of reservoirs and dams.

## SEWERAGE AND CONTROL AND PREVENTION OF POLLUTION OF WATERWAYS

Legislation is contained in the following enactments:—

Public Health (Northern Ireland) Act 1878
Water Act (Northern Ireland) 1972 (1972 C5)
Water and Sewerage Services (Northern Ireland) Order 1973 (1973 No. 70 (N12))

## Pollution of Waterways

The responsibility for the control and prevention of pollution of waterways rests with the Department under the Water Act (Northern Ireland) 1972.

Under the provisions of Part II of this Act a person commits an offence if he discharges or deposits, whether knowingly or otherwise, any poisonous, noxious, or polluted matter so that it enters a waterway or water contained in any underground strata.

Part II of the Act also makes provision for the control of effluent into waterways or underground stratum. Under this provision no person is permitted, without the consent of the Department, to discharge into a waterway or into underground stratum:—

*(a)* any trade or sewage effluent;
*(b)* any poisonous, noxious or polluting matter not falling within paragraph *(a)*.

The Department is also empowered under the Act to make regulations for the prevention of waterway pollution.

## Sewerage

The Department became the sole sewerage authority in Northern Ireland on 1st October 1973, under the general reorganization of local government. The new district councils, which also came into being on 1st October 1973, inherited the sanitary responsibility of the former local authorities. While drains and private sewers are the responsibility of the owners thereof, the district councils have a duty, under the Northern Ireland public health legislation and building control regulations, for the proper provision and maintenance of such pipes.

Under Section 29 of the Public Health (Northern Ireland) Act 1878, the Department can enter into agreements with persons wishing to erect buildings over public sewers. This Act also provides for penalities to be imposed for unauthorized building over public sewers.

The Department has a duty under the Water and Sewerage Services (Northern Ireland) Order 1973 to:—

(i)  provide and maintain sewers for draining domestic sewage, surface water, and trade effluent; and
(ii) make provision for effectually dealing with the contents of its sewers.

"Drains" and "sewers", etc., are defined in Article 2 of the Water and Sewerage Service (Northern Ireland) Order 1973.

## Trade Effluent Discharges

Part V of the Water and Sewerage Services (Northern Ireland) Order 1973, contains provisions for consent to discharge trade effluents to the Department's sewers and sewage treatment works, and for the review of existing discharges.

The responsibility for record maps showing and distinguishing public sewers is vested in the Department under the above-mentioned Order.

The Pollution Control and Local Government (Northern Ireland) Order 1978 [1978 No. 1049 (NI 19)] is not directly related to the prevention of pollution of waterways or for the provision of sewerage services, but Schedule 3 of this Order contains some amendments to the Water Act (Northern Ireland) 1972 and the Water and Sewerage Services (Northern Ireland) Order 1973. However, these amendments do not affect any of the provisions and responsibilities referred to in the preceding paragraphs.

## Land Drainage

Land drainage comes under the umbrella of the Department of Agriculture for Northern Ireland. However, there is close liaison between the two departments with regard to the implementation of land drainage and sewerage schemes.

## Acquisition of Water Rights, etc

The Department is empowered under the Water and Sewerage Services (Northern

Ireland) Order 1973 to impound or abstract water from any waterway or water contained in underground strata. The Department is required to inform statutory fisheries bodies of its proposals and to take all reasonable steps to inform persons who, in its opinion, will be affected thereby. The Department is also required to give public notice in the local press of its intention to impound or abstract. Any person aggrieved by the Department's proposals may appeal to the Water Appeals Commission for Northern Ireland within 28 days from the date on which the Department informed him of his proposals, or from the date of publication of the notice.

### Acquisition of Land

The Department is empowered under the 1973 Order to acquire land by agreement, or lease land, or acquire land compulsorily. The Department can also dispose of any land so acquired or taken on lease.

The Department is required to serve notice of its intention to acquire land compulsorily by Vesting Order, and at the same time to publish notice of its proposals in the local press. Objections may be lodged with the Department within one month from the date of service or publication of the notice. If valid objections are received, the Department may cause a local inquiry to be held to consider them. After taking all relevant factors into account, the Department may make an Order vesting the land concerned. Compensation negotiations with interested parties begin as soon as the Vesting Order becomes operative. If agreement cannot be reached, the matter can be referred to the Lands Tribunal for Northern Ireland, and its decision is final.

### Wayleaves for Water Mains and Sewers

The Department is required under the 1973 Order to serve notice of its intention to lay a water main or construct a sewer in on or over land not forming part of a public road, on the owner and occupier of the land concerned. Objections to the Department's proposals may be made within 28 days from the date of service of the notice. Such objections are considered and determined by the Department. After notifying the objector of its decision the Department may proceed to carry out the works specified in the notice, with or without modification.

### Compensation

The Department is required under the 1973 Order to make good, or pay compensation for, any damage caused by, or in consequence of, the execution of works under the Order. Any person aggrieved by an assessment of compensation can have the matter referred to the Lands Tribunal for determination.

### Financial Provision

Any expenses incurred by the Department under the 1973 Order are defrayed either out of monies appropriated for the purpose of defraying such expenses or, if the Department of Finance for Northern Ireland so directs, by means of sums charged on and issued out of the Consolidated Fund.

### Recreational Facilities

The Department may provide facilities on any land vested in it for the purposes of the 1973 Order, e.g. water catchment areas.

# Chapter 4

# ECONOMICS

## 1. FOREWORD

DEFINED by the Oxford Dictionary as the practical science of the production and distribution of wealth, economics remains a mystery to many, which is surprising, for natural economic skills have been displayed by mankind since civilization began. The present day water manager is no exception; his task is to husband naturally occurring water resources for the use of man, and to protect mankind and his environment from flood and drought and the potential hazards of water-borne waste products. Although water problems are solved chiefly through technology, economics assists in deciding the value and timing of resources to be used in the water services, the structure of the charges, and the degree of protection and standard of service to be provided for a public which on the one hand is increasingly bent on freedom from risk, and on the other neither understands the resultant charges nor welcomes them.

The chapter is in five parts. The first, Economic Background, describes the place of the water industry in the national economy, and the relevance of economics and planning to the water services. The remaining four parts deal with the main areas in which economics plays a role—Forecasting, Investment Decisions, Charging Policy, and Corporate Planning.

## 2. ECONOMIC BACKGROUND

### ECONOMIC AND SOCIAL DEVELOPMENT

Of all ancient peoples, the Romans paid most attention to water supply and were conscious of the importance of hygiene. After the fall of the Roman Empire urban civilization declined, and it was not until the nineteenth century that the importance of good sanitation and water supply was again recognized. The history of the water industry is covered in Chapter 1, but it is important to note that water services were generally not provided until the Industrial Revolution was over. The full consequences of large populations living close together in this period, prey to all infectious diseases including cholera, were disregarded until social reformers such as Chadwick made the provision of water services a matter of public concern.

The provision of abundant supplies of water and good sewerage systems was thus undertaken as a social reform and this colours our attitude to charges even today. The success of the programme of course enabled an economic gain, without which our present material prosperity would not have been possible.

Since the Second World War relative affluence, education and mobility have combined to make the public more aware of the environment and more concerned over pollution. While the foresight of the engineers who built the great reservoirs serving Manchester, Liverpool and Birmingham is applauded, new reservoirs have become environmentally sensitive projects. Now that a good and sufficient provision of water supply may be taken for granted, the growing economic value placed on the environment is becoming a new and important factor to be considered in the development of the industry.

## POSITION OF THE WATER INDUSTRY IN THE ECONOMY

Water has always been a service industry, responding to anticipated housing and industrial demands rather than leading them. Water is heavy and incompressible, and so more costly to convey over long distances than electricity or gas, and the absence of a convenient supply of fresh water and a means of waste disposal can impose constraints on new development in certain areas.

Although essential to every major human activity, the water industry currently takes a relatively small portion of the national economic resources. It employs only

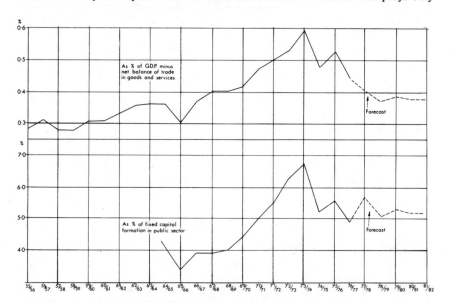

## Fig. 4.1. Capital investment in national water services as a percentage of national resources and public investment

*Source:* Thackray, J. E. 1977 I.W.E.S., Symposium on Water Services: Financial, Engineering and Scientific Planning, "1. Problems facing U.K. water authorities: the planning view".

0.4 per cent of the workforce*, and, in 1976 spent only 1.3 per cent of gross domestic product. In the same year its capital expenditure was 2.1 per cent of gross domestic fixed capital formation, or 5 per cent of public sector investment, although these proportions have varied in the past (Fig. 4.1). The average household bill for water supply, sewerage, and sewage services came to £0.61 per week in 1976, equivalent to 1.0 per cent of average household expenditure, while the cost of laying on these water services to a dwelling, including back-up resources and disposal works, approached 10 per cent of house building costs.

The water industry is highly capital intensive; Table 4.I shows that it has more fixed assets per employee, and spends more on capital investment compared to its revenue expenditure, than the gas or electricity industries or Imperial Chemical

*The following statistics refer to the 90 per cent of the U.K. population who live in England and Wales.

TABLE 4.I.    Capital Intensity of the Water Industry

| 1974-75 figures | Water | Gas | Electricity | ICI |
|---|---|---|---|---|
| Fixed assets per employee, £000 | 39 | 14 | 30 | 11 |
| Capital investment ÷ revenue expenditure, % | 68 | 25 | 18 | 15 |

*Sources:* Thackray, J. E. 1977 *I. W.E.S.*, Symposium on Water Services: Engineering and Scientific Planning,
    1. Problems facing U.K. water authorities: the planning view.

National Water Council 1976, Paying for Water.

Industries (ICI). Compared to ICI, it uses almost four times the capital per
employee, and invests over four times the proportion of its revenue expenditure.

In 1976-77 over one-half the Regional Water Authorities' capital expenditure was
for sewerage and sewage treatment and disposal and under one-third was accounted
for by water supply (Fig. 4.2), although the proportion has varied in the past (Fig.
4.3).

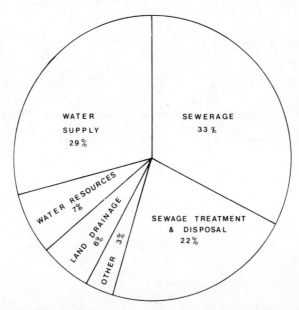

**Fig. 4.2.   Capital expenditure of water authorities in England and Wales**
*Source:* National Water Council, "Water authority annual accounts— 1976-77".

Almost one-half of revenue expenditure is used for servicing capital; one-quarter
is spent on employees, and less than one-quarter is devoted to other operating costs
(Fig. 4.4). It is probable that, if a realistic charge were made for the capital assets
used up each year, capital servicing costs would be much higher. The book value of
present capital assets, based on the prices actually paid for them when they were
built—some over 100 years ago—was about £4 billion in 1977; it is likely that their
residual value at 1977 prices was four times that figure. Even greater is their cost of
renewal, which for underground assets was reckoned at £40 billion (1977 prices).

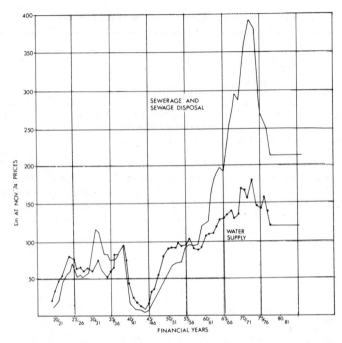

**Fig. 4.3.   Investment patterns in the water industry 1919-83**

*Source:* Thackray, J. E. 1977 I.W.E.S., Symposium on Water Services: Financial, Engineering and Scientific Planning, "I. Problems facing U.K. Water authorities: the planning view".

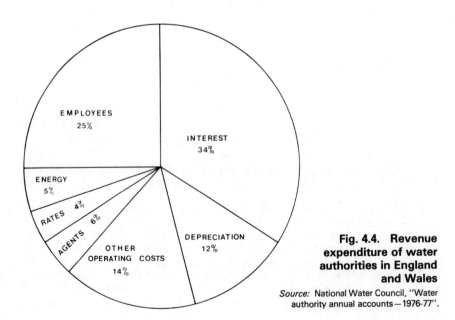

**Fig. 4.4.   Revenue expenditure of water authorities in England and Wales**

*Source:* National Water Council, "Water authority annual accounts—1976-77".

The significance of these figures is fourfold. Firstly, the capital requirement is large enough to be subject to political influence in the macro-economic management of the economy, so that the water industry can be, and has been, used to stimulate or temper national economic activity. Secondly, any political or economic decision affecting housebuilding or industrial growth may have an immediate effect on demand for water services and the need for new works. Thirdly, the production costs of water are small compared to the initial cost of the works. Short term Government adjustments in policy therefore are likely to be not only disruptive but uneconomic in their effect. Fourthly, the replacement of aged assets at many times their original cost cause real increases in charges for unchanged standards of service.

## INTERNATIONAL SCENE

In other parts of the world the capital demands for water services are even larger. Not only are many countries less favourably blessed with water resources, but most systems are less well developed and in most countries population growth rates are higher.

Whilst almost all the developed world receives a piped water supply, in the developing countries only 55 per cent of urban dwellers have a piped supply and only 20 per cent of the rural communities have access to safe water. Again, whilst 95 per cent of the total population of the U.K. is sewered this is true of only 25 per cent of people in the urban parts of the developing countries.

At the same time, population growth in the U.K. is almost static, yet in Mexico City it is 4.4 per cent per annum, in Bombay 4.2 per cent per annum, and in Sao Paulo 3.9 per cent per annum (Table 4.II).

The costs of meeting proposed World Health Organization targets in the developing world[1] at 1977 prices are £14 000 million to bring water supplies to 479 million people and £9 500 million for sewage disposal to 432 million. These figures represent average annual investments on water supply of £1.2/head and on sewage disposal of £0.8/head compared to 1978-79 U.K. investment[2] of £4.6/head and £4.9/head respectively, all at 1977 prices.

Labour productivity varies as well, the number of water employees per population served being 40 times greater in the developing countries than in the U.S.A.

The costs vary too, from 10 per cent of the consumer's gross income compared to less than 1 per cent in the U.K.

TABLE 4.II.   Population Growth of Cities

| City | Average annual rate of growth before 1975, % | Population 1975, millions | Predicted average annual rate of growth after 1975, % | Population 2000, millions |
|---|---|---|---|---|
| Bombay | 3.7 | 7.1 | 4.2 | 19.8 |
| Cairo | 4.3 | 6.9 | 3.6 | 16.9 |
| London | 0.2 | 10.7 | 0.7 | 12.7 |
| Mexico | 5.4 | 10.9 | 4.4 | 31.5 |
| Moscow | 1.8 | 7.6 | 1.4 | 10.8 |
| New York | 1.3 | 17.0 | 1.3 | 22.2 |
| Peking | 5.8 | 8.9 | 3.7 | 22.0 |
| Sao Paulo | 5.7 | 9.9 | 3.9 | 26.0 |
| Seoul | 8.3 | 7.3 | 3.8 | 18.7 |
| Tokyo | 3.9 | 17.5 | 2.0 | 28.7 |

*Source:* United Nations City Projections, December 1974.

Water is the key to health and the vital key to the elimination of poverty and the creation of wealth. A century of economic sanitary management in the developed world reduced the great nineteenth century killers of cholera, dysentery and typhoid into faint shadows, and made modern urban development possible.

## MONOPOLY INDUSTRY

In all countries water undertakers have a monopoly in the sense that there is no competition between them to supply the same service, each having been given exclusive rights and responsibilities in their areas by Government. This arises because, unlike gas and electricity which both supply power, there are no real substitutes for water supply and sewerage, except in the limited sense that industrialists can choose between private (licensed) and mains supplies etc., and in the area of water-based recreation. When consumers have to buy their services from a monopoly, they are largely at its mercy because there is no one to go to if they are dissatisfied. There may be little incentive for the water undertakers to produce efficiently, especially if profits are absent or restricted. Therefore, legal powers normally enable the State to safeguard the public interest by specifying obligations and methods of charging, and providing overall control.

These statutory obligations, none of which has absolute priority, are not as sharply defined as the words suggest and unfortunately, a monopoly lacks the guidance that market forces normally provide in establishing the appropriate standards for each service. It is a difficult task to ensure that the water industry is given its rightful share of national resources and no more, and it imposes on government an obligation to allocate those resources fairly through proper economic criteria rather than be swayed unduly by fluctuating opinion after, say, an extreme drought or flood. These criteria, and the problems of charging by a monopoly, are discussed later in this chapter.

## RELEVANCE OF ECONOMICS AND PLANNING

The size and nature of the water industry in the economy, its monopoly position and control by Government, and the social and political attitudes to water which have developed with its history, all impose external constraints on the way the industry is run. Economics provides a body of knowledge and a series of techniques which may be directed to improving the efficiency with which the industry's obligations may be met, within those external constraints. Planning provides a mechanism which takes each individual step—the forecast, the investment implication, the resultant charge, and the effect on the forecast—for each separate service, for each area, and determines priorities, policies and a programme for action. These steps are now discussed in detail.

## 3. FORECASTING

### INTRODUCTION

"Crystal balls" are no more prevalent in the water industry than elsewhere, yet their need is more acute, for due to the economies of scale it is frequently economic to construct dams, sewers and water mains to meet demand well into the twenty-first century. Sewers, for example, are usually designed to convey all flows imposed during the life of the property served, which is commonly 60 and may be more than 100 years. Perhaps because the problems of forecasting are so daunting, past techniques have been rudimentary and heavily reliant on the extrapolation of past data using more or less sophisticated mathematical techniques—or a convenient ruler. Recently, however, the water industry has begun to explore the reasons for growth in demand, and surveys have provided an improved base for forecasts.

Whilst all development inevitably imposes a demand for water services, the industry is conscious of the advantages of influencing the efficiency of water use. The most obvious influence—charging policy—is also seen as a way to improve management of the rivers. Whereas in the past forecasting has concentrated on the need for raw water resources and development of the piped systems, forecasts are now becoming necessary for the net and gross demands for river abstractions; the pollution loads imposed; and the demands for recreation and amenity. More attention is also being given to financial and manpower forecasting, and to forecasts of asset replacement, on which work is only just beginning[3].

## METHODS

In the past most forecasts were based on an extrapolation of historic data, sometimes adjusted, either up or down, by a "hunch factor". Although criticized for being no more than forecasting by blind faith, the method has a certain logic in that change of water use patterns tends to occur gradually. Local authorities, for example, began giving grants to improve housing amenities (baths and internal WCs especially) as far back as 1959 and some schemes remain in existence today. Washing machines began to be purchased in the early 1950s and it is only recently that market saturation has been approached. Although consumption will fluctuate due to meteorological and economic influences, the underlying trend should be smooth, making rapid changes unlikely. Hence, forecasts of total consumption up to 10 years ahead based on the trend of the past 15 years or so should not be greatly in error.

Efforts to improve accuracy by fitting sophisticated curves to past data using mathematical techniques such as regression (explained with great simplicity by Moroney[4]) seem less rewarding. Fig. 4.5, besides showing the doubling of per capita demand for mains water in the last 50 years, neatly demonstrates the potential pitfalls of this approach.

A second method seeks to develop forecasts by detailed projections of individual components of consumption. For example, a forecast of dishwasher ownership would be made and the figures multiplied by the average usage of dishwasher machines and an estimate of the probable frequency of use—figures which can be obtained from surveys.

A third method acknowledges the connection between demand for water and economic growth and attempts to associate consumption with various economic measures representing affluence and industrial activity, such as gross domestic product. Forecasts of economic activity are then translated into projected water demands, using the relationship established from historic data. Development of this approach is in its infancy.

Possibly the most comprehensive study of water demand was undertaken by Herrington[5] between 1969-73, who reviewed forcasts made in England and Wales over the period 1959-71 and then set out to show that the effect of income, appliance ownership, price, and rainfall, could be detected in the historic trends.

It is now considered preferable, even necessary, to attempt to identify growth in demand for most forecasts more than ten years ahead.

It is often said that the only certain thing about a forecast is that it will be wrong, and clearly different assumptions will lead to different figures. This has led to more consideration being given at the planning stage to the implications of forecasts being

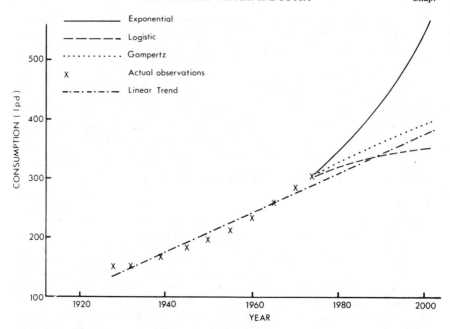

**Fig. 4.5. Alternative extrapolations of per capita water consumption from public supplies**

wrong; to the idea of testing strategies against a range of forecasts; and to the concept of confidence limits. Confidence limits may be calculated mathematically, using the variation in historic data to suggest potential divergence in the future, but again this approach may lead to a false sense of security if taken more than ten years ahead. A range of forecasts with different levels of probability may also be calculated by varying assumptions within reasonable bounds. Quite simply, the more that is known about water use and what influences it, the closer those limits can be.

## MAINS WATER SUPPLY AND SEWERAGE—COMPONENTS OF DEMAND

The major components of demand for water supply and sewerage are given in Table 4.III. Virtually all water supply is measured at either source or treatment works. Measured supplies are recorded on a more or less regular basis, but rarely more frequently than once a month. Leakage can be estimated from measurements of night flows in districts monitored by waste meters, but, in the U.K., where domestic water metering is almost entirely absent, domestic usage can only be determined by special measurement or survey.

Average daily flows (ADFs) recorded at most large sewage works include infiltration which will vary according to the rainfall during the year. Dry-weather flow (DWF), a better indicator of the trend in demand, is measured when infiltration is zero or at a minimum, and although there is no standard definition, it is often taken as the flow discharged during summer months (excluding industrial holidays) seven days after rain. Controlled or "consented" discharges from "dirty" industrial processes, i.e. the "trade" effluents, are also measured separately.

**TABLE 4.III.   Water Balance Showing Main Components on Demand**

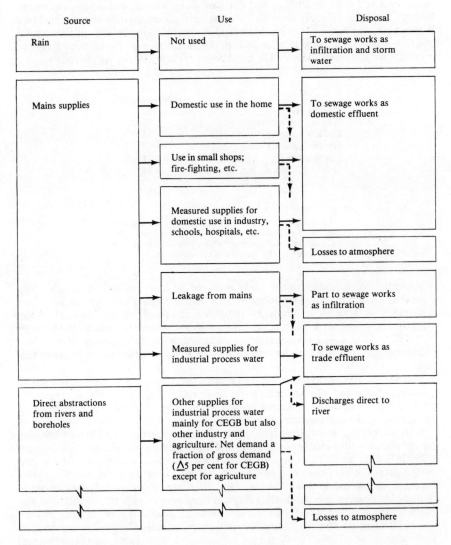

Supply and drainage areas are rarely coterminous. Moreover, some industrial water is obtained from private (licensed) supplies, and some mains water is either lost to atmosphere through transpiration of plants or cooling processes, or discharged directly to watercourses. The components of demand are dealt with in detail below.

## Use in the Home

Domestic use in the home accounts for about 40 per cent of the water put into supply.

In 1973 Jenking[6] undertook a study of water consumption in the Fylde Water Board area and work by Phillips and Kershaw[7,8] and Marsh[9] also deserves mention. Perhaps the most valuable work to date has been undertaken by the Severn-Trent Water Authority in their Malvern-Mansfield study (Thackray *et al*[10]). In 1976 a total of 853 households in these two towns kept detailed diaries of 13 different forms of water use for a ten week period. The breakdown of the main uses was as follows:—

|  | | | | *percentage* |
|---|---|---|---|---|
| Toilet usage | ... | ... | ... | 33 |
| Bathing/showering | | ... | ... | 17 |
| Clothes washing | ... | ... | ... | 13 |
| Garden watering | ... | ... | ... | 2 |
| Car washing | ... | ... | ... | 1 |
| Drinking, cooking and other uses* | | | | 34 |
| | | | | —— |
| | | | | 100 |
| | | | | —— |

*This figure is the residual quantity when the main appliance uses have been deducted. It derives mainly from the kitchen and wash basin taps and thus includes some clothes washing, personal usage, other regular and occasional uses.

Recorded consumption in the study averaged 98 l/person/day, although a few l/person/day should be added to allow for under-recording of meters at low flows and other factors. Consumptions measured in three other Regional Water Authorities, where work had not yet been published, have been higher, in the range 110-120 l/person/day. Evidence is now accumulating that supply pressure can affect consumptions, and this may be responsible for some variation in the experimental results.

The Malvern-Mansfield study showed again the very great scatter of household consumptions when plotted against rateable value (Fig. 4.6), but a reasonable relationship when bands of similar houses are grouped together—this information being of value in planning supplies to large estates.

It seems reasonable therefore to accept a 1978 base figure of 110-120 l/person/day for most areas with a mixture of housing and social groups.

Little further growth can be expected in the demand for toilet water (the largest part of present usage) and this consumption may even decrease if the dual flush toilet becomes widespread and is used correctly. However, other growth may occur as households develop the water-using habits of their more affluent neighbours. For example, the conversion to fully automatic washing machines may continue and the use of dishwashers and waste disposal units may increase. Central heating and the introduction of showers will make personal washing more comfortable and convenient. Swimming use may increase especially if it can be linked with solar heating, and other new uses may be introduced.

On the other hand, technical improvements to toilets, showers and taps being studied by the Building Research Establishment[11, 12] and other improvements encouraged by the National Water Council Approvals Board should curb total demand, so that it is considered by many that use of water in the home is unlikely to grow by more than 50 per cent of current use by the end of the century.

Data from the U.S.A. tends not to be directly comparable to U.K. practice due to high seasonal demands for garden water, even in the New England states.

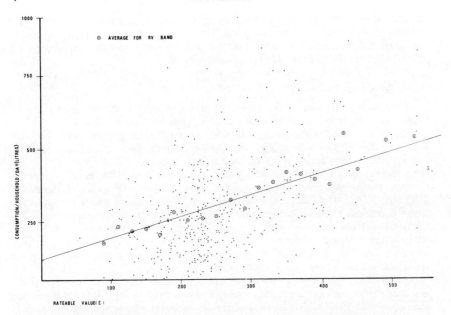

**Fig. 4.6. Variation in consumption by rateable value (Malvern)**

*Source:* Thackray, J. E., Cocker, V., and Archibald, G. 1978 *Jour. Proc. I.C.E.*, 64, 37, The Malvern studies of domestic water usage.

Nevertheless, the studies by Howe and Linaweaver[13] and the study in Akron County, Ohio[14] are of interest. Data for undertakers in continental Europe for 1971-72 have been recorded by Coe[15]. Recorded consumptions vary and it is difficult to determine a pattern, some appearing to be lower than would be expected by the affluence relative to the U.K. and others higher. It is interesting to note that domestic consumption in Stockholm is now reported to be 230 l/person/day compared to 237 six years ago, which suggest that consumption may be nearing a plateau due to saturation of the market for domestic appliances.

Details of the level of appliance ownership and other measures of relative affluence may be found in Social Trends[16]; the General Household Survey[17]; the Census reports[18]; and the Digests of Regional Statistics[19].

**Firefighting and Other Unmeasured Uses**

A small quantity of water, about 10 per cent of the volume of household use, is supplied to small shops and other premises and charged for on the basis of rateable value rather than volume. Water used for fire-fighting, gulley flushing, street cleaning and so on also comes into this category. It is probable that metering will be extended into this area of demand and the resulting curb will offset much of the potential for growth.

**"Domestic" Use in Industry, Schools, etc.**

The requirement for more comprehensive washroom facilities, canteens and so on at the work place seems likely to cause increases in this component of demand, although use here may offset some use in the home. Potential remains however for the adoption of more efficient water systems, and much attention is currently being given to control units for automatic toilet flushing systems whose purchase would be encouraged if sewage disposal charges (as well as water supply) were based on volume used rather than rateable value, as at present.

## Use in Industrial Processes

Very roughly one-half of the measured mains supply, or one-sixth of the total supply, is used for industrial processes and discharged as a trade effluent.

Industrial demand is important, however, not only for the gross quantity required but for the effluents produced which need both supervision and detailed consideration in the design of sewage treatment processes.

In recent years control over effluents has tightened and the costs of meeting consent conditions[20, 21] and the charges for trade effluent have risen considerably in most areas. The effect has been to reduce trade effluent volume and hence industrial water demands. Even in Birmingham, which has had comprehensive control for many years, trade effluent volumes dropped by about 40 per cent between 1970-76 whilst other measured consumption reduced by about 10 per cent. Trade effluent charges more than doubled in this period in real terms, suggesting that part of the reduction was caused by the impact of price.

Nevertheless, water charges remain one of the smaller bills in most organizations, and many firms lack the expertise to recognize potential savings. It is probable that the drought of 1976, which focused attention on water use, brought about savings which would otherwise have been deferred for several years.

Much new equipment however is designed to be efficient in water use; control systems are becoming automated, and recycling is increasing. Savings are being made both through greater process efficiency and greater perception of the minimum quality required.

Efficiency of water use is limited by the need to sustain quality of manufacture and improve standards of hygiene. For example, increasing the concentration of dye can lead to blemishes in the final product, and electroplating needs perfect cleanliness to avoid subsequent pitting. In some industries such as food processing, water use is in fact increasing as higher standards of hygiene (e.g. the spray washing of meat and poultry carcasses) are imposed.

Changes in industrial water demand and discharge quality can occur much more rapidly than domestic use. Industry, through mergers, rationalizations, and government incentives can move across the country, changing demand with a few months. Traditional industries can decline and new ones, with very different water demands, grow in their place. New practices in one firm will be copied by others to reduce competitive advantage.

It seems unlikely that industrial usage will grow very quickly in total across the country, but demands in specific industries and in different areas will vary. A study of the larger users and those with difficult effluents is a valuable preliminary to any forecast.

## Leakage and Infiltration

Leakage occurs from mains, service reservoirs, communication pipes, defective fittings, and overflows. Leakage also occurs on industrial sites, and it is common to save as much water on a site by reducing leakage as by improving the efficiency of water use, but this, having passed through a meter and been charged for is not normally included.

The economics of leakage control are discussed later. It is not clear whether forecasts of leakage are most appropriately expressed on a per person or per house basis, or as a percentage of total production. There are many difficulties in estimating the quantity of leakage and in deciding which costs to include in the analysis, and the work of the Technical Working Group on Waste of Water[22], which has led to the current programme organized by the Water Research Centre, will provide much valuable information.

Infiltration has received less attention than leakage. Indeed, in the past it has often been felt that a small quantity of infiltration may assist treatment at rural works by preventing deposition and septicity in the sewer and sustaining the bacteriological processes through low flow periods. Sewers are frequently designed with greater peak factors than water mains, so that the proportionate effect of infiltration tends to be less. Infiltration consists of direct inflow from unrecorded roof and surface water connections, and ingress of groundwater from often localized water tables. It tends, therefore, to be related to the intensity of recent rainfall and does not remain constant over the year.

Virtually all unmetered domestic and non-domestic and all metered supplies, except those to cattle troughs, discharge to sewers for most of the year. In extreme droughts it is believed a net loss to atmosphere reaching 20 per cent of the water put into supply may occur.

## POPULATION

Domestic water consumption in the U.K. is normally forecast on a per person basis and multiplied by a forecast of population. Industrial usage and other components of demand are also sometimes forecast on this basis. Each year the Registrar General publishes population projections for the country to the end of the century and beyond. He also publishes regional projections and he has published county projections which are constrained to the national figures. His assumptions of birth and mortality rates and migration are made explicit, and he is accepted as an authori-

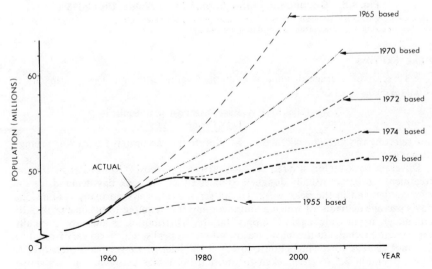

**Fig. 4.7. Actual and projected populations of England and Wales**

tative and impartial source. The County Councils, as strategic planning authorities, also produce population forecasts at county level and sometimes at district and sub-district level. The Registrar General and County figures do not always agree and can change markedly (Fig. 4.7) from year to year following changes in Government policy, as happened recently in the New Towns.

Nevertheless, there is normally sufficient population information on which to base a "best estimate", although it should be remembered that the official figures will normally relate to "resident" population, and allowances need to be made in tourist and other areas. Due to the variations in annual births, the age structure of the population will change. The ratio of "economically active" to "dependent" population will in fact become more favourable (Fig. 4.8) over the next few years. If the 15-65 age group uses more water than children and the very old, as is possible, consumption may increase more than is indicated by change in population alone, although the Malvern-Mansfield results[10] suggest the adjustment would be modest. This change in age structure could also accelerate the trend to lower household size, which tends to be associated with higher personal consumption.

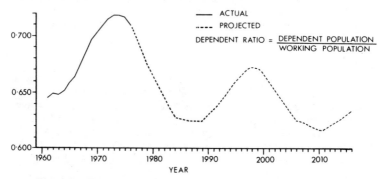

**Fig. 4.8.   Dependency ratio, England and Wales, 1961-2016**

Dependent population  = population aged 0-15 and population over retirement age
Working population     = population aged 16 to retirement age

## PEAK FACTORS

A forecast of average demand is of limited value to design. Design capacity is often taken as:—

$$\text{Design Capacity} = \text{Average Demand in year required} \times \text{Peak Factor} + \text{Margin}$$

and selecting the correct peak factor is as important as accurately forecasting average demand.

Different peak factors are required for different purposes. Raw water mains and treatment works are usually designed to meet either the peak day demand, or the average demand in the peak week. Urban service reservoirs normally contain one day's average demand, of which about one-quarter is required to balance peaks, the remainder to provide against supply failure. Distribution mains are normally expected to meet all but the most rare instantaneous peaks, which can vary from over 60 times average for a single house to 1.5 at the inlet to a large mains network. A figure of about 2.5 is often taken for most trunk mains between. Fig. 4.9 shows hourly consumptions as a percentage of average demand.

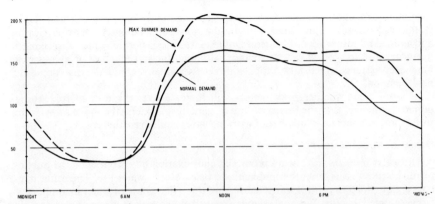

**Fig. 4.9. Hourly consumption of water as percentage of year's mean daily demand**

Local peaks also occur. For example, the manufacture of butter peaks in summer when milk yields increase, and cattle watering can cause severe peaks in the early evening when the grass is dry.

Combined and storm sewers are rarely designed to convey peaks arising from more than the 1 in 2 year storm, and overflows have historically been set to spill at about 6 × DWF. The attenuation of flow in foul sewers is equivalent to storage, so that the common design flow of 4 × DWF may be reduced nearer the sewage works. The size of smaller foul sewers is often determined by the need to avoid blockage rather than by flow requirements.

Peaks in biological load can also occur, for example, when washing down a slaughterhouse floor at the end of a day's work, and sewage loading will vary through the day (Fig. 4.10).

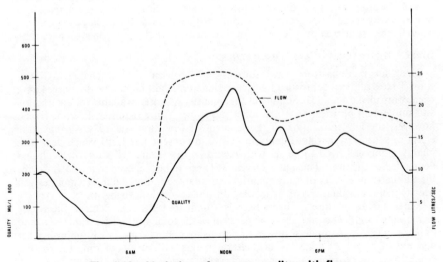

**Fig. 4.10. Variation of sewage quality with flow**

Storage can limit extreme peaks. Industry commonly provides one-half day's storage as a necessary commercial safeguard against supply breakdown or restriction, and as an extra insurance against fire. Domestic storage is normally provided to meet hot water and some cold water demands, although the introduction of pressurized hot water systems which take supplies direct from mains could increase domestic peak demand.

It is not clear whether peak factors will increase over the normal forecasting period. Some feel that the increased use of garden sprinklers, the move away from shift work, and increased number of working wives could have this effect.

## DEMAND MANAGEMENT

The water industry has always promoted conservation by encouraging the public, through school visits and other publicity, to be careful in water use. The water bye-laws are intended to control wasteful use, and the efficient use of water in appliances is encouraged by the National Water Council Approvals Scheme. Considerable advice is given to industrialists in water use, leading frequently to reductions in overall demand and trade effluent load.

Charging schemes, dealt with more fully later, have generally been designed simply to meet revenue requirements at the minimum administrative cost, and domestic metering, although debated at great length over many years, has so far been rejected. It seems likely that in the future charging schemes will become more sophisticated and will begin to be used to influence demand.

Domestic metering could become economic as a result of charging for both water supplied and sewage discharged on the basis of volume used, and although a nationwide programme of domestic metering would take 10-15 years to complete, it is possible that domestic consumption could be reduced by about 10 per cent of forecast levels by the end of the century, or more if the pricing policy led to greater consumer support for technical improvements in water use appliances.

Using the potential demand management tools of price, law, education, and technology, not only total demand, but peak demand may be curbed as well. Some industries are already required to release concentrated effluents over a period of 24 hr using storage tanks on site to reduce extreme loadings. There is no reason in principle why special supply contracts could not be negotiated with large consumers, whereby they restricted themselves to an "off-peak" supply for a concessionary rate.

## DIRECT ABSTRACTIONS AND DISCHARGES

Direct abstractions from water sources and "consents" to discharge to water-courses have all been controlled by licence since 1963, although new discharges have been controlled since 1951. So long as the quantity of water available for abstraction and subsequent purification is abundant, no forecasts are required. In some rivers, however, the implementation of the Control of Pollution Act 1974 will have the effect of setting river water quality targets, and consent standards which deal with quality alone will need to be set with regard to the future gross and net volumes demanded of the river. Thus, many rivers will need to be managed to a greater degree than hitherto in respect of both quantity and quality, and modelling techniques will need to include evaluations of environmental and recreational benefits.

Water taken by direct abstraction is dominated by the Central Electricity Generating Board who take about 48 per cent of the total abstraction from rivers and upper estuaries[23]. A modern power station using cooling towers will impose a net demand of about 30 $m^3$/MW/day, although this will vary according to weather conditions. The gross demand for a direct cooled station would be 3 000 $m^3$/MW/day although all is returned to the river, but at about 10°C warmer than before. Total water demands for any station are frequently highest in the early years of the station's life, with demand dropping as more efficient stations come on line, so providing a margin that other consumers may be able to use.

The other major group of net abstractors are spray irrigators. Irrigation equipment is expensive to install and operate, but crop yields can be increased considerably and some farmers, using a trickle feed system, find irrigation to be economic, even when using mains water. Yields will vary from year to year and even from field to field, but Table 4.IV gives attainable figures in the U.K.

TABLE 4.IV.  Typical Yields of Crops with and
without Irrigation (Tonnes/hectare)

| Crop | Rain alone | Rain and irrigation | Increase, % |
|------|------------|---------------------|-------------|
| Cauliflower | 21.6 | 28.8 | 34 |
| Early potatoes | 13.3 | 18.5 | 40 |
| Peas | 10.3 | 16.0 | 56 |

*Source:* Taylor, J. A. 1970 "The role of water in agriculture",
Pergamon Press, London.

Not all soils are suitable for irrigation, but irrigation demands must be expected to grow at perhaps 1-2 per cent per annum to the end of the century. The timing of irrigation demands varies with the crop. Onions and spring cabbage, for example, require water in March, but celery needs water from May to September.

Crops have varying tolerances to river water quality and upstream consents to discharge to rivers used for irrigation may need to have regard to the concentration of boron and certain other substances.

## RECREATION AND AMENITY

As affluence increases, the preference for more leisure will grow, and the demand for all forms of recreation will also grow. Unfortunately, the wish for cheap effluent treatment can conflict with the demand for fishing; fishing can conflict with the demands for boating, and boating with the need for land drainage.

The efficient management of the river systems will thus depend in part on good forecasting of all the demands.

The Central Water Planning Unit, in their Technical Note No. 13[24], summarized most of the available information on the benefits of recreation and further findings have been published by Gibson[25] and in the Trent Economic Model[26]. Most researchers have found a logical link between demand and distance travelled to the recreation activity, and have assessed benefits using the Clawson approach[27] but more survey work is required and a general policy as to how the expense of recreational development is to be funded is needed.

## 4. INVESTMENT DECISIONS

### INTRODUCTION

Engineering is mostly concerned with transforming one set of resources into another of higher value as efficiently as possible. By taking natural materials like clay and timber and using men to convert, assemble and construct works from these and other raw materials, value is added to the nation's wealth which can be used, consumed or enjoyed. The more the total value of the products created (benefits) exceed the total labour and material resources used up (costs), the more affluent the country becomes.

Usually, costs and benefits are measured by market value, that is the pound notes that would be paid when or if a resource is sold, e.g. a gallon of petrol. At times of inflation, however, the number of pound notes paid for a resource will change year by year, even though the resource, i.e. the gallon of petrol, remains the same. *Economic analysis is concerned with resources: financial analysis with pound notes*, and it is possible for financial and economic analyses to justify different solutions. Financial analysis must consider inflation: economic analysis needs only to consider relative changes in costs.

## COSTS AND BENEFITS

Cost benefit analysis is readily associated with land drainage and flood alleviation projects where it is less difficult to estimate benefits than in other areas. Cost benefit analysis is undertaken to determine firstly whether benefits exceed costs, and secondly, in what proportion. When resources are limited those projects with the highest benefit-cost ratio should be undertaken first. For example, if land drainage works costing £100 000 can raise the value of land by £150 000, the benefit cost ratio is 1.5, and this scheme should be ranked before another costing £200 000, but yielding only £280 000.

Flood alleviation schemes are considered in the same way, except that a further variable—the degree of flood protection—is introduced. In addition, flood schemes are implemented not only to realize the potential of land, but in some cases to reduce the probability of damage, loss of property, or even loss of life. The cost of flood protection against a very rare flood with return period of once in 100 years will be much greater than for one of once in five years, but the benefits arising from the gain in flood protection may not increase at the same rate as the costs. Thus, it becomes necessary to seek an optimum, and the optimum flood frequency will vary according to the type and extent of the property to be protected. Buildings and built-up areas generally merit high levels of flood protection from about 1 in 25 years upwards, according to the potential damage that could be caused. The Thames tidal barrier protecting London, for example, is designed to give 1 in 1 000 year protection in the year 2030, whilst Nottingham on the river Trent has 1 in 100 year protection.

Alleviation of flooding of agricultural land depends on the latent potential of the soil, and the optimum level rarely exceeds 1 in 10 years unless there is an associated risk of loss of life[28].

Flooding can also cause disruption to traffic, services, and community life generally, and even anxiety and stress. An interesting paper by Bennet[29] linked a flood in Bristol in 1968 with an increase in deaths, notably cancer, postulating psychological distress as a cause. In so far that a community would pay to avoid disruption, it is a proper benefit of flood protection and may be included in the analysis, although its value will be difficult to assign. The most detailed work on flood economics in this country has been undertaken by the Local Government Operational Research Unit[30] and by staff at Middlesex Polytechnic[31] who not only explain the theoretical basis of analysis but suggest costs for different types of property damage, for loss of time, and for other related costs, and document the effect of actual floods in detail.

In theory, it should be possible to apply cost benefit analysis to revelant water supply and sewage disposal schemes. For example, the decision to provide a first-time water supply to a rural community could be made on cost benefit grounds. The principal benefit might be a reduction in the risk of sickness and loss of life, but it is difficult to assess both the reduction in risk and the value of life. Similarly, it is not easy to compare benefits arising from reliable and less reliable sources in time of drought.

The decision to provide main drainage is also justified principally on health grounds and improvements to sewage works effluents to gains to environment and recreational interests.

None of the benefits listed above, however, is easy to value and the problems associated with cost benefit analysis are diagnosed neatly by Self in the case for the Third London Airport[32]. Although work is continuing on the measurement of benefits, especially those arising in the field of transportation (DoE[33]), the only practical method at present is to describe the benefits and give the costs, and seek a judgement from the consumer or his representatives.

## RATE OF RETURN

Whilst costs often occur substantially at the beginning of a project, benefits frequently arise over a period of years. The increased value of land or any new asset is determined by its increased yield and the "going rate", i.e. the annual percentage return, for similar ventures carrying similar degrees of risk. Thus, in the example above, the annual increase in yield required to justify an increase in land value of £150 000 if the "going rate" were 8 per cent (per annum), would be £12 000. The benefit-cost ratio of 1.5 in the example is equivalent to a rate of return of 12 per cent (8 per cent × 1.5) and schemes may be measured either by ratio or rate of return. More complex examples can be found in ICE[34], and in Kuiper[35].

For public sector projects the Government, in a 1967 White Paper[36], set the minimum acceptable "going rate" at what it believed was the normal real return on "low risk" projects in private industry. Then 8 per cent, the *Test Discount Rate* (TDR) as it was called, was later raised to 10 per cent. The 1978 White Paper[37] on the Nationalized Industries replaced TDR with a *Required Rate of Return* (RRR) applicable to new investment as a whole. Initially set at 5 per cent, RRR will be reviewed within 3 to 5 years. The Government argues that the public sector should not undertake investment whose rate of return is less than can be achieved in private industry, before tax, for this will be wasteful of resources. In other words, the public sector should have regard to alternative "opportunities" elsewhere, and the RRR is another term for what economists call the "opportunity cost" of capital.

The RRR can, of course, be used as a rationing tool. High rates could cut public sector expenditure by limiting capital investment to schemes capable of a high rate of return. Low rates would encourage expenditure by the public sector, possibly at private industry's expense.

## PAY NOW OR LATER—DISCOUNTING

In the water industry, however, it is more usual to be faced with two or more alternative proposals which achieve the same objective, e.g. a new supply of water. The benefits will be the same for all options and the benefit cost ratio is not calculated. The exercise is then to seek a solution at least overall cost. Often the alternatives will vary, with one having higher capital costs and the other higher operating costs. It may be to choose a large dam or a phased groundwater scheme; to stage a pipeline or not; to continue repairing a main or replace it; to use lagoons or a sludge press; and even whether to convert WC cisterns to dual flush or supply more water. The essential economic problem is to balance the advantage of using resources now against using a greater quantity of resources over the life of the scheme.

There is a general agreement that society weighs the cost of say, 20 man years of work required in 10 years time less than 20 man years required now, but there has been great debate by how much the cost should be reduced or "discounted". 20 man years of work 10 years hence would in fact be written down to 7.7 man years discounting at 10 per cent per annum, 12.3 man years at 5 per cent, and 16.4 man years at 2 per cent. These figures would be referred to as the "present value" or "present worth" of the work.

Selection of a discount rate can have a dramatic effect on the choice of scheme[38]. The current opinion is, however, that a figure of about 5 per cent is about correct for most use in this country[37, 38, 39]. Some economists hold the view that this figure

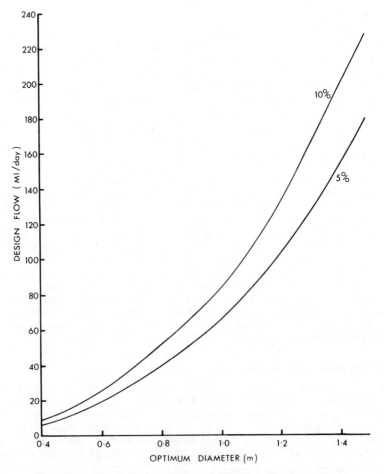

Fig. 4.11.  Pipeline size: effect of different discount rates

equates to the "social time preference rate", and should be expected to remain constant over many years.

Whatever its basis, the discount rate has a different purpose from RRR. Whereas RRR provides a measure of whether to proceed with a project, the discount rate gives guidance on the use of resources over time.

The mechanism of discounting has been explained by many authors, including the ICE[34]. Davies[40] has shown its application to gravity pipelines and Paine and White[41] and Greenwood[42] have applied it to pumping mains. One considerable advantage of the technique is that it can accommodate operating costs which can be greater than the capital cost themselves. For example, annual operating costs of one-tenth capital cost are equivalent to double the capital cost when the discount rate is 5 per cent. Any costs, capital or operating, occurring in say year 10 can be converted to a present value by dividing by $(1 + i)^{10}$ where $i$ is the discount rate, and added to the other costs occurring in different years, converted in the same way.

The effect of the discount rate on optimum pipeline size is illustrated for one specific set of C values, power tariffs, etc., in Fig. 4.11.

## To Build Big or Small!—Staging

Generally, the bigger the works, the less the average cost per unit of capacity, due to the economies of scale. On the other hand, the bigger the works the longer does its full capacity remain unused, using extra resources that could have been better employed elsewhere.

The Water Research Centre have published several scale factors for different types of works in TR 61[43] using the general formula—

$$Cost = Constant \times (Capacity)^s$$

Examples of the value of "$s$" the scale factor are:

| Works | | | Scale factor |
|---|---|---|---|
| Service reservoir (conventional) ... | ... | ... | 0.64 |
| Sewage treatment works ... | ... | ... | 0.82 |
| Water supply pumping stations ... | ... | 0.79 |

Thus, the cost of a conventional sewage treatment works built to last 20 years could be written $£K \times (20)^{0.82}$, where $K$ is a constant. The same works built in two stages at 10-year intervals, however (assuming straight line growth—which does not always apply) would cost in discounted or "present worth" terms:—

$$£K \times (10)^{0.82} + \frac{£K \times (10)^{0.82}}{(1 + i)^{10}}$$

where $i$ is the discount rate

The two alternatives would be compared to decide whether or not to stage.

In practice, a general formula can be developed for works staged for any number of years $(Y)$ for any scale factors $(s)$ and any discount rate $(i)$, assuming straight line growth, so that:—

$$\frac{Present}{Worth} = Constant \times Y^s (1 - \frac{1}{(1 + i)^Y}) - 1$$

The optimum staging interval can be found for any known value of "$s$", and selected value of "$i$", by graphical plotting or interpolation of Table 4.V.

Thus, the theoretical optimum staging interval for sewage works ($s = 0.82$, $i = 5$ per cent) would be about 8 years.

TABLE 4.V.   **Theoretical Optimum Staging Intervals** (years)

| Discount rate, % | Scale factor | | | | |
|---|---|---|---|---|---|
| | 0.9 | 0.8 | 0.7 | 0.6 | 0.5 |
| 12 | 2 | 4 | 6 | 8 | 11 |
| 10 | 2 | 5 | 7 | 10 | 12 |
| 8 | 3 | 6 | 9 | 12 | 16 |
| 6 | 4 | 7 | 12 | 16 | 22 |
| 5 | 4 | 9 | 14 | 19 | 25 |
| 4 | 5 | 11 | 17 | 24 | 32 |
| 2 | 11 | 22 | 34 | 48 | 64 |

These figures need to be treated with due caution. Some works cannot be extended without considerable disturbance to the public or disruption to works operation. Sometimes there are advantages in building big. Large sewage works for example may produce a better than designed effluent provided they are not grossly under-loaded, although low flow rates can lead to septicity in sewers and operational problems and high unit costs at rural works. Works built too large of course may preclude the use of new technology.

## LIMITING YOUR MISTAKE—SENSITIVITY TESTING

Sensitivity testing has two purposes:—

(1) To identify the factors most critical to the choice between alternative schemes so that attention can be focused on their accuracy.
(2) To assess the possibility of one or more factors (the forecast of growth of demand, discount rate, design parameter, etc.) being wrong, so that the consequences of error can be minimized.

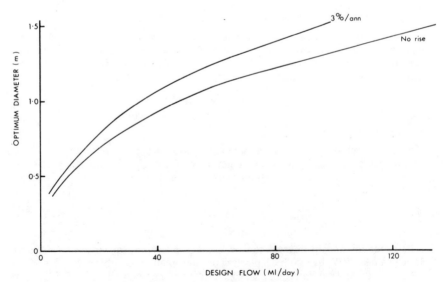

Fig. 4.12.   **Pipeline size—effect of rise in power costs**

For example, the most critical factor in the choice of pumping main is likely to be the trend in fuel prices. Energy is a scarce resource and some believe it could increase in real value relative to the cost of pipeline construction, by as much as 3 per cent per annum. The effect of a 1, 2 or 3 per cent rise compounded annually would be to increase the unit cost of electricity to 122, 148 and 181 per cent of present-day prices after 20 years. Fig. 4.12 shows the effect of such a change on optimum pipeline size, again for specific C, power tariff, and other values.

As to purpose (2), suppose despite a soil survey, the corrosive nature of ground remains uncertain. Sleeving a pipe or providing cathodic protection would be a known extra expense, whilst the consequences of not taking precautions could be corrosion leading to premature replacement after, say, 15 years. The choice reduces to weighing the extra cost of protection against the discounted cost of the replacement pipe (including the costs of disturbance), which will depend on estimated life and pipe route. The relative risk and consequent costs may be acceptable in a rural area but unacceptable in an urban area.

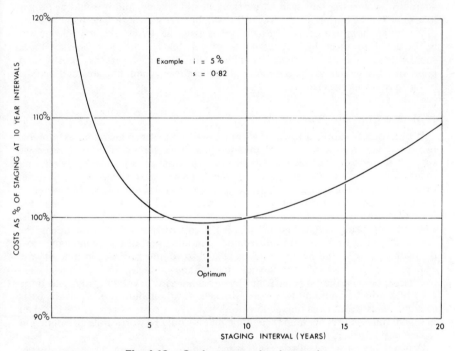

**Fig. 4.13.  Optimum staging interval**

The consequence of error in the forecast may be relatively modest. Works capacity may suffice for longer or less than the economic optimum, but fortunately the optimum curve (Fig. 4.13) plotted from the formula on p. 165 is relatively flat and the error is limited to 6-7 per cent even if the outcome is half or double the forecast made, although this 6-7 per cent may represent a large sum over a number of schemes. Real waste of resources occurs, however, if the forecast growth never occurs. Where there is any doubt of the growth, or any prospect of premature obsolescence of the technology (e.g. in the fast developing telemetry field), it is prudent to *under* rather than over provide; to consider the use of construction materials with limited life, or to use units which can be transported elsewhere. Any error in the forecast will, of course, be reflected in the consequent costs and it is sometimes a valuable exercise to present the possible range of costs at the time of presenting a scheme, and indeed to weigh the accuracy of the costs especially if one alternative is venturing on new ground[44].

## TO PATCH OR REPLACE

The decision to replace old plant with new which is more efficient, or to go for "cost saving" schemes like automation or some other change in working practice, is made on essentially the same grounds as a dam versus a groundwater scheme. A high capital cost option is being compared to another with higher operating costs. Note that any costs that have been incurred (the "sunk" costs), play no part in the analysis which is solely concerned with future expenditure. Frequently, the proposed alternative will be less labour intensive than the old scheme, and it would be proper to assume (in the option not to proceed) that labour costs will rise, perhaps by 3 per cent per annum in real terms if historic trends continue. Often, the new scheme will be expected to meet higher standards of reliability, and may provide more sophisticated control, reducing standby, call out and emergency costs, and improving the service to the consumer. These are true economic gains and may be included to justify the change.

## IS WASTE CONTROL WORTHWHILE?

If two sources supply a town, the "marginal" cost of producing an extra cubic metre of water will be the cost of the more expensive supply as the less expensive supply will normally be fully committed first. Marginal costs are especially relevant in the economics of waste detection. Suppose that a new waste detection district is set up and waste found to be 200 m³/day. Suppose the level is reduced to an average of 100 m³/day and held there for a year. The water saved will be 36 500 m³, and the immediate cost savings will be equivalent to the production cost, what the economist calls the 'short run marginal cost", that is the cost of chemicals for treatment; the cost of all power from source to distribution; and that part of the maintenance cost of treatment works and pumps which is related to volume rather than time, if any. The production cost will not include debt charges, wages, or any other fixed overheads, because they are unaffected by any change in the volume produced. If the costs of production amount to 2 p/m³, the savings will amount to £730. If the costs of regular waste meter reading and inspection, plus the costs of repair, are less than £730, not only is the programme economic, but it would be worthwhile attempting to reduce waste further.

Demand in the waste district will grow. Suppose peak demand in the district reaches a rate of 1 000 m³/day and is growing at 2 per cent or 20 m³/day/annum, so that a new main costing £10 000 has to be considered unless total demand can be held to 1 000 m³/day. This would mean reducing waste by 20 m³/day, i.e. from 100 to 80 m³/day. The value of deferring expenditure one year has been shown earlier to be

$$£10\,000 \times (1 - \frac{1}{1.05})$$ or about £480, using a discount rate of 5 per cent. The

immediate cost savings, i.e. the production cost of the water saved, would be £146 (20 m³/day × 2 p/m³ × 365) but the total value would be £626 (= £146 + £480). If waste can be reduced by 20 m³/day for less than this sum, the works should be deferred for at least one year by intensifying the waste effort. For this year the "marginal" value of the water saved will rise from 2p to about 8.6 p/m³ (£626 ÷ (365 × 20)). The effects of water savings on capital as well as running costs have profound effects on waste control decisions.

In an integrated water supply network where either source works, trunk mains, treatment works or service reservoirs are added every year, a policy to reduce waste permanently will have a long term effect on the capital works programme. In such a case the value of the waste reduction will equate to what is called the "long run marginal cost", and this can be calculated by comparing the present worth costs of that part of the capital works programme required to provide new demand to the planning horizon, with and without change in waste detection effort. The discounted costs would of course include operating costs. The method of calculation is demonstrated in an interesting example by the NWC Working Group on Waste of Water[45].

Generally, the marginal value of waste detection is highest in areas where new works are imminent, and higher in areas served by more expensive treatment works or supplied to higher elevations. Waste effort is normally given priority in this order of ranking.

PROJECT APPRAISAL

Finding and justifying the best way to meet additional demands for water services by the construction of capital works is an area of work known as Project Appraisal. Project Appraisal seeks answers to four questions.

Why is the works necessary?
What will it achieve?
How was it chosen in preference to other alternatives?
When is it required?

These questions provide a useful summary of this section.

## 5. CHARGING POLICY

INTRODUCTION

Current charging schemes and possible developments in those schemes are described in Chapter 5. This section discusses the reasons why a charging "policy" is necessary, what it can achieve, and the economic principles on which policy may be based.

Charging policy in the water industry may have one or more of three main aims. At its simplest the sole aim may be to recover costs at the least administrative expense. The second aim is to recover costs equitably between consumers. Thus, although it is more expensive to collect revenue through domestic metering this may be a price worth paying for greater equity. Thirdly, charging policy can be used to influence demand. High prices could curb demand and low prices encourage it.

The ideal charging policy would achieve these three aims simultaneously. In practice the ideal cannot be achieved and charging policy is a compromise. In the U.K. it must satisfy the Water Act 1973, in particular that (a) the charge for each service should have regard to the cost of providing it, and (b) after 1st April 1981 charges must not discriminate unduly between classes of persons. This Section attempts to explain the various factors behind charging policy and how it would be possible to move closer to the ideal in some areas.

## THE PROBLEMS OF EQUITY

Behind all the current disputes on incomes lies the question, what is equitable? Should lower paid workers be given more because their needs are greater? Should skilled workers be paid more because their economic worth is higher? Should the highly paid be taxed more severely than the lower paid? Each view is coloured by position and experience. Equity is, after all, only what people believe to be fair. Charging for water on the basis of rateable value is considered fair to many because the rich on average pay more per litre than the poor. Others, pointing to the single occupant living next door to and paying the same as a large family, believe metering is a better method.

Most believe that it is right to make the same charge for the same service, yet houses on remote hills impose higher costs for the same service than those in compact towns. Should equitable charges then be based on a uniform price or costs imposed?

In sewage disposal there is a simple view that "the polluter should pay", but the polluter will explain that the people who purchase his products actually pay, and the beneficiaries of his treatment may only be a few fishermen. Should the fishermen pay more to maintain the river?

Equity may be judged by historical, social, or economic criteria and there is no consensus view. The water industry is reluctant to change its charging methods because that change may disturb the widespread acceptance of charging schemes which, though imperfect, are widely understood.

## RATEABLE VALUE BASED CHARGES

In Britain almost all household water supplies, some commercial water supplies, most foul and storm sewage and sewage disposal services (apart from industrial effluents) and most environmental services, are charged for on the basis of *Rateable Value* (RV). They are, in fact, a tax on property, not a charge for water use, and discrepancies are shown clearly in Fig. 4.6. This charge has a long history, arising from the original concept of the water industry as a social service. It is supported even today when the historical campaigns against poor sanitation and water-borne disease are long over, when the quantity of consumption is much higher than that needed to maintain life and health, and when other essentials of life like food and heat are acceptably distributed by the market.

This charging method is cheap to operate and its acceptability turns on the "fit" between the scale of payment and service taken, which, although poor for individual consumers, is reasonable for RV bands as demonstrated by the Malvern and Mansfield Study (Fig. 4.6)[10]. The fit could be better if a two-part tariff were used.

So long as the unmetered consumer pays his water rates, however, he can have as much water as he likes. The "marginal" cost to him of the extra water used and thus its price, is zero, but to the water undertaker the "marginal" cost will be at least the cost of treatment and pumping, and ultimately the cost of bringing forward new works.

Some consumers may, therefore, misuse water and others may use more than they would if required to pay the full cost.

The effect of RV charges is likely to lead to some additional consumption—how much we do not know—with consequent demands for investment which consume more resources than consumers' demands justify, and which could otherwise have been diverted to say, hospitals or other services with greater need.

The RV charges also deprive management of information necessary for efficient decision-making. If all water services were charged by price rather than tax, excessive investment would raise charges more than consumers would be prepared to pay. As a result, demand would be curbed and revenue lost, providing management with a powerful incentive to economy. Such signals from consumer to supplier and vice versa would help the water industry to allocate resources more efficiently, but so long as supply failures are penalized more heavily than excessive investment, managers will be motivated to be safe, not efficient.

In the absence of these price signals, economic efficiency can only be promoted by encouraging consumers to indicate their preferences for the standards of service they desire through representation on the boards of water undertakers, consultation, market research and attitude surveys.

## CURRENT METERED CHARGES

Most industrial, agricultural, and some commercial users pay for water supply by volume and most water discharged from industrial processes is charged for as a trade effluent by volume and strength. This is more efficient and more equitable than the RV-based charges but more expensive to administer, especially in respect of trade effluent which involves the costs of regular sampling.

The charges however are based on average costs which include debt charges founded on historical rather than replacement values of assets. It is believed that this average unit cost is less than the "marginal" cost of providing additional supplies. If this is true, the current charges, while more efficient than RV charges, are still liable to inflate demand.

The effect of inefficient pricing is to *increase* costs and charges above what would otherwise be required.

## MARGINAL COSTS

The marginal cost of supply or disposal is the cost of an extra unit at the "margin" of demand, that is the next increment of output. When this increment of output requires no change in plant size, the cost, as was shown on p. 168 is (for water supply) the short run marginal cost, i.e. the cost of treatment and pumping only.

To illustrate the properties of short-run marginal costs, take the example of pumping through a pipeline. It will be remembered that unit pumping costs vary with throughput. Using the Hazen-Williams formula for friction losses in a pipeline, it may be shown that power costs are proportional to $Q^{2.85}$ where $Q$ is the throughput. This means that whilst average power costs per unit pumped are proportional to $Q^{1.85}$, marginal power costs per unit pumped are proportional to $2.85\,Q^{1.85}$, as can be seen in Fig. 4.14. The interested reader can also demonstrate that when capital charges for the pipeline are added to power costs, the average cost per unit pumped equals the short run marginal cost when the pipeline is working at the optimal point. At higher throughputs, marginal cost exceeds average cost.

The significance of Fig. 4.14 for charging is that it demonstrates how the *Short Run Marginal Cost* (SRMC) can rise as spare capacity is taken up becoming very large when a new pipeline is required and then reducing to a new low level when it has been installed.

Due to this continuous fluctuation, SRMC is not a satisfactory basis for charging and economists advocate charging on the basis of *Long Run Marginal Cost* (LRMC) which smooths out the short term variations by spreading the injection of capital over the increased output. For in practice, a new works will be built large enough to absorb not only the immediate increment of demand but all anticipated increments for perhaps 10 years ahead. It is cheaper to do it this way due to the economies of scale (p. 165) resulting in long periods of surplus capacity when SRMC is relatively

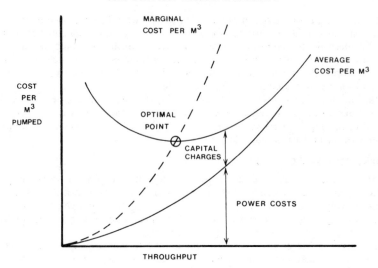

Fig. 4.14.  Pumping costs for pipeline of given diameter

low. There will also be occasional periods of shortage when SRMC is extremely high. But overall, if investment is optimal average SRMC should equal LRMC.

There are various ways to apportion the costs over all increments of demand over the period ahead and alternatives have been put forward by the Water Resources Board[46], Saunders et al[47], Turvey[48] and others. The LRMC so derived is a better basis for charging than SRMC, as explained by Walker[49], and provides a satisfactory compromise between price stability and economic efficiency.

Marginal costs could be calculated for each separate supply and drainage network, and would differ considerably. Here we would run foul of the objectives of equity and administrative simplicity, for consumers within an undertaking's area would not expect to pay different charges, and separate calculations would be expensive. Equalization of charges then normally conflicts with economic efficiency.

### APPLICATION OF MARGINAL COSTING

Despite the difficulties and imperfections, charging on some basis that approximates to marginal cost is to be preferred. See the White Papers[36, 37], the Third Jukes Report[50], Rees[51], Webb[52], and Boiteux[53].

In so far that marginal costs are likely to be higher than present unit charges, a surplus of revenue would be generated unless a two-part tariff were used, as discussed in[50] and by Williams[54]. However, charging the last few units of demand only at a high cost might result in unpredictable variations in revenue, and some interesting problems would arise in deciding the ration of low cost units.

Marginal costing can also be used to influence peak demands. Some direct abstraction charging schemes are designed to encourage winter and to discourage summer consumption, and large users supplied from the mains could be subject to a tariff, such as those employed by the electricity industry and telephone service, to encourage "off peak" use. The marginal costs in this case would include that localized part of the distribution network designed on an instantaneous peak basis. Several fascinating schemes in use on the Continent in this context are listed in a series of booklets entitled "European Plumbing Notes"[55].

### ELASTICITY OF DEMAND—DOMESTIC METERING

The administrative and equity arguments for and against domestic metering have been given earlier, and clearly charging by volume would assist the aims of economic efficiency. Paradoxically, metering may not be economic due to the additional expense of providing, installing, and maintaining meters, and reading and billing. In their appraisal of universal domestic metering, the National Water Council[56] compared the cost of metering per unit of water saved with the estimated cost of supply and disposal of additional supplies which would otherwise have been required. Their conclusion was crucially dependent on the permanent saving in water consumption, which in that exercise was assumed to be 20 per cent. Middleton *et al*[57] explained how metering decisions should be appraised and concluded that one should not be "for" or "against" metering, but should treat each case on its merits.

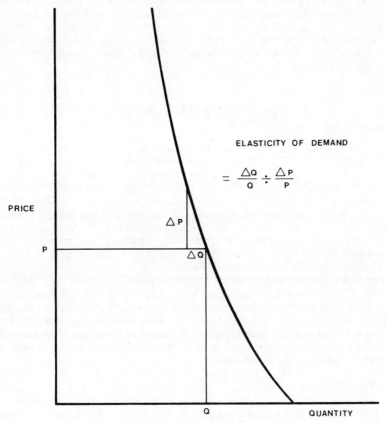

**Fig. 4.15. Demand curve**

A typical demand curve for water showing the quantity a consumer is willing to buy at each price is shown in Fig. 4.15. The shape of the curve in British conditions is not known at present.

Foreign evidence confirms that demand (the *quantity* of a commodity consumers are willing to buy at a particular *price*) falls as the price rises but conclusions on the effect of water metering in the U.K. are mixed. See Rees[58], Phillips and Kershaw[8], Smith[59] and, for international evidence, Hanke[49].

Whether metering would be economic in the U.K. or not depends on water's "elasticity of demand". If a 20 per cent increase in charge provokes a 10 per cent decrease in use, the elasticity is —0.5. Most water for domestic use is supplied effectively at zero price, and although U.S. experience suggests that the elasticity of "inside" household use is about —0.2 at prices ruling, it is not clear what impact "first time" metering would have. This can only be determined by experiment.

## THE ROLE OF MANAGEMENT

In Britain water charges have a greater influence over the standards of service demanded than the quantity of water demanded. Whether charging policy will curb quantity demanded in the future remains to be seen. The economic principles which influence charging policy are unambiguous, but practical application is subject to measurement problems, and conflicts between objectives. The role of management is to initiate research and to seek the best compromise through the exercise of judgement. Such judgements are best made in the context of an ordered view of ends, means, and constraints. The provision of this ordered context is the function of corporate planning.

# 6. CORPORATE PLANNING

## INTRODUCTION

The application of corporate planning to water was first discussed in the Second Jukes Report in 1974[60], and was subsequently endorsed in Department of the Environment Circular 142/74[61]. Corporate planning is the means by which all aspects of the water services are brought together to devise a strategy for the future, balancing the need for investment against charges and other constraints. Planning takes as its starting point the objectives of the undertaking, interprets them as policies and priorities, and explicitly devises programmes of action and targets to meet future demands. The physical and technical aspects of investment proposals are considered alongside the financial and economic consequences, so that the implications for charges may be clearly seen.

The planner, at regional, divisional or company level acts rather like the navigator on the bridge of a ship, considering alternative routes and the inevitable consequences. Corporate planning provides a water authority with a framework whereby it can account systematically to its consumers and government for the money it spends and the action it takes. It enables the planning efforts of various disciplines to be co-ordinated, and so corporate planning is practised in some form for much of the time by most managers.

## PLANNING CYCLE

Planning is a series of activities linked one with another in cyclical fashion (Fig. 4.16). Forecasts of demand have to be made in terms of both quantity and the levels of service to be provided.

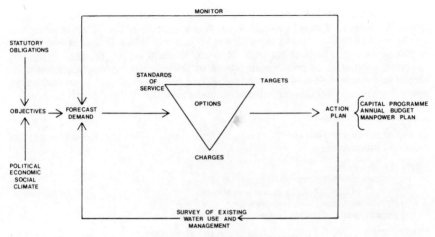

**Fig. 4.16.  Planning cycle**

Defining levels of service is a practical means of bringing existing situations and future requirements onto a common scale of measurement so that priorities can be determined and targets set. Monitoring, which is an essential part of planning, will identify shortfalls and provide a means of controlling progress. Feedback from monitoring also enables adjustments to forecasts and policies to be made in the light of the latest information.

Annual budgets for revenue and manpower provide the vital link between plans and execution. Formerly, the annual budget was primarily a financial exercise. Because it reflects the financial effect of policy decisions on capital investment, it is now regarded as part of the planning process, providing a bridge from planning to execution and control. Likewise, the manpower budget demonstrates the manning consequences of future plans. Annual budgets are tied to the corporate plan, but financial timing and tactics normally lie outside the strategic planning process.

Planning is a dynamic process involving continuous re-evaluation of a changing scene in which only the water authority's objectives remain relatively stable from year to year. A plan is therefore a "snapshot" in the planning process.

### WATER AUTHORITY OBJECTIVES

The water industry's objectives follow from statutory obligations and from political and social pressures, in which public opinion is an important force. No objective has absolute priority, although measures to safeguard health come very high. Most are expressed in general terms so that flesh has to be added to the bare bones of the statements to generate detailed definitions of service which can be quantified and measured. Whereas the objectives of a water authority describe the general direction in which it intends to move, it is the target level of service which maps out the destination and enables progress along the way to be monitored.

The standard of water resource reliability is a good example. The drought in 1976 brought the public face to face with the dilemma of how "reliable" a water supply should be. The general view seemed to be that the standard was acceptable so long as piped supplies could be spun out by voluntary reductions, but that restriction to stand-pipe supplies was tantamount to failure. That complete certainty of supply can only be provided at infinite cost is not a conclusion that either the public or their political leaders find easy to comprehend. It is analogous to the "I never thought it would happen to me" syndrome which is so common when individuals are faced with a rare event. The problem with flood and drought is that, though infrequent, the population affected press for improvements which may be totally uneconomic. Continual failure to maintain a standard service even to small groups of consumers may merit special attention on political grounds, although it is not strictly economic.

## LEVELS OF SERVICE

As suggested by Thackray[49], there are four types of demand for water services requiring investment:—

Demand arising from:—
   (i) Maintenance of current levels of service.
  (ii) Growth of throughput by existing consumers.
 (iii) Provision of services to new consumers.
  (iv) Improvements in quality and reliability of service.

In practice, there is limited discretion in the allocation of resources to (i) and (ii), and at the moment little opportunity to manage demand and therefore growth of throughput by price. The options reduce to variations in (iii) and (iv). Even in (iii), the provision of services to new housing and industrial development is largely automatic and it is only "first time" piped services to existing rural properties over which there is debate. The greatest area for choice is therefore (iv) in such things as the reliability of supply, the quality of sewage works effluents, and so on. The object is to set these demands which raise the standard of service to the consumer in order of priority. The Department of the Environment jointly with Water Authorities has

TABLE 4.VI.  **Purpose Classification of Capital Expenditure**

| Purpose | 1978-79, £million |
|---|---|
| To meet public health requirements (including health and safety of employees) | 12.7 |
| To maintain or replace the existing system (at present levels of service and environmental standards) | 91.2 |
| To meet growth in demand by existing consumers (at present levels of service and environmental standards) | 63.0 |
| To increase operating efficiency (through cost savings) | 10.2 |
| To meet anticipated housing development (including infilling) <br> To meet anticipated commercial and industrial development | 145.3 |
| To improve the present quality of potable water supply rivers <br> To improve the present quality of other non-tidal rivers <br> To improve the present quality of estuarial waters and beaches <br> To improve the present quality of coastal waters and beaches | 38.9 |
| To improve present levels of service to the consumer | 46.9 |
| To improve recreational facilities and amenities (including fishing) | 1.9 |
| To provide first-time services to existing properties | 5.3 |
| To achieve other purposes | 14.4 |

*Sources:* Department of the Environment 1977, Guidance on water authorities' annual plans and programmes to be submitted under Section 24 of the Water Act 1973.
National Water Council 1978, water industry review

developed a purpose classification (Table 4.VI). In absolute terms the list is roughly in order of priority. In 1978-79, however, £12.7 million will be spent on public health, whereas £38.9 million will be spent reducing pollution and this emphasizes that priority is not an absolute but a matter of degree, consequence, and cost.

The most impressive justification for any scheme is brought out by asking the promoter of a project the searching negative question—What are the consequences of not going ahead? The risk of pathogens in water supplies, with the potential devastating implications of water-borne disease, is rightly weighted far more heavily than, say, the risk of inadequate water supply pressure. The significant distinction is between preserving health and consumer confidence on the one hand and providing a better service on the other. In either case, the relative value of investment is most readily judged by reference to accepted standards of service. A situation requiring additional sewerage to solve a flooding problem, and a water supply pressure deficiency requiring mains reinforcement, for example, are difficult to compare, but the choice is assisted if standards of flooding frequency and water pressure have previously been established as practicable and economically justifiable minima. The gap between actual and standard will also be a guide to the relative urgency of works.

The question then remains whether standards for the water services should be uniform or left to local decision. Walker[49] concluded that it was difficult to delegate the fixing of standards to operating divisions of a Water Authority, due to the uniformity of service consumers expect to receive across an area where charges are equal, although national and even international standards might be appropriate for wholesomeness. The move towards uniformity, however, may be conducted slowly and selectively for attitudes and expectations will vary. City dwellers, for example, may expect higher standards than rural water users, and one of the skills of the water manager is to detect these local variations. Local decisions are more acceptable for effluent standards affecting river quality, now being reviewed on the basis of the assimilative capacity and use of the river.

Standards should be fixed from the consumer's rather than the operator's point of view. A consumer is not interested in how many hours' storage are provided in the service reservoir but he is concerned at the frequency of interruption to his supply. The water industry is currently endeavouring to determine appropriate minimum standards[62]. Table 4.VII gives some of the main areas under consideration with possible standards, bearing in mind that many different standards can apply (e.g. the difference between urban and rural). In practice, an acceptable minimum will often reduce to "what people are used to" and criticism will be muted if managers show concern and understanding and take the trouble to apologize for inconvenience caused.

The practical difficulty of fixing standards should not be under-estimated. Market research could be used, but consumers do change their minds. Moreover, the consequences of failure leading to water-borne disease are so traumatic that the professional view must prevail. The fundamental advantage of standards in this context is that they bring out into the open what service can reasonably be expected and acknowledge that perfect performance is impossible. Thus, unwarranted demands for expenditure can be resisted from without as well as from within the industry.

The use of standards as a test of whether or not to proceed with new works is now developing in the industry. Davies[63] suggests an approach whereby standards are used to determine the degree of actual or potential deficiency and thus the priority of remedial action. For instance, a measure of the significance of a mains reinforcement

### TABLE 4.VII.  Standards of Service

| Service | Minimum standard |
|---|---|
| Water resources | *Reliability:* Traditionally full yield except in droughts more severe than 1 in 50 or 1 in 100 years. In future may be defined by frequency of restriction, e.g. hose pipe ban 1 year in 10, Section 1 Drought Act 1976 restrictions 1 year in 25, etc., with standpipes and rota cuts less than once a lifetime. |
| | *Raw Water Quality:* Minimum qualities recommended by EEC or the NWC in "River water quality—the next stage, review of discharge consent conditions" (1978). |
| Water supply | *Interruption (a)* Planned: Probably 3 or 4 times in 2 years |
| | *(b)* Unplanned: Action required at greater than 1 in 2 years, less in rural areas. Pressures often 15 m residential, 25 m industrial, normally, with restrictions at high points not exceeding 2 hr, 2 or 3 times a year. Probably no minimum standard at times of peak sprinkling demand. |
| | *Quality:* Action in all cases not complying with WHO European standards, HMSO Report No. 71—Bacteriological examination of water supplies and future EEC directives. |
| | *Dirty Water/Infestation:* Investigate all persistent complaints. |
| Sewerage | *Foul flooding:* Action in all instances involving public health risk. |
| | *Storm water flooding:* Dependent on cost benefit analysis of potential damage caused, but often one flood/year is accepted. |
| Sewage disposal | *Effluent:* Investigate failure to comply generally with consent standard or coastal pollution parameters. |
| | *Nuisance (odour, flies):* Investigate persistent or recurring nuisance. Level of nuisance will depend on locality. |
| Land drainage | *Flood frequency:* Dependent on cost benefit analysis. |
| | *Flood warning:* Minimum of 6 hr if potential loss of life. |

scheme may be expressed in points which give credit to the duration and frequency of inadequate pressure and to the population affected. For example:—

$$\text{Points} = \frac{1}{\text{Actual \% days tested when pressure less than 15 m}} \times \text{population}$$

Such evaluation of physical factors helps to quantify the benefits of restoring standards by installing works and by means of the simple formula:—

$$\text{Priority} = \text{Points} \div \text{Cost}$$

schemes may be ranked in priority order. This order may be deliberately adjusted if there are other unquantifiable factors, e.g. political pressure, history of neglect, etc., to be taken into account. It would be obviously wrong to choose the schemes with high points values and hence high benefits if they individually cost too much. Hence, dividing by cost recognizes it as a constraint.

In the formula, cost is taken as capital plus discounted operating costs less discounted operated savings. Thus, capital intensive schemes do not receive unfair treatment as well they might if cost were taken only as pure capital cost. Due account is also taken of cost saving schemes.

### WATER AUTHORITY ANNUAL PLANS

The statutory obligations of regional water authorities to prepare plans and programmes are specified in Section 24(1) of the Water Act 1973. The principal planning requirements are:—

   (1) A survey of existing use and management covering quality aspects of present and likely future uses.
   (2) Estimates of future demand over a period of 20 years.
   (3) A plan of the action to be taken during that period to meet future demands for water and to restore and maintain the quality of rivers and coastal waters.

Although these provisions do not apply to land drainage functions, regional water authorities are required to carry out similar land drainage surveys by Section 24(5) of the 1973 Act.

Section 24(6) requires a water authority to prepare from time to time and submit to the appropriate Minister programmes for the discharge of its functions. Precise details of the means of meeting the requirements of Section 24 for the preparation and submission of plans and programmes are described in a guidance document[64] issued by the Department of the Environment. As well as specifying the five-year period for a capital investment programme, the guidance covers the breakdown of expenditure over functions and purposes required by Government. Upon approval by the Minister, a Water Authority must act in accordance with the Section 24(6) programme subject to an expenditure tolerance on each water service of 5 per cent of the annual total or "Capital Ceiling".

The submission of planning documents by water authorities to Government departments is timed to fit in with the annual public expenditure survey, by which forecasts of expenditure by all public authorities are collected in a common format and to a common timetable. Known as the PESC (Public Expenditure Survey Committee) process, it provides the basis for Government decision and control of public expenditure, which culminates in the January publication of a White Paper describing the Government's spending plans for the four year period commencing in the April following. So a programme for 1979-80—1982-83 is drawn up at what are called "1978 survey" prices, which are in fact November 1977 actual prices.

The Second Jukes report[60] describes the basis for medium and long term planning in relation to the statutory requirements of Section 24. Originally, an annually submitted medium term (five year) plan was recommended to record and justify decisions in the capital investment programme, but as indicated in a 1977 White Paper[65], the Government now accepts that water services planning is more accurately reflected in regional plans spanning both the medium and long term. Regional water authorities now produce a single plan rolled forward annually, which covers not only the five year period of the capital programme, but also provides a comprehensive look at the longer term some 20 years ahead, giving details of policies and priorities across the whole range of functions, and incorporating a report of the survey of existing use and management. Besides justifying the capital programme as a whole, the plan demonstrates the physical and financial effects of variations in estimated expenditure. The concept of updating the plan continuously, so that planning is considered a dynamic process rather than one which erupts and then dies every few years, is now established. Part of the challenge of planning is the lack of governmental direction about future economic activity. Because plans of a service industry like water are so dependent on national economic factors, planners could find themselves second-guessing the Government whose plans, if they exist at all, are subject to enormous short-term variations. The answer appears to be never to deal in a single set of outcomes, nor close options, until it is necessary but to develop ranges of outcomes which widen with time.

## Monitoring Progress and Assessing Performance

An essential activity in any continuous planning process is the means by which the learning which comes from experience is injected back into the planning cycle. This process includes two overlapping aspects, namely, monitoring progress and assessing performance.

Monitoring progress is done by comparing actual expenditure, physical work done, and so on with forecasts of these quantities. It includes the comparison of service standards with service targets and the related costs.

If actual results are found to diverge from the expected outcome, reasons should be sought, for it is by understanding how that appropriate adjustments can be made to improve future forecasts.

Performance assessment is a responsibility of management, but the efficiency with which services are provided will affect the outcome of the plan. Information on past performance is seen as desirable both to estimate the resources to execute future plans and to motivate management. Whereas estimating needs and assessing performance are conceptually distinct, similar information relates to both. However, the relationships between increments of service, themselves difficult to measure, and resources for their achievement have yet to be developed.

The contribution of performance assessment to planning is found in identifying where a source is being used wastefully. Approached through comparison between the achievements of one management unit and another, it is invariably revealing to each. Unfortunately, such comparison of public authorities is not popular and can endanger relations unless it is tackled with understanding and in the knowledge that, like all techniques, it is by no means infallible.

Performance comparison is complex. Strictly, for each kind of comparison to be valid, things other than the quantity compared should remain the same. Unit costs will vary according to local conditions. However, if operational costs from various locations are analysed, it is possible to develop empirical relationships which distinguish inherent cost differences from variations in efficiency. It is then possible to locate where use of a resource is deviating from the norm, a small but material step towards the refinement of a future forecast and plan, and above all towards greater efficiency.

In the 1978 White Paper[37], the Goverment considered that Nationalized Industries should account to Parliament for their progress against published performance and service aims, including valid international comparisons if relevant. It seems probable that key performance indicators for the water industry will be expressed as the costs of meeting specific standards of service. This emphasizes the importance not only of monitoring progress, but of pursuing from the start policies and methods based on sound economics.

## 7. REFERENCES

**Economic Background**
1. World Health Organization, 1976, *WHO Chronicle*, 30, "Community water supply and wastewater disposal".
2. National Water Council, 1978, "Water industry review 1978."

**Forecasting**
3. Department of the Environment and the National Water Council, 1977, "Standing Committee on Sewers and Water Mains: a national assessment".
4. Moroney, M. J., 1969, "Facts from figures", Pelican Books, London.
5. Herrington, P. R. 1973, University of Leicester, Department of Economics, "Water demand study—final report".

6. Jenking, R. C., 1973, "Fylde metering: a research study", Fylde Water Board.
7. Phillips, J. H., 1972, *Journ. I.W.E*, 26, 6, "Domestic metering—an interim review".
8. Phillips, J. H., and Kershaw, G. C., 1976, *Jour. I.W.E.S.*, 30, 4, "Domestic metering—an engineering and economic appraisal".
9. Marsh, G. J. W., 1971, "Marley plumbing technical publication no. 5—water for 6", Marley Extrusions, Maidstone, Kent.
10. Thackray, J. E., Cocker, V., and Archibald, G., 1978, *Jour. Proc. I.C.E.*, 64, 37 and discussion, "The Malvern and Mansfield studies of domestic water usage".
11. Rump, M., 1976, Building Research Establishment Note 50/76, "Water economy measures in dwellings: their feasibility and economics", H.M.S.O.
12. Ball, E. F., and Rump, M., 1976, Building Research Establishment Note 82/76, "Water economy measures for WCs and urinals", H.M.S.O.
13. Howe, C. W., and Linaweaver, F. P., 1967, *Jour. Water Resources Research,* 3, 1, "The impact of price on residential water demand and its relation to system design and price structure".
14. Murray, C. R., and Reeves, G. B., 1972, U.S. Geological Survey, U.S. Department of the Interior, "Estimated use of water in the U.S. 1970".
15. Coe, A. L., 1978, "Water supply and plumbing practices in continental Europe", Hutchinson Benham,
16. Central Statistical Office, London Annual, "Social trends".
17. Office of Population Censuses and Surveys, 1976, "General household survey".
18. Office of Population Censuses and Surveys, 1971, "Census reports".
19. Central Statistical Office, London Annual, "Regional statistics".
20. Barrett, J. W., 1978, *Jour. Product Finishing,* "A case of unfair treatment".
21. Barrett, J. W., 1978, *Jour. Product Finishing,* "A case of unfair treatment".
22. Department of the Environment and the National Water Council, 1977 and 1976, "Technical Working Group on Waste of Water: Reports of September 1976 and December 1977".
23. Pipe, E. J., 1972, ICE Management of National and Regional Resources Symposium, "CEGB and Regional Water Authorities".
24. Central Water Planning Unit, 1976, Technical Note no. 13, "Water-based recreational activities".
25. Gibson, J. G., 1974, *Jour. Planning Outlook*, Summer pp. 1-105, "Recreation cost benefit analysis: a review of English case studies".
26. Trent River Authority, 1970, "The Trent economic model—vols. 11 and 12", Water Resources Board.
27. Clawson, M., 1959, Resources for the Future, Washington, "Methods for measuring the demand for and value of outdoor recreation—report no. 10".

## Investment Decisions

28. Ministry of Agriculture, Fisheries and Food, 1974, "Field Drainage Leaflet no. 16".
29. Bennet, G., 1970, *British Medical Journal,* August, 451, "Bristol floods 1968—controlled survey of effects on health of local commmunity disaster".
30. Local Government Operational Research Unit, 1973, Reading, "The economics of flood alleviation—report no. C155".
31. Penning-Rowsell, E. C. and Chatterton, J. B., 1977, "The benefits of flood alleviation: a manual of assessment techniques", Teakfield Ltd., Farnborough, Hants.
32. Self, P., 1975, "Econocrats and the policy process", Macmillan, London.
33. Department of the Environment, 1972, "The COBA method of appraisal".
34. Institution of Civil Engineers, 1969, "An introduction to engineering economics", chapter 5.
35. Kuiper, E., 1971, "Water resources project economics", Butterworths, London.
36. Command Paper CMND. 3437, 1967, "Nationalized industries: a review of economic and financial objectives", H.M.S.O.
37. Command Paper CMND. 7131, March 1978, "The nationalized industries", H.M.S.O.
38. Balmer, R., 1975, *Jour. I.W.E.S.*, 29, 390, "Discounting—its use in project appraisal".
39. Herrington, P. R., 1977, *I.W.E.S.*, Symposium on Water Services: Financial, Engineering and Scientific Planning, "6. Choices within the water industry: does economics help?"
40. Davies, G., 1968, *Jour. I.W.E.*, 22, 281, "Trunk pipelines selection—what size and when?"
41. Paine, N., and White, J. K., 1969, *Jour. I.W.E.*, 23, 435, "Water transport costs."
42. Greenwood, R. H., 1978, *Jour. I.W.E.S.*, 32, 509, "Optimal sizing and staging of pumping mains".
43. Water Research Centre, 1977, Technical Report TR 61, "Cost information for water supply and sewage disposal".
44. Lambert, P. A., 1978, "Error sensitivity", unpublished paper.
45. National Water Council, 1977, Working Group on Waste of Water, "Optimization of waste control expenditure".

## Charging Policy

46. Water Resources Board, 1973, "Water resources in England and Wales", H.M.S.O.

47. Saunders, R. J., Warford, J. J., and Mann, P. C., 1977, World Bank, Washington, staff working paper no. 259, "Alternative concepts of marginal costs for public utility pricing: problems of application in the water supply section".
48. Turvey, R., 1969, *Economic Jour.*, 79, 2, "Marginal cost".
49. Institution of Water Engineers and Scientists, 1977, Symposium on Water Services: Financial, Engineering and Scientific Planning.
50. Department of the Environment, 1974, Third Report of the Secretary of State for the Environment, "The water services: economic and financial policies", H.M.S.O.
51. Rees, R., 1976, "Public enterprise economics, Widenfeld and Nicolson, London.
52. Webb, M. G., 1976, "Pricing policies for public enterprises", Macmillan, London.
53. Boiteux, M., 1949, "Peak-load pricing", Prentice-Hall, London. (Also in Nelson, J. R. 1964 "Marginal cost pricing in practice", Prentice-Hall, London).
54. Williams, A., 1975, Chartered Institute of Public Finance and Accountancy, "Long term charging policy for the water industry".
55. Building Research Establishment, October 1971, "European plumbing notes".
56. National Water Council, 1976, "Paying for water".
57. Middleton, R. N., Saunders, R. J., and Warford, J. J., 1978, *Jour. I.W.E.S.*, 32, 111, "The costs and benefits of water metering".
58. Rees, J. A., 1972, Report to Social Science Research Council, "Factors affecting metered water consumption".
59. Smith, R. J., 1974, *Jour. I.W.E.*, 28, 47, "Some comments on domestic metering".

**Corporate Planning**

60. Department of the Environment, 1974, Second Report of the Secretary of State for the Environment, "The water services: economic and financial policies", H.M.S.O.
61. Department of the Environment, 1974, Report on corporate planning—DoE Circular 142/74, "The water services economic and financial policies", H.M.S.O.
62. National Water Council, 1978, "River water quality—the next stage, review of discharge consent conditions".
63. Davies, G., 1978, Public Works Congress and Exhibition Council, "Project selection in the water services".
64. Department of the Environment, 1977, "Guidance on water authorities annual plans and programmes to be submitted under section 24 of the Water Act 1973", H.M.S.O.
65. Command Paper CMND. 6876, 1977, "The water industry in England and Wales: the next steps", H.M.S.O.

# Chapter 5

# FINANCE

## 1. INHERITANCE

ON 1st April 1974 ten newly formed Regional Water Authorities in England and Wales inherited the accumulated assets of:—

29 river authorities
157 water undertakers
1 393 sewage undertakers

These organizations transferred to the new authorities assets valued at that time at £2 400 million together with the associated debt which amounted to £2 200 million.

The new water authorities had access to a market of some 49 million people and in the first year their income amounted to more than £600 million with a capital expenditure of over £400 million.

Thus, in a rapid reorganization there was put together a new water industry, having a workforce of about 59 000 and a degree of capital intensity which placed it, in relative terms, significantly above the current league leaders of electricity generating and post office telecommunications.

That inheritance has inevitably affected the early life and existence of water authorities and the customers they serve. Indeed, the heavy burden of inherited and continuing capital expenditure has been one of the most significant factors to concern the management of the water industry. Further, government could see clearly, perhaps for the first time, its impact on public sector funding, its share of national investment resources, and the implications for the consumer.

The response to these problems coloured both government and management's actions over the next few years and will almost certainly influence their joint thinking for many years to come.

From previous chapters in this book the reader will have noticed several other major problems which were present at "vesting day". Those included doubts about the level of future demand projected to the end of the Century, questions about the condition and capability of the distribution and conveyance systems (the underground assets), the question of metering, the degree of service which consumers would require and perhaps a changed attitude to the environment. These questions, and many more, created the backcloth to the financial problems which faced the new industry.

## 2. ECONOMIC AND FINANCIAL POLICIES

In the period leading up to reorganization in April 1974, and progressively from that date, a number of changes occurred in the accounting attitudes of the water industry. Some of these changes were introduced by the water companies with their commercial approach, in other instances the new industry led and the Companies followed. Again, some were instigated by the arrival within the industry of outsiders

---

who were accustomed to different accounting attitudes. Some issues were new to the industry, but were long-established conventions elsewhere.

These changes were highlighted, introduced and discussed in a way that created a new atmosphere for the Industry. The debate was fostered by a number of Committees, described below, as well as a host of papers and articles by groups of individuals, which together have resulted in the creation of the new financial structure for the water industry.

## THE WOODHAM REPORT

This Report, titled "The Water Services Estimates and Accounts" was produced in 1974 by a Committee under the chairmanship of J. B. Woodham. It dealt with accounts and estimates, management accounting, accounting principles, and the publication of financial information. Some of the accounting concepts covered were:—

Depreciation
Reserves
Debt servicing
Units of performance
Current cost values
The treatment of deficits and surpluses
The concept of the physical values of capital
Cross subsidization

## THE JUKES REPORTS

Three further Reports were produced by a Committee under the chairmanship of J. A. Jukes, all entitled "The Water Services: Economic and Financial Policies", published by Her Majesty's Stationery Office.

The *First Report* (1973) considered economic and financial objectives in the water services, and the short-term economic and financial issues facing the industry.

The *Second Report* (1974) surveyed present water use and management, and discussed long-term and medium-term plans in the context of corporate planning for the industry.

The *Third Report* (1974) considered the financial background of the industry, the current basis of charges, and recommended charging principles to be followed in future.

The main issues that emerged in the Reports are considered in this Chapter.

## 3. THE CONCEPT OF CAPITAL

### CAPITAL EXPENDITURE

The Woodham Report (para. 4.9) led water authorities into a concept which was a departure from the practice of many of its predecessors, i.e. a definition of *capital expenditure* which was derived from its nature rather than its source. The principle is sufficiently important to express it in full:—

"We recommend therefore, that accounting conventions in the Water Services should develop from the view that capital expenditure, irrespective of the source from which it is financed, is expenditure received in the expectation that it will contribute to the operations of the Authority beyond the current year of Account".

This concept was accepted throughout the industry. In time it has led to a greater clarity of thought on many associated issues such as depreciation accounting, self financing and the general debate which took place on the burden of debt financing, and notably the questions of interest on loans and depreciation rates on assets.

At a later date the lead given by the Woodham Report was followed by the Water Authorities' Directors of Finance Working Party who defined *capital expenditure* as:—

"Expenditure (including design salaries and supporting costs) on the construction, provision, purchase, replacement and improvement of fixed assets, or on their major renewal".

This definition has been followed throughout this Chapter.

The Woodham Report gave a further lead to the industry in para. 4.11 by indicating that:—

"We believe that a capital asset account should be regarded as an account in which the unconsumed portion of expenditure, contributing to more than the current accounting period, is carried forward to future accounting periods".

Clearly, such a policy must include such assets as reservoirs, mains and treatment works, but it also includes items of shorter life such as motor vehicles and plant and can include a more nebulous asset in the form of major expenditure upon research and development, continued over more than one year and having possible benefits over the course of further years.

## DEPRECIATION

Arising from this concept of the nature of capital is the associated one that having created an asset by spending money—the investment decision and commitment—then that asset could be used, and each time it is used it is likely to diminish its expected life by some increment. Gone therefore was the "loan charge" concept imposed on the predecessor authorities, which required them to pay off loans for capital expenditure within a fixed period, which varied only according to the nature of the works. "We believe therefore that 'loan charge' accounting should find no place in the accounting techniques of the new water services" (para. 4.14, Woodham Report) and in its place—"We recommend that the Water Authorities should develop depreciation techniques relevant to their various classes of asset" (para. 4.17, Woodham Report).

It is appropriate at this point to show a form of accounts for the recording of an asset or assets, and which includes the recognition of the diminution in value of those assets by use or through time (Table 5.I).

The various forms of depreciation—straight line, reducing balance, sinking fund—all have their advantages and disadvantages, and their proponents and opponents. It is not intended in this Chapter to enter into this debate, but any student on this subject will find the arguments detailed at length in accounting text books.

If one accepts the concept of depreciation as *a measure of diminution of an asset by virtue of the effluction of time or of its use*, then similarly one should accept its corollary, that where an asset depreciates its true value could, or even should, be reflected in the asset account. This leads us into the realms of *current cost accounting* which is briefly discussed later in this section. If, however, an asset, for whatever reason, increases in value at a rate in excess of inflation, it could be argued that its value should be increased—a form of "negative" depreciation.

The Woodham Report makes a positive recommendation that land should be treated in the same way as other assets, whilst recognizing that depreciation may be calculated at a zero rate. The Report emphasizes the importance of compatability of the treatment of depreciation.

TABLE 5.I. Assets/Depreciation Statement

| Type of assets | Cost | | | | Depreciation | | | | Depreciated value 31st March 1975, £000s |
|---|---|---|---|---|---|---|---|---|---|
| | Transfers at 1st April 1974, £000s | Addition, £000s | Sold or written off, £000s | As at 31st March 1975, £000s | Transfers at 1st April 1974, £000s | Provision, £000s | Sold or written off, £000s | As at 31st March 1975, £000s | |
| Freehold lands and buildings | 650 | 381 | — | 1031 | 227 | 17 | — | 244 | 787 |
| Leasehold land and buildings (more than 50 years) | — | 1314 | — | 1314 | — | 93 | — | 93 | 1221 |
| Leasehold land and buildings (less than 50 years) | 29 | 16 | — | 45 | 27 | 1 | — | 28 | 17 |
| Motor vehicles | 21 | 15 | 4 | 32 | 10 | 4 | 2 | 12 | 20 |
| Plant and equipment | 131 | 34 | 86 | 79 | 107 | 5 | 63 | 49 | 30 |
| Furniture | 93 | 2 | 93 | 2 | 70 | — | 70 | — | 2 |
| Total | 924 | 1762 | 183 | 2503 | 441 | 120 | 135 | 426 | 2077 |

## ASSET LIVES

Implicit in the concept of depreciation, as a measure of diminution in the value of an asset by time or use, is some assessment of the life cycle of that asset. Before 1974, with "loan charge" financing, this concept commanded less importance because "expected life" tended only to indicate the period of loan to be associated with the funding of that asset. However, with the acceptance of depreciation accounting the two "cycles", asset life and replacements, and funding and its repayment, can be regarded more as two separate cycles.

A report of a Working Party established under the Water Authority Directors of Finance stated that the average of asset lives within the industry had been assessed at 55 years. It is important to understand that this was an average of various classes of assets. With this report, and its indication of average asset lives, each water authority could consider or re-consider its depreciation policy. Some believed that the average of their asset lives was approximately that of the report; others believed that this estimate may have been too optimistic in relation to their own range of assets, so that in reality a variety of circumstances could so threaten the expected life as to make the possible average of 55 years unrealistic. Currently, over a range of water companies and water authorities, asset lives ranging on an average from 25 to 55 years are in operation. This range undoubtedly leads to problems of compatability, particularly in view of the questions of supplementary depreciation, which is now explored.

## SUPPLEMENTARY DEPRECIATION AND INFLATION ACCOUNTING

As has been indicated earlier, several factors can effect the value of an asset:—

(1)  The consumption of that asset by "use" or "time" (e.g. plant).
(2)  The obsolescence factor.
(3)  The increase in the value of that asset in real terms (e.g. land).
(4)  The effect on the historic cost of an asset, particularly a "long life" asset, of inflation.

It is the last of these factors which will be considered now. There has been a growing realization of the erosion of monetary value measures of an asset's worth. Current convention expresses the cost of an asset, and thus its depreciation rate, in terms of what it cost to acquire—its "historic cost value". With a high inflation rate, however, this convention expresses only the apportioning use of that asset in the context of historic cost. It does not recognize that "use" of that asset is in real money terms, where income is likely to be in inflated money terms.

Concern about this subject was sufficiently serious for the Government to set up the "Sandilands Committee"*, which recommended that a form of inflation accounting should be adopted to recognize the deficiencies of the historic cost conventions. The Committee was relatively silent on the applications of inflation accounting principles to the public sector and nationalized industries, while the accounting profession as a whole did not receive the report with great acclaim and required further work to be carried out on the subject.

Nevertheless, it was recognized that the current consumer, even in the public sector, was paying an inadequate charge for his period of use of the assets which supplied him with, amongst other things, his water services. As a result of this recognition the Government introduced legislation which allowed the nationalized industries to increase their depreciation charge by a factor of 40 per cent, as a first step towards recognition of the full current cost accounting depreciation charge.

It is interesting to compare the charge for depreciation which emerged from the historic cost approach with the possible charge from a current cost accounting

*Report of the Inflation Accounting Committee (HMSO, 1975)—Chairman: F. E. P. Sandilands.

TABLE 5.II.  Financing of 1977-78 Capital Expenditure of the Water Authorities
(excluding expenditure on sewerage, but including sewage treatment and disposal)

|  | Historic cost basis* | | CCA basis | |
|---|---|---|---|---|
|  | £ million | Percentage | £ million | Percentage |
| Depreciation | 110 | 34 | 170 | 53 |
| Borrowing and other | 210 | 66 | 150 | 47 |
| Total | 320 | 100 | 320 | 100 |

*inclusive of up to 40 per cent supplementary depreciation

approach. The disparity is clearly seen in Table 5.II which, although acknowledged to be a very imperfect attempt to assess the early thoughts on this complicated subject, does highlight the major implications of the current cost accounting debate.

## 4. CAPITAL INVESTMENT

### CAPITAL PLANNING

With the inherited problems of the new industry and faced with similar problems to those dealt with by water companies as they had become rationalized over the previous decade or so, the water industry was forced to make major decisions on capital investment, priorities, standard of service and by inference the effects on charges.

Fig. 5.1 sets out the actual or planned *investment* by all water authorities up to 1982-83.

Fig. 5.2 shows, by way of note, the incidence of *debt servicing* (broadly interest and depreciation) as a proportion of the industry's revenue budgets over the period 1974-78.

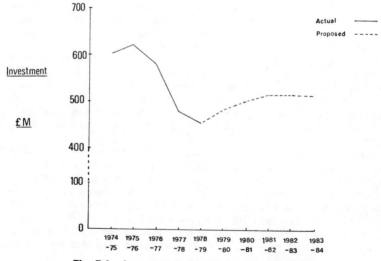

Fig. 5.1.  Investment by all water authorities

5

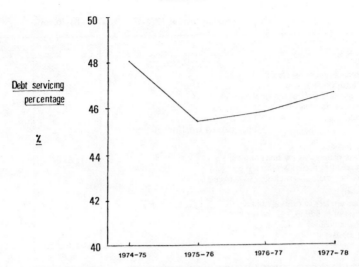

**Fig. 5.2. Dept servicing (depreciation and interest) percentage of revenue expenditure**

Close attention to the level of spending gave rise to a series of steps which will have a profound effect on the long term structure of the industry:—

(*a*) greater care, thought, and planning was given to the overall investment levels in the industry;
(*b*) greater attention was paid to the composition of individual programmes and their constituent projects;
(*c*) more management effort was put into the planning and support of existing assets, plant, and machinery; and
(*d*) by these and other influences greater attention was given to the "value for money" concept.

As a result of problems of investment levels the industry and government together established a better level of capital allocation for the industry which led to the identification of a 14-purpose category analysis which itself led to some forms of "priority assessment" within the industry (Table 5.III).

In planning capital investment a number of techniques are employed which have been discussed in other chapters, and are covered by the general description of assessment and appraisal, i.e. the inspection of a capital proposal from every facet before authorization is sought, before physical engineering commences, and before any money is invested. In most major industries some form of capital expenditure planning, authorization, and control procedure is in use and follows a certain basic pattern.

**Stage 1:**
The first outline concept will emerge from some strategic plan or some tactical disposition of resources. To this, outline approval is given or withheld.

**Stage 2:**
Having cleared Stage 1, a detailed investigation will be required leading to a preliminary specification and drawings, etc. This will involve the organization in time and money (perhaps feasibility studies), so that Stage 1 approval implies approval to some level of

TABLE 5.III   Capital Expenditure in 1978-79—Analysis by Purpose

| | £ million | Percentage |
|---|---|---|
| **Renewal** | | |
| Maintenance and replacement | 91.2 | |
| Public health requirements | 12.7 | |
| Improvement of present service (50 per cent) | 23.4 | 31 |
| Improved operational efficiency (50 per cent) | 5.1 | |
| **New development** | | |
| New housing and industry | 145.3 | 34 |
| **Increased demand** | | |
| Growth in demand by existing consumers | 63.0 | |
| Improvement of present service (50 per cent) | 23.5 | 21 |
| Improved operational efficiency (50 per cent) | 5.1 | |
| **Improvement** | | |
| First time services to existing houses | 5.3 | |
| Reduction of pollution | 38.9 | |
| Improved recreational facilities | 1.9 | 14 |
| Other purposes | 14.4 | |
| | 429.8 | 100 |

expenditure. With draft proposals the organization is now capable of seeking authorization in some detail and in assessing the benefit and cost with some precision. It is at this point also that consideration should be given to such other issues as planning approvals, manning and operational costs, ordering lead times, planned maintenance, demand growth, short-term training and recruitment, the cash profile of expenditure throughout the project life, together with funding and interest rates. In addition, the implications of concurrent projects which depend upon or need synchronizing with the project in question should be considered.

### Stage 3:

Having carried the approving body (e.g. board, authority, or a level of management) so far, the proposal is separated into various convenient units and is then carried to the final stage where authorization is sought to commit the organization to specific sums, and the full physical engineering process gets under way.

The engineer, having established that a proposal is valid, is worth doing, and may show some benefit, now has to ensure that the proposal is physically undertaken to plan. Men have been engaged or transferred, some benefits are waiting, funds have been provided and other linked schemes may await the completion of this project. On top of this, the proposal will be in a capital programme, and subject to the control of either a capital allocation by government or of a borrowing or cash limit, each of which will relate to a specific period(s). Any stoppage in payment during the period(s) in question is likely to result in repercussion on these limits.

It is during this process that the provision of information to the project engineer is vital. In turn, he should ensure that information passes from him to his colleagues—delay or haste, variations, technical change, tender price information and change in estimated final cost are all relevant information to management who are dove-tailing their efforts into the final completion date expected by the engineer.

During the whole of this process the exchange of information for better control will result in progressive re-assessment of final cost, linked where necessary to supplementary approvals. It is by no means unusual for a point to be reached where the growing costs of a project can be re-assessed, and a decision taken that any expected benefit may be so damaged by increasing costs that an alternative course of action can be implemented. Such a course of action may well include scrapping the proposal altogether.

## Review

Having undertaken a project in this manner a review is often undertaken to establish where and why departures from plan have occurred, not so much to recriminate but more to improve the estimating and planning process for the future. This review process is part of a cycle by which the capital investment process is constantly tuned and improved.

## GENERAL

This broad outline of the cycle of the investment process may sound complicated, but is very similar to procedures operated within most well managed organizations large and small, in public and private sectors, within this country and abroad. It underlines the very nature of capital expenditure which is given earlier. Capital, by its nature, has a life which exceeds an accounting period—indeed much of its category is of extremely long life. Thus, once a good investment has been approved and brought into being, its benefits will usually give benefit for many years. Conversely, the results of a poor decision will be present to bedevil management usually longer than the management itself, and can often only be salvaged by additional cost—or at worst the completed project has to be scrapped. That sort of decision is always difficult because, although damaging operations can be eliminated, men re-deployed and alternative proposals put in hand, there is a continuing burden of debt. In conclusion, it could be said that decisions in the highly capital-intensive water industry tend to have a long life, and that decisions in a labour-intensive industry have a much shorter one.


## 5. FUNDING

### DEBT FINANCING

Table 5.IV sets out the disposition of the borrowing portfolio of the water industry at the date of the 1974 reorganization and in each of the three following years.

TABLE 5.IV.   Disposition of Water Authority Borrowing

| Source | Loans outstanding at | | | | | | | |
|---|---|---|---|---|---|---|---|---|
| | 31st March 1974 £ million | % | 31st March 1975 £ million | % | 31st March 1976 £ million | % | 31st March 1977 £ million | % |
| National loans fund | — | — | 266 | 11 | 687 | 25 | 701 | 23 |
| Other central Government | 348 | 16 | 324 | 14 | 308 | 11 | 286 | 9 |
| Local authority | 1513 | 69 | 1466 | 61 | 1412 | 52 | 1370 | 44 |
| Foreign | — | — | 173 | 7 | 194 | 7 | 613 | 20 |
| Other loans | 325 | 15 | 175 | 7 | 133 | 5 | 109 | 4 |

It will be seen from Table 5.IV that the vast majority of borrowing in the early days of the new industry was linked to the loans inherited from their predecessor local authorities and their loans pools.

Table 5.V indicates the level of borrowing by age or redemption distribution. It may appear attractive at a time of soaring interest rates to have a preponderance of long-dated low-interest funds, but at the same time a more balanced portfolio would be a safer basis upon which to structure the funding of an industry. It was along this path that those responsible for the funding operation set their sights, and the change in age distribution of borrowing within the industry within the three years since 1974 gives some indication of that attempt.

TABLE 5.V.   Age Distribution of Water Authority Borrowing

| Age | Amount repayable from | | | | | |
|-----|---|---|---|---|---|---|
| | 31st March 1975 £ million | % | 31st March 1976 £ million | % | 31st March 1977 £ million | % |
| Less than 1 year | 53 | 2 | 24 | 1 | 14 | 1 |
| 1-5 years | 271 | 11 | 242 | 9 | 642 | 21 |
| 5-10 years | 260 | 11 | 241 | 9 | 231 | 7 |
| Over 10 years | 226 | 10 | 339 | 12 | 332 | 11 |
| Instalment loans | 1594 | 66 | 1889 | 69 | 1861 | 60 |

Initially, in 1974 access by the water authorities to long-term borrowing was limited to funds available from the National Loans Fund for periods of:—

(i)   ten years for refinancing
(ii)   25 years for new borrowing.

Access to other sources was strictly limited, overseas funds only being available by approval of the Secretary of State. From 1974 the industry made direct approaches for such overseas borrowing and with the close co-operation of both the Treasury and the Bank of England it sought and obtained very substantial sums from overseas sources. This is reflected in the distribution shown in Table 5.IV.

At the same time as these changes were taking place approaches were being made to the European Economic Community, the European Investment Bank and, later, the European Iron and Steel Community for support from the funds available to disadvantaged regions, particularly those designated as regions of high unemployment or intermediate regions. Over the period covered in Table 5.IV a gradual pattern of European support emerged in the form of direct grants and loans to support industry in those depressed regions. This will be seen in Table 5.V as a slight shift of the age distribution of the borrowing pattern. However, the preponderance of long-dated funds still heavily weights the overall borrowing portfolio of the water industry.

SELF-FINANCING

Whilst these changes were taking place, another effort was being made to remedy one more undesirable fluctuation. In 1974-75 the self-financing element of capital expenditure in the water industry was only 20 per cent, compared with figures of 67 per cent in electricity and 78 per cent in the gas industries. With the Government's co-operation, attempts were put in hand to extend the proportion of self-financing available to the water industry.

Although these moves were agreed as desirable, were sympathetically understood by Government, and were considered to be in the long-term interests of the consumer, it was equally true that self-financing is a shift of borrowing from one individual lender (e.g. the Government) to millions of lenders—the public (i.e. the consumers). Such individual borrowing is enforced in the charges made for water, and the proposal arose at a time when the consumer was subject to price pressures for a number of reasons, e.g. a high rate of inflation and the removal of Government subsidy (some 60 per cent of sewerage and sewage treament costs had, before 1974, been subject to a form of subsidy through the "rate support grant"). These pressures, taken together with the wish to increase the level of self-financing, required a most cautious approach on the part of water authorities, coupled with strict oversight of the situation by government in the form of:—

(1) Ministerial directions,
(2) scrutiny and oversight of charges by the Price Commission*.

Ministerial directions have, for example, limited the amount that any water authority could put aside to reserve in any year to two or three per cent of revenue expenditure for that year. At the same time, the Price Commission have applied a strict scrutiny to the charges made by water authorities, and to the levels of depreciation and inflation, interest rates, and surpluses. Nevertheless, even with these constraints, a very gradual move towards a greater degree of self-financing has emerged in the industry.

As a source of funding, self-financing has a most important role to play. Effectively by "borrowing" a small sum by increasing the charges to individuals it becomes possible for the "borrower" to avoid dependence upon a single lender of large sums for long periods at possible high interest rates, while the payment of "interest" on the involuntary "loans" from the individual consumers occurs by way of reduction of future charges.

Self-financing has the effect of increasing the charges to the present consumers; in the longer term it will reduce charges and allow the burden of debt finance to be reduced thereby allowing greater flexibility and reduced borrowing. Funds so obtained are, of course, applied to new investments as loans would be.

## OTHER FUNDING

Just as the generation of funds for investment or working capital can be provided by either borrowing or "self-financing", so other methods are available. For example, the facility of *leasing* releases the investor from providing cash of significant proportion over one year or so, and replaces that investment by an annual sum of longer continuing duration. At no time, in this situation, does the ownership of the asset pass into the "investors" or water industry hands. Extreme examples have occurred of this type of situation, where an organization could for example, in proper circumstances, sell off the whole of its transport fleet whilst simultaneously leasing those vans and cars back on an annual rental basis. The principle may well have application in the industry.

Other forms of raising finance are available with less obvious consequences. For example, the organization may extend its "borrowing" from its suppliers by refusing to pay its debts quickly, or from its customers by collecting its accounts very quickly. Each of the techniques can be strongly criticized, but here again the principles are applicable. It would be just as open to criticism for a finance manager to pay his organization's debts too quickly—that is, faster than the conventional trade terms—or to recover sums owing to his organization in a lethargic manner.

One further financing consideration may be relevant—that is to look at the

---

*The Price Commission is a Governmental agency established in 1973, operating under Acts of Parliament, and having powers to investigate price increases. These powers cover water service charges, but not land drainage precepts.

"borrowing" tied up in a stores system. An unnecessary sum tied up in stores could be replaced by a profitable investment of the same sum. The manager will clearly have to balance the desirability of one investment with the attractions of the other.

## 6. RESERVES

When they came into existence in April 1974, the regional water authorities inherited very few reserves or balances from their predecessors; odd specific reserves, small losses, the occasional profit, but little else. Water companies had, on the other hand, had many years to create some reserves.

It was the Jukes Report (see p. 184) which initially recommended that charges should be sufficient to contribute to the building up of reasonable working balances over the first three years from 1st April 1974. The suggested level of such a working capital reserve was put at 10 per cent.

All water authorities welcomed the guideline, but achievement has been slow, many authorities not yet have reached 10 per cent, some may never do so. With time, and the use of overdraft facilities, levels below 10 per cent could be satisfactory in some circumstances. With the possibility that too much of a burden may have been put on the consumer in an effort to reach a satisfactory reserve position, the Price Commission and Government together intervened and the Secretary of State in successive years had applied directions to limit the amounts which water authorities may put aside to reserves (see "Self-financing", p. 192).

Initially, the level of application to reserve was 2 per cent, and only in 1978/79 was this increased to 3 per cent. It was this constraint, and concern about levels of charges, that prevented water authorities from reaching the suggested 10 per cent level of reserve within a period of three years. Even after five years (1979) some authorities will have only reached a level of 7 to 8 per cent.

Ministerial direction has not so far been applied to land drainage account and for this service, whose accounts are kept separate, there is a more healthy reserve position.

It should be noted that the creation of a reserve has two effects. On the one hand, a buffer is provided for those periods when major problems arise. Of even more importance, however, is the creation of surplus funds to reduce the dependence upon external borrowing, or in other words to increase the self-financing ratio in the industry.

Water companies are no strangers to this question of reserves and their contribution to the self-financing capability of their operation. For funding, they either have to rely on conventional loans, call on their shareholders, or provide the capability from internal sources—frequently a combination of two or more of these sources.

Efforts to create a sound reserve position have, as has been indicated, created an improved self-financing position, which has allowed each organization to avoid the burden of borrowing at high rates of interest. In order to be realistic, where reserves are created in any one activity then the use of those reserves attracts a rate of interest. Thus for funds borrowed from inside or outside, the organization pays interest on those funds, the internal interest being itself put to reserve.

## 7. ANNUAL ACCOUNTS

Water authorities are obliged, under the terms of paragraph 38 of Schedule 3 to the Water Act 1973, to prepare audited statements of accounts in respect of each financial year. Copies of these statements must be sent to the Secretary of State, Ministry of Agriculture, Fisheries and Food, and local authorities within their regions and made available to the general public.

The Woodham Report (see p. 184) recommended the overall format and broad outline of water authority accounts. This recommendation was for an analysis reflecting the services provided, namely, a set of service revenue accounts for which each relevant service would indicate the degree of success achieved in recovering the costs from the users of the service. The entries contained within the service accounts were to reflect the consumption or movement of real resources, the use of employees, power, materials and utilization of assets, but not to show any allocation of surpluses from current revenues, which would be shown in a separate revenue account.

The actual form of the published accounts is agreed between the Department of the Environment and the water authorities, although the Department of the Environment has the power, with the approval of the Treasury, to issue directions on the form of the statement of accounts should agreement not be forthcoming. The accounts follow the basic pattern of:—

| | | |
|---|---|---|
| *Balance Sheet* | ... | showing the total cost of assets held, loan debt, extent of reserves. |
| *Summary Revenue and Appropriation Account* | ... | showing the surplus or deficit of charge over expenditure on each service, together with the allocation to reserves. |
| *Source and Application of Funds* | ... | showing how funds either borrowed or generated internally from surpluses were utilized. |
| *Service Revenue Accounts* | ... | showing income and expenditure within objective headings. |

Plus *a statement* showing a subjective analysis of the service revenue accounts and schedules of loans outstanding and fixed assets.

A standard form of approach is absolutely essential if inter-authority comparisons are to have any credibility. The accounts, as now published, may still be too detailed, but there is a conflict between trying to provide the fullest possible information about the financial aspects of the services provided and the need to keep the presentation simple and readily understood. The published columns of figures, which are essential for management needs and budgetary control, are of limited value to the general public.

## 8. BUDGETING

A budget is an expression of the future plans of an organization, in financial terms. In the water industry, both revenue and capital budgets are prepared and used for three prime functions:—

(a) As a basis for setting charges.
(b) As a basis for the control and monitoring of progress against the plan.
(c) To provide a means of allocating resources.

When setting their charges, water authorities are under a number of conflicting pressures:—

(i) They have a duty to ensure that, taking one year with another, they do not spend more on carrying out their activities than they collect in charges.
(ii) The consumer tends to expect an improved service.
(iii) Government has investment programmes which they want to see carried out.
(iv) There is a limit to the increase in charges which the consumer will bear.
(v) With the exception of land drainage precepts, the charges are subject to the approval of the Price Commission.

It is essential for a carefully considered budget to be prepared to ensure that sufficient income is obtained to enable an authority to carry out its policies and to balance these conflicting pressures. Having established the revenue budget for charging purposes, this also provides a yardstick against which progress can be measured on a regular basis throughout the year.

The purpose of making regular comparisons of actual expenditure and income against the budget is to bring to the attention of management, at the earliest possible time, significant variations from the budget. This will enable correcting action to be taken before it is too late. The use of budgets for management acccounting purposes is dealt with below.

Capital expenditure is essentially different from revenue in that it is the result of a series of individual projects each of which may take from a few weeks to a number of years to complete. This poses additional problems in controlling the budget because of the effects of inflation over such a time span, coupled with the difficulties which are inevitably encountered in working in difficult site conditions subject to the vagaries of the weather. However, in view of the significant effect which capital expenditure has on charges and therefore on the resources available for revenue expenditure, it is important that progress is regularly reviewed so that corrective action can be taken at the earliest opportunity.

In the foreseeable future there is always likely to be a shortfall between resources available and those desired. This applies to both capital and revenue requirements, and the production of a budget provides a means of assessing the claims of competing proposals for the resources available.

## 9. MANAGEMENT ACCOUNTING

Management accounting has been defined as:—

"The application of professional knowledge and skill in the preparation and presentation of accounting information in such a way as to assist management in the formulation of policies and in the planning and control of the operations of the undertaking".

From the definition it can be seen that the principal function of the management accountant is to help managers to manage—that is to carry out the processes of management efficiently and effectively. This help goes beyond the mere provision of financial information. The management accountant should play an active and positive part in the decision-making process so that no major decision is taken without its full financial and economic implications being known by all parties.

The importance of management accounting to the water industry has been recognized nationally. The subject features prominently in the Woodham Report (see p. 184), and further work on the subject has been undertaken by a group of officers drawn from the ten regional water authorities in England and Wales. Their paper, entitled "Management Accounting in the Water Industry"*, begins with the general thesis that a system of management accounting should be founded upon the principles of "accountability" and "value for money".

*Accountability* is achieved through budgetary control, whereby the total budget of the undertaking is built up from individual cost centres which are assigned to the control of specified managers. A cost centre is defined as "the smallest unit of the operation—a location or item of equipment or group of these—for which costs may be ascertained for the purposes of cost control, fixing charges, and monitoring efficiency". Each manager's sphere of control may span one or more cost centres and is termed a responsibility centre, for which he is held accountable.

*published by the National Water Council.

*Value for money* is measured by relating the physical outputs achieved to the resources required to achieve them, and by establishing key output measures and performance indicators for each cost centre, and thereby for each responsibility centre as an integral part of the budgetary control process. A management accounting system should allow for actual results in terms of expenditure, output and output measures to be recorded within the budget framework and then provide meaningful control information and a suitable basis for managers to take corrective action.

Management accounting systems are not standard as between the different undertakers within the industry, and in the following example of what has been done in one water authority it should be remembered that this is not necessarily representative of management accounting throughout the industry.

In the Wessex Water Authority a computerized general accounting system has been developed which, although providing the medium for producing the authority's annual accounts, is aimed primarily at providing accounting information for consumption by internal management. The system produces routine budgetary control reports tailored to meet the needs of the various levels of management. In addition, the facility for obtaining *ad hoc* information is made available. The structure of the accounts code is complex, but allows cost to be analysed in a number of different ways:—

    (1)  by cost centre (i.e. *where* costs are incurred);
    (2)  by operational reponsibility (i.e. according to the *manager* responsible for the operation of the cost centre);
    (3)  by their objective (i.e. *why* the costs are incurred);
    (4)  by their *nature* (e.g. wages, materials, etc.); and
    (5)  by *resources* responsibility.

The last mentioned analysis allows the total annual resources budget to be allocated to spending officers in accordance with responsibility for initiating the expenditure of those resources. It is therefore an analysis made *before* any complications arise from the internal transfer of charges, and has proved to be a valuable aid to the control of expenditure, particularly in the early years of developing the management accounting system.

The development of the Wessex system has not been achieved without problems. It is well recognized, for instance, that the value of any management accounting system is totally dependent on the quality of the data input, and it has been, and still is, a battle to ensure the reliability of this data.

One important further step is the introduction of unit costs and other performance measures as a supplement to management information which is purely financially based. At present such unit costs are being produced selectively and on a manual basis. In due course, it is hoped to achieve greater integration with the rest of the management accounting system.

## 10. AUDIT

**STATUTORY REQUIREMENTS**

Paragraph 39 of Schedule 3 to the Water Act 1973 provides that the accounts of a water authority (and of the National Water Council) shall be audited in accordance with Sections 154 to 167 of Part VIII of the Local Government Act 1972.

Section 154 of that Act requires the audit to be carried out by either a district auditor or an "approved auditor", the choice resting with the authority. The qualifications of an approved auditor are set out in Section 164, which also provides that the appointment must be approved by the Secretary of State. Section 157 defines, in general terms, the duties of an auditor including the duty to consider whether, in the public interest, he should make a report on any matters arising from the audit. Section 158 specifies the auditor's right of access, at all times, to all such documents relating to the accounts as appear to him to be necessary for the purposes of the audit. It also gives him the right to require, in respect of such documents, such information and explanation as he thinks necessary. The authority must provide the auditor with every facility and all information which he may reasonably require for the purposes of the audit. Section 159 defines the rights of the public at each audit to inspect the accounts and to challenge them. Sections 161 and 162 describe the procedures to be followed when it appears to the auditor "that any item of account is contrary to law".

Under Section 166 of the Act the Secretary of State has made the Accounts and Audit Regulations 1974 relating to various aspects of the preparation of the acounts, and of the audit of them. Regulation 6 requires "the responsible financial officer" to "maintain a current internal audit of the accounts", and gives an internal auditor the same right to require explanations as is given to an external auditor. This provision serves to confirm that the role of the internal auditor is complementary to that of the external auditor.

In their Circular No. 79 (1973), the Department of the Environment listed amongst the matters of concern to an auditor that "the accounts do not disclose any significant loss arising from waste, extravagance, inefficient financial administration, poor value for money, mistake or other causes". This emphasizes the duty of audit to verify that resources are used honestly and efficiently.


EXTERNAL AUDIT

Since external and internal auditors are both complying with a statutory duty to undertake an audit of the accounts, it follows that their work must, to some degree, cover the same ground.

Experience has confirmed that the external auditors expect internal audit to maintain an interest in most of the matters they are themselves involved in, and to co-operate with them in carrying out their duties. They have a specific duty to assess the adequacy of internal audit.


INTERNAL AUDIT

The statement of the Chartered Institute of Public Finance and Accountancy, on the "Role and Objectives of Internal Audit in the Public Sector" defines the responsibility of Internal Audit as "to review, appraise and report upon:—

(a)  The soundness, adequacy, and application of financial and other management controls.
(b)  The extent of compliance with, relevance and financial effect of, established policies, plans, and procedures.
(c)  The extent to which the organization's assets and interests are accounted for and safeguarded from losses of all kinds arising from:—
     (i)   fraud and other offences
     (ii)  waste, extravagance, and inefficient administration, poor value for money or other cause.
(d)  The suitability and reliability of financial and other management data developed within the organization".

The common thread which runs through these four requirements is the need to verify that resources are used honestly and efficiently. The specific significance of them is as follows:—

(i) The effectiveness of the management controls will determine the efficiency in the use of resources.

(ii) Policies, plans, and procedures are approved with a view to determining what resources are required and how they shall be employed.

(iii) The need to ensure honest and efficient use of resources calls for the recording of those resources and for safeguards to prevent their misuse. These records and safeguards must be adequate.

(iv) Plans and procedures, and control of the use of resources, will depend in part on the management data which are provided. It is essential that the data be relevant and accurate.

The Woodham Report (see p. 184) suggests that there is great scope for increasing the value of internal audit by making it a responsibility of multi-disciplinary teams to examine aspects of management not confined to the financial field. The internal audit teams of some water authorities include members of disciplines other than accountancy. Although internal audit benefits from a multi-disciplinary approach, the bulk of the work will always be of a financial nature.


## 11. INCOME

### STATUTORY REQUIREMENTS

The Water Act 1973 lays these requirements upon water authorities:—

*(Section 29)* — "It shall be the duty of every water authority so to discharge their functions that, taking one year with another, their revenue is not less than sufficient to meet their total outgoings properly chargeable to revenue account".

*(Section 30(4))* — "In fixing charges for services, facilities or rights a water authority shall have regard to the cost of performing those services, providing those facilities or making available those rights".

*(Section 30(5))* — ". . .it shall be the duty of every water authority to take such steps as will ensure that, as from a date not later than 1st April 1981, their charges are such as not to show undue preference to, or discriminate unduly against, any class of persons".

It is clear that the industry has to balance its costs with its income over the years. Cross subsidies of any kind are discouraged, although they are likely to remain in some form or another because of the impossibility of exactly defining "any class of persons".

### SOURCES OF INCOME

The industry derives its income from a range of activities which can loosely be described as *the provision of a water service*—which in the specific case of a water company can be as precise an area of charge as the supply of potable water. The sources of income of water authorities broadly include water abstraction charges, water supply charges, charges for sewerage and sewage treatment, trade effluent and environmental service charges, fishing licences and charges, land drainage and internal drainage board precepts, together with a host of miscellaneous income which can include consultancy fees, charges for rechargeable works and income from investments and lands.

Table 5.VI lists the main sources of expenditure for water authorities, and gives some indication of the sums involved and the proportion between services.

TABLE 5.VI.    Water Authority Expenditure 1977-78

|  |  | £ million | Percentage |
|---|---|---|---|
| 1 | Water resources | 34 | 3.1 |
| 2 | Water supply | 447 | 40.3 |
| 3 | Sewerage | 250 | 22.5 |
| 4 | Sewage treatment and disposal | 318 | 28.7 |
| 5 | Water quality regulation | 9 | 0.8 |
| 6 | Pollution alleviation and environmental improvement | 1 | 0.1 |
| 7 | Recreation and amenity | 3 | 0.3 |
| 8 | Navigation | 2 | 0.2 |
| 9 | Fisheries | 4 | 0.3 |
| 10 | Land drainage and flood protection | 40 | 3.6 |

## WATER RESOURCES

The income from the main "wholesale" users of water tends to be grouped and allocated as a whole against the costs of the resource account. The principal customer of the resource account is usually the water authority itself, or a water company, although many large consumers of an individual type are also included. One other large group of wholesale customers is farmers, who use large quantities of water for spray irrigation.

## WATER SUPPLY

Broadly, the income from this service can be broken down between those customers who pay for their consumption by meter and those who are charged for the use or availability of a supply irrespective of the quality consumed. The clearest example of this latter group is the ordinary householder, who is charged according to the rateable value of his property—i.e. by a form of "property tax".

One area of uncertainty exists in the parity of charging between measured and unmeasured consumers, because nobody is charged directly for leakage in water mains systems upstream of consumers' meters. Various estimates put this leakage at between 15 and 35 per cent of the supply and unquantified levels of waste of this magnitude make calculations difficult.

## SEWAGE DISPOSAL

The bulk of income in this category, at present, is the rate-derived income from domestic consumers for the disposal and treatment of domestic sewage. Much income is also derived in the same way from effluents of a similar sort from commercial or semi-commercial nature, although in the latter case the rate-based income may be out of all proportion to the effluent load received. Charging concessions are being considered on a national basis, and gradually the position may change.

One particular problem concerns the receipt, conveyance, and disposal of surface water run-off, either by way of direct discharge to a sewer or by way of infiltration into that sewer. The problem of deriving income from surface water run-off is a difficult one, and could merit a chapter to itself. Readers will be aware of the approximate design criteria of six times dry weather flow, and the costs involved in the provision of storm water retention tanks in treatment works and similar works provided to cope with surface water run-off.

## ENVIRONMENTAL SERVICE CHARGE

Although small, this income is rate-based and is intended to support those aspects of sewage treatment which can be regarded as social or environmental or relate to amenity and pollution control generally.

## TRADE EFFLUENT CHARGES

Although this source of income has been established for some long time, it is only in recent years that it has emerged as a significant source of income in the water industry. The charges are calculated upon a formula which takes into account the combined effects of suspended solids, chemical or biological oxygen demand, and volume.

## FISHING LICENCES AND CHARGES

These sources of income which fall, to some extent, on the fishing community at large, are mostly small in impact but have strong emotional reactions. The rod licence income falls upon anyone wishing to use a rod within the region and is usually adjusted in level to suit his quarry—a high charge for salmon and game fishing, a lower charge for coarse fishing, and separate and specific charges for such interesting and unusual activities as eel traps, putcher nets, and the varied forms of fishing which seem to abound in the estuaries around this country.

## LAND DRAINAGE

This source of income to water authorities is the one true tax-based charge remaining. It involves a precepting* process. The precept is notified to certain Councils and Internal Drainage Boards, and is then aggregated and charged to the public.

## 12. GRANTS

### GENERAL

Generally, water authorities have to raise their own income—only a small proportion is met by grants or subsidies of any kind from central government. Grants which are available are listed below.

### LAND DRAINAGE

This is the most significant grant-aided area of water authorities activities, and grants are available from the Ministry of Agriculture, Fisheries and Food under provisions of the Land Drainage Act 1976. Grants of this kind normally amount to less than one-half of the total cost of schemes, which have to be approved in detail by the Ministry before any grant becomes payable.

### RURAL WATER SUPPLIES AND SEWERAGE

The Rural Water Supplies and Sewerage Acts 1944 to 1971 provide for a limited amount of grant aid to schemes for water supplies and sewerage in rural areas. A scheme will be eligible for grant aid where it:—

(1) serves a rural locality defined as:—
   most localities in rural districts, except where a development is urban or suburban in character, in particular where it is near a town, or in other areas where schemes will

*A "precept" is a charge which one authority can make upon the income of another. Land drainage costs of water authorities are largely met by precepts upon County Councils and London Borough Councils, under the provisions of Section 45/46 of the Land Drainage Act 1976.

serve less than 100 properties (including prospective development) per mile of main sewer, will be considered if
(a)     prima facie rural and
(b)     effectively separated from the nearest substantial urban development (normally taken as one mile);
(2)   has the primary purpose of serving *existing* properties for the first time (although the imminent development up to 25 per cent of existing properties is admissable for grant purposes);
(3)   links the locality for the first time to an adequate water source or to effective sewage disposal arrangements.

Apart from the grants available under the provisions of the Land Drainage Act 1976, the Ministry of Agriculture, Fisheries and Food will make supplementary grants towards the cost of rural water mains extensions. Grant is limited to a maximum of 75 per cent of the assessed agricultural benefit, which is calculated from the possible increased cropping and stocking arising from the availability of a piped water supply.

## 13. MARKETING

Water, as a resource or service, is available in adequate quantities currently and at most times; it is reasonably cheap, committing only 1 or 2 per cent of earnings and has a monopoly supplier. It is therefore not surprising that *marketing* has been neglected in the water industry. There are no marketing departments or functions, and the question of "selling water" is not regarded as a priority.

However, with the impact of higher prices there has arisen a more commercial approach, with growing interest in attempts to recycle used water, and interest in the return on investment by the industry and an expectation of benefits to be achieved.

At some point there comes the major question: is the water industry in the business of selling water and other services or is it in the business of rationing use by price? If the latter, this section may be unnecessary; if the former, then the industry may have to come to terms with marketing its products and services.

Other substantial questions arise in this context. It is easy to see the logic of attempting to sell by-products of the sewage function, such as soil conditioners, fertilizers, and even methane. The industry is already in the consultancy market, and at some time it could well be in the protein food market. But what of the main product—water is to most a colourless liquid, necessary to support life and useful or even essential in many commercial processes. It can also be regarded from another viewpoint as a conveyance mechanism for many dissolved chemicals, examples of which are organic acids, carbonates, sulphates, nitrates, chlorides, bromides, fluorides, and iodides. Many users of water in industrial, commercial, or agricultural processes would be delighted to receive more of one and less of another, and might well require additional additives. The time may be approaching when the marketing of such a "tailormade" specification water will be both attractive to the supplier and the consumer. In such a situation a recalculated charge would result, and there would be an opportunity to enhance the return on investment at which each investor looks so critically.

Examples already exist in this country where purpose-specified water at an attractive price has created advantageous contracts between supplier and consumer. Some organizations have similar arrangements for the disposal of high quality recovered water from sewage treatment works for use as cooling or other process water.

Already, the chemical content of potable water may be critical to certain horticulturalists, particularly where intensive cultivation under glass takes place. It is not too great a step to imagine that such a customer would be interested in a particular "made water" with nutrient added.

As this section has attempted to show, there has, for good reasons, been a minimal need for marketing managers in the industry in the past. The time may be coming when that situation will need to be reviewed, and the industry could see the emergence of a new discipline.

# Chapter 6

# MANAGEMENT

## 1. PROLOGUE

THE theory and practice of management has, over recent decades, been the subject of much study, writing, and argument—management courses, schools, theories, qualifications, systems, techniques, teachers, savants and cranks have abounded. Throughout it all, the practising manager has had to maintain his work, wits, and equilibrium.

In a single Chapter of this Manual it is impossible to do more than introduce the engineer or scientist (or other professional) to the responsibilities of management, and to the techniques with which to approach the problems of directing and controlling affairs which extend beyond the confine of a single skill or handful of people.

This Chapter cannot even dabble in the subject of management training. At best it can indicate the skills which the manager needs to possess, and encourage him to read, study, and practice to acquire them.

## 2. NATURE OF MANAGEMENT

There are almost as many definitions of management as there are managers. Many years ago it was defined as deciding what other people are to do, and getting them to do it in the best possible way. Nowadays, this sounds both remote and arbitrary, but at least it does recognize that management is about people, a fact overlooked in more recent propositions such as "management consists of decision-taking concerning the allocation of available resources to meet defined objectives", or even "management consists of the effective realization of a corporate plan".

Remembering always that management is a social process, something that people do in relation to other people, the following elements can be identified; they are each discussed later in this Chapter:—

(1) **Planning**—the analysis and identification of objectives, resources, constraints, and priorities;

(2) **Organization**—the structuring of individual activities to act as a corporate whole;

(3) **Direction**—the motivation of people, determining their duties and targets, and guiding the organization as a whole; and

(4) **Control**—collecting and using information to identify and correct deviations from the desired course of events.

Styles of management can vary infinitely between the two extremes of absolute autocracy, where a "king" whose word is law makes every decision, and "communes" where every voice has equal weight. Even these two extreme styles may be quite effective in small organizations, but as so often in human affairs the best choice lies somewhere in the middle. That choice will not be the same for all organizations, but will vary with the times and circumstances, and inescapably with the people concerned. The reference to "times" is a reminder again that management is a social process, and a style of management has to be acceptable to the society in which it operates, and for efficiency will have to change as that society changes. Today these changes can be quite rapid, and management must accept the task, always unwelcome, of changing its ideas with equal rapidity. This is easier said than done, and it has been argued that our politics and culture are often nowadays unable to change with sufficient speed to keep in phase with social and economical developments.

Antony Jay (in "Management and Machiavelli"\*) calls not only Machiavelli but Milton and Shakespeare to the aid of his argument that management is a political process, and that modern corporations are so similar to independent states of the past that they can only be understood in terms of political and constitutional history, and management can only be properly studied as a branch of government. Certainly, the modern manager, seeking through management aids and data processing to reach correct decisions, nevertheless constantly finds the old Adam re-asserting himself; no man in a position of power can escape the power game, and he may well turn to the cynical Machiavelli for advice.

Certainly, too, management is not a human activity that started with the twentieth century.

### 3. CORPORATE MANAGEMENT

The concept of corporate management is now widely applied and is also used in connection with a number of management activities—corporate planning, corporate objective, corporate approach, etc. The basic significance is an awareness that an organization's activities should be planned and directed as a whole, and not be the simple sum of the contributions of various sections of that organization.

This concept is by no means new, it has existed in various forms ever since organizations became large enough to split into separate specialized parts, followed by the awareness that those parts were pursuing their own ends rather than that of the organization as a whole. Corporate management seeks to bring the heads of those sections together, and to impose on them an individual responsibility for ensuring that each problem is examined in a corporate manner, before a decision is taken or advice given. The concept is particularly valuable in some public authorities, including water authorities, where otherwise the heads of specialist departments might give advice directly to their governing body, without provision for their separate advice to be co-ordinated in the light of some previously defined policy or objective of the authority as a whole.

It will be seen that corporate management is to some extent an antidote for departmentalism, to the tendency of a department acting in a non-corporate manner to feel that the department's own objectives are necessarily those of the authority as a whole. The references to corporate management as a "concept" are deliberate, as its success depends upon a deliberate intention on the part of managers to seek to attain the corporate objectives of the organization as a whole, rather than those of the section for which they are responsible. Provided that this concept is accepted and applied, then the actual mechanisms for corporate management are not so important. It is however important that the concept should be held and applied throughout an organization, and not only at top management level.

The strengths of corporate management are obvious. To make the best of these, it is necessary to recognize and minimize the weaknesses, which include:—

    (*a*)  a tendency to carry the search for co-ordination, for a corporate identity, too far; and to degenerate into a mass of committees and meetings;

\*Jay, Antony, 1967, "Management and Machiavelli", Hodder and Stoughton, London. (Pelican Book 1970.)

(b)  a danger that the search for a consensus will inevitably lead to a compromise decision for which no individual feels himself fully responsible;

(c)  the fact that most people are motivated by other people as individuals, and less frequently by teams;

(d)  it can place a heavy burden upon a departmental head who is a specialist rather than a manager, when he and his fellows are grouped together and told to act as a management team. After all, they may originally have been chosen for quite different talents.

Attempts have been made to solve this last problem in other organizations by introducing the generalist administrator, an officer to take charge of the specialists, presumably on the assumption that a jack of no trade must be master of all. The results hardly recommend this proposal to the water industry, but it is the duty of every specialist officer appointed to management to be prepared to submerge his previous professional interests and pursue the corporate end. In every case it is an important duty of the leader of the team to ensure that the other members run together, and truly follow the corporate approach to their duties as members of that team. Perhaps the next most important duty is to ensure that their decisions draw from the combined skills and wisdom of the members, and do not decline to the determination of a lowest common denominator nor become a means to avoid personal responsibility.

Members of a management team must be competent and senior people, likely to hold views of their own. With such people a consensus is not always possible, and provision must be made to recognize honest disagreement. However, dissent should be distinguished into two classes. Where there are disagreements from the majority opinion, the dissenter must be prepared to accept collective responsibility and to support the decision of the team, once this has been made.

The second form of dissent is much more serious. Some members of the team will be senior professional or specialist officers, and if the team reject a member's specialist advice, he may feel it his professional duty to record his dissent. There can be no question of a professional officer in such a case meekly accepting collective responsibility for a decision which he regards as not just wrong or mistaken, but improper or disastrous.

## 4. PLANNING

A manager at all levels has to accept responsibility for the direction of planning activities, to ensure that they are linked to reality and ultimate action and that the cost of the planning process is justified by its benefit. He must also ensure that the two chronic temptations of planners are resisted, firstly to carry out elaborate analyses which are not justified by the reliability of the original data, and secondly to pursue planning as an end in itself. Small deeds done are better than great deeds planned.

The discipline of orderly planning demands, as far as possible, a quantification of data, and quantified economic and financial comparisons and appraisals. This, however, can never be the whole of the story, and it is the duty of the manager rather than the planner to ensure that the process takes account of unquantifiable constraints such as social pressures, the attitudes and expectations of consumers, as well as the realities of power and the art of the possible. If he can, he should also add that touch of vision and imagination without which the planning process can decline to mechanical sterility.

Finally, it does no harm to take an historical view, and while planning for the future to keep an eye on how successful were forecasts and plans made in the past. It is surprising how rarely a check is made on past planning performance, although it is highly significant to recall the simplicity and cheapness of earlier planning processes compared to those of today. Refinement of forecasting is useless unless it produces predictions nearer the ultimate events, in such a way as to justify the cost of the refinement.

## 5. ORGANIZATION

A manager should be aware of current studies and theories of organization, and know the forms of organization design which are available, and how they may be selected and applied after an analytical approach to the organization's objectives and tasks. This is particularly important if he is to be responsible for the design of any new organization, however small, as there is a recurring temptation—from which the water industry is far from immune—to base organizations on the needs and habits of the past and to ignore lessons that have been hard-learnt elsewhere. Once an organization has been set up, it is extraordinarily difficult to change it; a little study and thought beforehand can save years of creaking inadequacy.

Once the organization is in being, it must be kept under review; and it is important to distinguish between the establishment—which is, as it were, the ration of manpower resource allocated by the governing body—and the organization chart which shows how the people within that establishment are deployed and work in relation to each other. The establishment may remain unchanged, except in details, for a long period of time; the organization may have to be quite flexible and change rapidly and frequently. Because of these changes, and of the human element that is involved, an organization is rarely what it seems and may exist at several levels of reality. The organization that top management believes to exist may not be the same as that which has been established at a lower level. In turn this may be different from the way things actually work at still lower levels. For these reasons, management must keep a fairly frequent review of the organization structure as it actually operates and correct it as necessary.

A number of common faults that this review may demonstrate include:—

(i)   Spans of control may be too wide. The number of people that one person can directly control is surprisingly small; six is rather a lot, and if their activites are different and require a high degree of involvement, two or three may be plenty.

(ii)  The organization may be fussily over-divided into small units, requiring a complicated system of communication and co-ordination to bring them together again to act in a corporate manner—in other words in a way to seek the objectives of the organization as a whole, and not to pursue sectarian interests.

(iii) The chains of control, responsibility, communication, etc., may be unclear or over-long.

(iv)  Responsibilities may not be sufficiently clearly defined, so that different groups poach each other's preserves.

(v)   Over-large gaps between the pay of successive posts may indicate future problems of succession, or show that senior staff are being under-employed, or vice versa.

In England and Wales the regional water authorities face a complex problem of organization. In many ways, particularly at the level of the executive divisions in each authority, they were originally not so much new organizations as an amalgam of earlier ones. Another problem is that the authorities are multi-functional, and in many ways have multiple objectives, all within fairly small organizations. Their duties, and the dispersion of their staff, means that they face the problems common to organizations which are divided between a head office and dispersed executive

units, while the application of corporate management following the Ogden Report*
has to some extent fixed a departmental structure, where each department is headed
by a member of the management team.

The Report recommended an organization structure for water authorities based on
the concept of *line-and-staff*. Briefly, this comprises a headquarters management
team of functional chiefs—operations, finance, scientific services, etc. Outside
headquarters the activities are carried out by divisions, each under a manager, whose
staff will include specialists of the same kinds as those who form the headquarters
team. The *line* is the executive link from headquarters to divisional manager (the *line
manager*), the *staff* link is from the functional chief (director) at headquarters to
senior officers of the same speciality in the divisions. It may be noted that this
organization has for many years been adopted by armies, where a specialist officer
such as an engineer, with functional responsibility to a chief engineer at
headquarters, finds himself under a *line manager*, the local field commander. Ogden
added a gloss to the concept by suggesting the establishment of management teams
within divisions.

Within the general framework of the Ogden Report, the various water authorities
tackled their organization problems in different ways. It is hoped that this flexible
approach to organization will continue, and not be stultified by further
centralization of control and power.

## 6. DIRECTION

The direction of an organization takes planning into practice. Having determined
tasks and objectives and planned the structure, it must then be operated as a going
concern. In direction we become much more concerned with people; we have to
respond to changing circumstances by guiding people to meet them.

Direction of an organization requires information about its performance.
Nowadays "management information" is offered in quantity, as data processing
makes it possible to produce all sorts of figures said to be indicators of performance.
As usual, this information is only as good as its input, which is often treated with
much less care than the output. There is a tendency for managers to be bombarded by
the professional producers of data, whose attitude is "we can provide all the
information you need, just tell us what you want" the inference being that *we* have
done *our* duty, and *you* can now take the responsibility! All managers are aware of
how easy it is for valuable information to be submerged in a flood of figures. The
manager must have strong control over the production of this kind of information,
its credibility, and its use. There is no way to manage when drowned in such a
flood, nor has the practising manager the time to sift the wheat from the chaff; he
must ensure that is done for him, and that only significant and credible information
is presented to him.

When it comes to directing the organization there is no field in which it is more
important for the manager to assign priorities than his own time. Events crowd in on
him, and he has to distinguish sharply between those things that matter and those
which do not. This is often far from obvious, and a test of managerial skill is for him
to decide where he will apply his own limited resources. All else must either be
forgotten or delegated. One of the commonest failures of management is to be
become submerged in items of low priority, and have no time to deal with the real
problems.

*The Report "The New Water Industry, Management and Structure" of the Management Structure
Committee to the Secretary of State for the Environment, June 1973. The recommendations were largely
adopted by the Regional Water Authorities formed in England and Wales in 1974.

## 7. CONTROL

The manager must monitor and control the performance of his organization, to check that it is proceeding on the lines selected. There are a host of methods and techniques, some of which are discussed under the section "Management aids and techniques" (p. 215). Generally, however, monitoring of performance must depend upon financial or quantitative data, and too much of this can soon submerge the mind. The manager must also be wary as to validity of such data; "garbage in, garbage out" is a saying which has deservedly become well known, while quantitative data has its limitations. For example, quite apart from inflation and the concepts of real or current cost, a purely financial approach cannot show whether a sensible policy is being pursued—even with the most detailed analysis it can only reflect the assumptions made. Life seems to become more complicated much faster than we can identify and pin down its vagaries in quantitative terms.

Inexperienced managers tend to shy away from decisions until they have sufficient data to make it easy. But experience soon teaches that there never is enough data, and management decisions must always involve an element of guess, an element of risk.

## 8. THE PEOPLE FACTOR

Whatever management is or is not, it is certainly about people. The organization and direction of the impersonal affairs of an organization may be administration, or accountancy, or whatever; it is only when the personal factor is included that it can be called management.

### MOTIVATION

Management must work through people, and it follows that it is the manager's first duty to motivate those people, so that they give of their best and offer their abilities in a positive way to the performance of their work and the advantage of the organization. Lack of motivation is a failure of management.

All this is readily and widely acknowledged, but motivation is a tender plant difficult to foster, quick to wilt. It has been the subject of numerous behavioural studies, and most people, from their own experience, can clearly recall examples of good and bad motivation; but it is often far more difficult to apply the lesson. At least, however, there are certain means which will help to motivate people; they include:—

(1) **Fairness**—consistent standards consistently applied, a clear and consistent pay structure, no favouritism;

(2) **Reward**—"stick and carrot" is perhaps too crude an image for modern management, but a manager must seek to reward effort and success, and penalize idleness and neglect. On the other hand, rewards must be truly earned, few would claim that a very common form of reward—"productivity bonuses"—have done much at all for motivation.

(3) **Control**—failure of the manager to correct an error may not much affect the motivation of the employee concerned, but his colleagues will quickly become careless or apathetic;

(4) **Interest**—almost everyone has been in a situation where they are convinced that management cares nothing for their efforts, which diminish accordingly.

(5) **Accessibility**—this is a closely related matter, delay deadens minds and convinces employees that management has no real interest in their work. Apart from anything else the pure cost of hanging around waiting for decisions can be tremendous, and its affect on morale devastating;

(6) **Delegation**—this is discussed in more detail below, but the feeling that one is empowered to get on with one's job is a great motivator;

(7) **Example**—unless the manager himself shows some enthusiasm for the job, some urge to get things done well, few others will.

Two great opponents of good motivation are pettiness of mind, and management by interference; and perhaps it is not too old-fashioned to suggest that a manager should show a high level of courtesy and respect when dealing with everyone, at all levels, in his organization. Certainly, lack of courtesy and bad manners seem all too frequently to be the trigger, if no more, of industrial disputes.

## DELEGATION

Since delegation involves getting other people to do work for you, it should be popular; but is easier said than done. The terms of delegation must be clear, the area of responsibility must be defined, and the policy within which the delegated power is to be exercised must be clear; adequate authority to carry out the duty must also be delegated.

A manager, by delegation, does not divest himself of responsibility—and this creates the prime difficulty which tempts so many managers not to delegate, but to do it all themselves. The delegation of a duty must carry with it the authority to carry out that duty effectively, but the manager remains responsible for seeing that the duty is discharged.

Once a job has been delegated, subsequent interference in the detailed work of the subordinate indicates that either he, or his senior, are incompetent. The senior may, of course, discuss the details chosen by the junior, but in no case should he alter details which are within the responsibilities delegated. To do so is to practice management by interference, a deadly enemy of efficiency and good motivation. The best advice on delegation is old and traditional—don't keep a dog and bark yourself.

The best managers delegate as much as possible, and always remember that freedom to make decisions means that some bad ones must occur, and that the man who never made a mistake never made anything.

## SOCIAL BEHAVIOUR

A great deal of work has been done in the fields of the behavioural sciences and studies of social behaviour at work, and of means of utilizing those sciences and studies in management. To complaints that the behavioural sciences are inexact and woolly, their protagonists are quick to retort that managers have a choice between those sciences, such as they are, and no science at all. This Manual is not the place to even start to summarize any of the work carried out in this vast field, but every manager should make and keep himself familiar with the main works and theories.

Perhaps it is worth pointing out that behavioural sciences do not seem to be able to produce good managers, but they may help a good manager to become a better one—rather like the way in which a polishing filter can make a good effluent better, but has little effect upon a bad one.

## 9. PERSONNEL MANAGEMENT

### THE PERSONNEL OFFICER

The trends towards greater specialization, larger units, and the proliferation of employment law all make it difficult for a manager to handle relations with his workforce without skilled professional assistance. There is nothing new about this, managers are accustomed to needing and receiving professional advice from accountants, engineers, lawyers, etc., and the personnel officer is only the latest of a long list of essential management helpers. It is important that the personnel officer should not usurp the function of management itself, a problem that arises with all specialist advisors if they are unfairly used by management as cover to hide from problems, and as protection against hard decisions.

Similarly, if a manager uses his personnel officer to shield him from "people problems", then the personnel man comes to be regarded by the employees as a front man, a tool of management, and loses stature and acceptability accordingly. In many ways a personnel officer can only function efficiently if he is regarded both by management and employees as a sort of honest broker—one may compare this with the role of the engineer as quasi-arbitrator under the ICE Conditions of Contract, where his decisions may bind both contractor and employer.

## THE PERSONNEL FUNCTION

These are some of the functions which are normally undertaken by the personnel department:—

**Pay and Conditions**—Personnel must be the experts upon schemes of pay and conditions of service for all employees, to provide management with information and advice, to ensure all agreed variations are noted and the rules applied.

**Recruitment**—Administration of the whole system of approving the filling of a post, checking budgetary allocation, advertising, interviewing, and selection; and assisting directly in this final stage, ensuring that proper procedures are followed and all applicants properly informed of where they stand.

**Appointments**—Compliance with the legal requirements as to contracts of employment, etc., updating personal records, arranging for first reporting and induction training, arranging that newly-appointed employees are paid on the proper scale, and watching for legal problems arising from temporary and probationary engagements.

**Retirements and Resignations**—Administration of insurance, tax, and pension requirements, closure of records, and termination of pay arrangements.

**Discipline**—Operating (and if necessary helping to determine) disciplinary rules and records, ensuring that the law regarding dismissal is closely followed and that the employer is protected in any legal or quasi-legal actions by dismissed employees.

**Industrial Relations**—Assisting with negotiations between employers and employees about pay, promotion, practices, and procedures. It is in this field particularly that the personnel officer must seek to earn the confidence and trust of both sides.

**Consultation**—Serving joint consultation and negotiating machinery, ensuring compliance with agreed procedures concerning grievances or disputes, and for appeals such as those for regrading or against dismissal. The water industry has well established machinery, jointly agreed, in all these fields, and it is the function of Personnel to "know the ropes", to advise. management, and to deal with administration.

**Manpower**—To analyse manpower needs and advise management on recruitment and training policies to meet future manpower requirements.

**Employment Law**—To keep abreast of the complexities of employment legislation, and to guide management through them.

**Training**—To plan the training needed for replacing and updating existing employees, including the preparation of a training plan so that training can be matched to needs and resources, and then to administer the actual training, organizing internal courses (some of which may be designed to cover quite local needs) as well as training at courses run by the National Water Council (Training Division), or at colleges and other educational establishments.

**Health and Safety**—Personnel have the duty of assisting management to comply with the Health and Safety at Work legislation, as well as meeting the requirements for the reporting and recording of accidents, compliance with Factories Acts and similar legislation, and administering the requirements for the appointment of safety representatives and safety committees. All this becomes rather impersonal unless they also undertake responsibility for staff welfare beyond the bare legal requirements.

## WORK STUDY

Work Study is often grouped with Personnel. This may be satisfactory in smaller organizations, but there are arguments for separation. It is sometimes difficult for the personnel officer to win trust and confidence as the "honest broker" if, at the same time, he is responsible for looking after management's interests in the kind of horse-trading negotiations inseparable from bonus payment schemes. He must always be closely involved in productivity schemes and work study generally, but it is sometimes better if he can act from a separate position. In addition, there is a trend towards the use of work study skills in the organization of all kinds of work activity, including clerical and professional duties; and this is rather separate from the personnel function.

## "INDUSTRIAL RELATIONS"

Good employer/employee relations (often rather misleadingly called "industrial relations") nowadays depend upon the existence of previously agreed systems for negotiation and consultation, and for the settlement of disputes. The ability to refer in this way, properly used, can remove personal heat and acrimony from disagreement at local level. In the water industry the arrangements for joint consultation and negotiation are well established. In England and Wales the National Water Council, under the Water Act 1973, have an overall duty to promote these arrangements, and the following bodies cover all employees in the industry. Each comprises members appointed by employers and by employee organizations, and each is the subject of an agreement governing its constitution, activities and powers; each publishes agreements upon pay and conditions of service for the employees covered.

(a) **National Joint Committee for Chief Officers of the Water Service**—covering chief executives and directors, and equivalent staff.

(b) **Joint National Council for Water Service Senior Staffs**—covering assistant directors, divisional managers, some members of divisional management teams, and equivalent staff. There are a number of Regional Committees established under the National Council.

(c) **National Joint Council Water Service Staffs**—covering the vast majority of the non-manual staff in the industry; this Council's publication on pay and conditions of service is familiarly known as *"The Blue Book"*. It sponsors subordinate organizations, Regional Joint Councils, which enjoy a measure of delegated powers of negotiation and decision.

(d) **National Joint Industrial Council for the Water Service**—covering all manual employees, except for some craftsmen, of water authorities, water companies and affiliated internal drainage authorities, its publication on pay and conditions of service is familiarly known as *"The Green Book"*. It sponsors Regional Joint Industrial Councils similar to those for non-manual staff.

(e) **Craftsmen**—there is a national agreement on rates of pay and conditions of service for craftsmen in the water service, which is made between the Employers' Side of the National Joint Industrial Council for the Water Service on the one hand, and the

Confederation of Ship Building and Engineering Unions and the Operatives' Side of the National Joint Council for the Building Industry on the other. The two employee organizations concerned represent between them 25 constituent trade unions.

As explained in Chapter 2 (Organization of the Water Industry from 1974) most of the duties of the water authorities and water companies in England and Wales are undertaken in Scotland by local authorities and in Northern Ireland by the government. In Scotland pay and conditions of all employees engaged upon water services are determined, in theory at least, by the various joint negotiating bodies established for Scottish local authorities; with the exception of the Central Scotland Water Development Board where the *Green Book* (see above) is applied to manual employees. In practice there are arrangements under which the *Green Book* also applies to some other manual employees (but not craftsmen) in the *water supply* service in Scotland.

In Northern Ireland the *Green Book* applies to manual workers (except craftsmen) in the water service. The pay and conditions of craftsmen and all non-manual employees are governed by the appropriate negotiating bodies for the British civil service.

## NEGOTIATION AND CONSULTATION

It is important to distinguish between these two activities. *Negotiation* takes place in a bargaining situation, where there are differences to be bridged and where agreement has to be sought. In negotiations both sides have to be prepared for a certain amount of give and take, and to seek eventual joint agreement. If this cannot be reached immediately, there is usually provision for the disagreement to be referred to the next level in the joint machinery. *Consultation* applies to situations in which management must make the responsible decisions, but where employee interests are affected, and where the manager would be wise to seek the comments and advice of employee representatives before reaching his decision.

The manager must take care not to allow these two situations to become muddled, or he will find himself *negotiating* about decisions which are his responsibility, and with which employee involvement should be limited to *consultation*. The new manager may find the process of consultation tedious, slow and unrewarding, but present day society demands an increasing degree of employee participation, and this is a repeated reminder that management is a social process that has to be acceptable to the society in which it operates.

## 10. TRAINING

In the previous section it is suggested that the administration of training should be a duty of the personnel officer. This does not detract from the duty of management, at all levels, to ensure that the people under their control are properly trained for their present and potential duties.

The Water Act 1973 lays a duty on the National Water Council to prepare a scheme for training and education throughout the water industry, and unlike the other activities of the Council this duty extends to Scotland and Northern Ireland. The Council runs a number of residential training centres where courses are held continuously while, in addition, a great deal of training is directly arranged by employing authorities at universities and colleges of all kinds. In addition the larger size of units in the water industry now makes it possible for an increasing number of in-house courses to be mounted, whereby an authority makes its own internal arrangements for the transfer and acquisition of skills.

Money can easily be wasted on training that is not really required, and it is essential that a proper training plan be prepared, so that people can be trained in advance to meet the real needs of the organization, without the waste involved in expensive over-training. People should not be trained at the expense of their employer merely because it is thought likely that they can acquire a new skill or obtain a qualification, unless there is a reasonable chance of that skill or qualification being of use to the employer or the industry, otherwise a great deal of money can be wasted and frustration generated.

A training plan must be based on a training policy dealing with the general approach and attitude towards training. In the water industry this is partly determined by the requirements of the Water Act 1973 and the work of the National Water Council under the provisions of that Act. The next stage is an analysis of training needs, under headings such as:—

(i)   replacement of staff who resign or retire;
(ii)  training for succession, so that wherever possible staff may be promoted within their capability and that management may have a choice of such promotions;
(iii) training for new skills, and up-dating existing ones; and
(iv)  training to meet changed needs and circumstances.

This leads to the preparation of the training plan itself, which should include programmes for training and means of organizing and controlling them. In particular, a training plan should include clear statements of what training is to be done, how it is to be carried out, who is to be trained, and who will be responsible for organizing, carrying out, and monitoring the training. Not least, the plan must include estimates of cost and resources required.

Not the least need for training is that of managers themselves, and the National Water Council's Training Division offers both advice and a number of courses for training in management. There are full time courses leading to qualifications in management or business studies, while the Diploma in Management Studies is a practical means of gaining rigorous grounding in management theory and practice through part-time courses which are held at many local colleges.

## 11. MANAGEMENT AIDS AND TECHNIQUES

### THE USE OF MANAGEMENT AIDS

Until recent years all management aids were primarily financial in character, designed to keep the organization solvent, to show overall profitability, to identify costs, to guard against dishonesty, and so on. Although these accountancy techniques have been highly refined over the centuries, they are often crude and intermittent as controls and indicators, and by themselves can give a misleading picture.

Partly as a result, attention has in recent decades been given to developing other management aids, and this has led to an enormous output of writing and theorizing on the subject, while everyone involved in management has been subject to pressures to adopt all sorts of techniques to improve their performance. This is all to the good, and very stimulating, but in looking at results it is difficult to avoid a certain scepticism; so many techniques have been praised and promoted, and all too soon have faded into the background. This is unfortunate, because many useful techniques have become devalued because they were oversold in the first place, or became an end in themselves. All new ideas attract enthusiasts, and new management techniques are often promoted by people who are enthusiastic about them, and who suffer the usual enthusiast's defect of being absorbed in their own activities. Their vision may be limited by the confines of their techniques, and they may never have stopped to wonder what it is all about, or whether it is worthwhile, or to acknowledge that anything really matters outside their particular speciality.

The manager should therefore approach the use of such techniques with an open and enquiring mind, but with a critical eye; with a tendency to trust his own observation and judgement rather than the claims of enthusiasts and those with an axe to grind. If he is a little allergic to jargon, so much the better.

There are many good aids to management, but none better than the ability to take a detached and balanced view, avoiding these extremes:—

(1)   to believe that management aids are an elaborate and inefficient substitute for sturdy commonsense, or
(2)   to abdicate managerial responsibility, and to believe that to apply sufficient management techniques is all that a manager has to do.

Avoiding these extremes, each technique should be approached in a similar way to many other problems, such as:—

(a)   What is the objective?
(b)   Will this technique help to meet it?
(c)   What are its disadvantages?
(d)   What will it cost?
(e)   Is it worth it?
(f)   Is there another way to do it cheaper/better?

The question of disadvantages is most important. Everything brings its own disadvantages, and it is a great pity that the sales atmosphere generated around many management aids means that their good points are fully publicized, but there is a tacit silence about the inevitable associated disadvantages.

### MANAGEMENT TECHNIQUES IN USE

Some management techniques currently in use are:—

### Cost-Benefit Analysis

A comparison between the total *costs*, direct and indirect, financial and social (quantified as far as possible), of carrying out a service or activity, and the total *value* of that service or activity quantified in the same manner. (See "Investment Appraisal", below).

### Cost-Effectiveness Analysis

An analysis to find the cheapest way of attaining a defined objective, or the maximum value from a given expenditure, sometimes leading to a decision as to the point at which diminishing returns cease to justify further investment, whether of cash or other resources.

### Costing

The techniques of ascribing expenditure to particular activities. Types of cost and costing include the following:—

#### Types of Cost

(i)   *Direct Cost*.—A cost which can be identified directly with a particular activity.
(ii)   *Fixed Cost*.—A cost unaffected by variations in volume of output.

(iii) *Marginal Cost.*—The amount at any given volume of output by which total costs are changed if that volume is increased or decreased by a single unit.

(iv) *Opportunity Cost.*—The maximum amount obtainable if assets or resources were to be sold or otherwise put to the most valuable practical alternative use.

(v) *Replacement Cost.*—The cost of replacing an asset at a given point in time, either now or in the future.

(vi) *Variable Cost.*—A cost which tends to vary directly with volume of output.

## Types of Costing

(1) *Absorption Costing.*—Charging both variable and fixed costs to products or services.

(2) *Direct Costing.*—Charging all direct costs to products or services, leaving other costs to be written off against profits.

(3) *Marginal Costing.*—The ascertainment of marginal costs and the effect of changes in volume of output on profit, differentiating between fixed and variable costs.

## Cybernetics

The study of communication and control mechanisms in machines and the human brain, or the means of controlling an activity to keep it directed towards a particular objective. Cybernetic control is dependent upon the adequacy of the feedback of relevant and reliable information to the point at which action can be taken.

## Investment Appraisal

Assessing whether expenditure of capital on a project would show a satisfactory rate of return. The analysis involves the use of discounting techniques, and is usually associated with a cost-benefit analysis. The application of these two techniques in the water industry is described in Chapter 4, "Economics".

## Job Evaluation

Methods of determining the relative worth, in terms of pay, of jobs within an organization. There are several systems for job evaluation; in practice none can be applied effectively without the consent and co-operation of the employees concerned.

## Management by Exception

Arrangements under which only exceptional items are reported to management, all others being dealt with according to previous instructions or statements of policy. A good analogy is that of automatic plant controls, which only signal alarm states if predetermined limits are exceeded. As with such controls, the technique of management by exception only works if the limit states are defined beforehand.

## Management by Objectives

A technique under which agreed and realistic targets are fixed for achieving greater effectiveness throughout the whole or any part of an organization (even a single person). This system includes the fixing of targets in readily identifiable terms, and must provide for periodical appraisal of progress and, if necessary, revision of targets. Any work programme, if it includes dates for completion of certain stages and is agreed, is an application of management by objectives.

The application of this technique sometimes leads to a mass of paperwork, which can obscure and destroy the essential elegance of the concept, which is that targets are *agreed* and *accepted*, and that the people who work to achieve them are therefore personally committed to doing so.

## Method Study

(See under "Work Study", below).

## Network Analysis

The process of analysing the activities within a project to component parts and recording them in a network to illustrate the inter-relation between the activities necessary to carry the project to completion. The technique is widely used for physical projects, but can equally be used for any managerial or organizational activity.

Other titles for the same process are Critical Path Method (CPM) and Programme Evaluation and Review Technique (PERT). These names refer to network analyses that were originally somewhat different in concept, but which have developed on similar lines until there is now no fundamental difference between them.

## Operational Research (OR)

The application of scientific processes to operational problems, usually involving the development of a symbolic model of the system, incorporating measurements of factors such as chance and risk, with which to predict and compare alternative decisions. Several techniques are used, they normally have a mathematical or statistical basis, and involve computer simulation to predict the effects of a range of forecast conditions and choices of action.

## Organization and Methods (O and M)

The systematic study of the structure of an organization or any part of it, and its procedures and methods, leading to action to increase efficiency by improving procedures, methods and systems, communication and controls, and organization structure. Part of this activity is a specialized application of Method Study (see under "Work Study", below).

## Value Analysis

The comparision of the cost of a project with the value obtained from it, to determine whether the value justifies the expenditure. The term is also used to describe studies of the cost of employing people or carrying out procedures in relation to the object to be achieved. *Value Engineering* is used for the application of value analysis at the planning stage.

## Work Study

A management service based on those techniques, particularly *Method Study* and *Work Measurement*, which are used in the examination of human work, and which lead to the systematic investigation of the resources and factors which effect the efficiency and economy of the situation being reviewed, in order to effect improvement.

(a) *Method Study.*—Systematic recording and critical examination of the factors and resources involved in ways of doing work, as a means of developing and applying easier and more effective methods and reducing costs.

(*b*) *Work Measurement.*—The application of techniques designed to establish the time for a qualified worker to carry out a specified job at a defined level of performance.

In the water industry work study has largely been linked with the payment of bonuses for increased productivity in manual activities, although from the above definitions it will be seen that the techniques have a very much wider application.

## FUTURE DEVELOPMENTS

By the time this Manual has been printed and read, it is likely that a few more techniques will have been invented and promoted. The reader is advised to approach them with an open but critical mind, as advised at the beginning of this section.

## 12. COMMUNICATION AND PUBLIC RELATIONS

### COMMUNICATION SKILLS

Good communications are a somewhat negative virtue—they will not secure the efficiency of an organization but without them inefficiency is guaranteed. It is the duty of a manager to foster and secure effective communications for his organization.

Communication is essentially a two-way process, the reciprocal transmission of information; one way communication is like talking to the deaf. Half of communication skills lie in receiving—listening or reading. The communications which the manager must foster fall into three classes:—

(i)   **Personal**—contacts between people, and individual communication skills.

(ii)  **Organizational**—the channels of communication within the organization.

(iii) **External**—contact with other organizations, and with the public.

Everybody, working with others, needs some personal skills of communication—at the lowest level, the ability to speak and hear; but a manager must foster these arts to a higher degree. In speech and in writing he must seek clarity, simplicity, and avoid misunderstanding; these are not always natural skills and he must foster them through personal effort and by formal training or study. There are other skills to be taught and learned, in the field where behavioural sciences have mapped various aspects of interaction between individuals. These are particularly in evidence at meetings of groups, where gestures and other "signals" as well as words may firstly give a key to a person's thoughts and attitudes, and secondly give the opportunity to direct and control the discussion. This is a field in which a manager, unless unusually gifted, may usefully himself seek training.

### COMMUNICATIONS WITHIN THE ORGANIZATION

Communications within an organization need fostering with great care. Not that they will wither—far from it, people may spend too much time communicating and not working, but there may be bad communications in the sense that they are carrying too much or useless information, or—more frequently—false information. It is the duty of management to seek to improve the situation by keeping a steady flow, in all required directions, of sound information and instructions. An exceptionally vigorous and misleading bush telegraph is a sure symptom of bad communications. It is a common and disconcerting experience to find, even in an organization with good communications, how a message has failed to reach the person concerned, or has reached them in a garbled form. It is equally common to find that information which is common knowledge in one group is never transmitted to another, because everyone assumes that they are sure to know about it anyway.

It must be remembered that communications go in all directions. Downwards, from the chief to a subordinate, is the commonest direction considered, and perhaps the easiest; all that is often required is to ensure that the message does not become diluted or distorted as it goes down the organization tree. It is very difficult to ensure that upward communication is as efficient as downward, although it is quite as important. Every manager has to obtain information for making decisions, and this includes information on the attitudes and the feelings of his subordinates, the effects at their levels of his previous decisions, and facts which they know and he does not. It is also necessary for checking the interpretation which subordinates are placing on downward communications, an interpretation often different from that which was intended. There are formidable barriers to upward communication which must be appreciated. Difference in type of work being done, in social attitudes, education and speech, in habits of communications, may all be significant obstacles. Errors in policy which have to be corrected at high level are often only detected at low level. If upward communication fails, the errors flourish.

A manager must ensure that the *means* of communication within his organization are good. People must have the skills, fostered by training if necessary, to speak and write clearly and adequately, necessary meetings must be properly chaired and minuted, papers must be circulated to everyone concerned, and so on. . . at the same time he must keep a severe check upon the tendency for meetings papers and copies to proliferate.

## PUBLIC RELATIONS

Outside the organization, communication with other bodies is fairly simple and often stylized by rules or tradition. The real problem lies with communicating with the public, the customers of the water industry, and with the press. In these two areas of communication the industry has a poor record; although like other public services it often starts with a grave disadvantage because people (at least in a democracy) always seem anxious to believe the worst about their public services and respond with horrid delight to tales of their errors and shortcomings. Naturally, the press respond to this pressure from *their* customers—and who can blame them? They have to sell their papers, and print what they think their readers want to read. This fact of human nature must be faced, few people want to read tales of the success or virtue of the water industry. This is rather sad, and somewhat disturbing when it is common experience that if a talk on the industry is given to any gathering of people, they usually express surprise at the complications of the work involved, and at the level and the low cost of the service. It seems that the industry is much better at face to face communications than with the written or transmitted word.

Even batting on this rather sticky wicket, there is much that the industry can do to foster and maintain better public relations, such as:—

(1) The employment of specialist staff with the requisite knowledge of methods of publicity and the requirements and customs of the press. Nowadays, it is virtually essential for an organization to employ qualified public relations staff in this way. At the same time, public relations officers should not be allowed to drift into becoming the sort of "official spokesmen" whose main job is to cover up for their employers and stave off unwelcome questions.

(2) All employees who make public contacts, either in person by telephone or in writing, must be aware of the need to be helpful and courteous. A brusque response

can lose the industry a friend very quickly, and it is important to remember that customers bringing queries are often confused, and even a little fearful at having to deal with "authority".

(3) It is a true saying that an organization is judged by the manners of its telephone operators. Extending this a little, people's impression of an organization is often conditioned—sometimes permanently—by their first reception. Courtesy from the telephone operator or receptionist, and perhaps a touch of style about the reception area, can work wonders.

(4) Good relations should be established with the press. Nobody likes to do more work than he has to, and papers prefer to have news sent to them than to have to scratch it up for themselves. Rapid circulation of any stories which might make news will provide a steady coverage of "good" news and a sympathetic public reaction. For instance, if a large main bursts, a quick issue of the report of the facts has a good chance of being printed. Neglect this, and all the public are going to read are the outraged reactions of a disgusted housewife whose water went off without warning. Feeding the press with information in this way means accepting that a proportion of stories may never be printed. It also means that the people whose activities may come into the news must be aware of the need to get the information fast to the press, and managers must ensure that the organization can get this done by somebody who knows about press requirements such as deadlines.

Finally, it is worth remembering that it is no use providing the press with material that you want them to print, unless it is such that their readers will want to read. All information likely to be of interest to the public should be fed to the press, but in a form that may make interesting reading, and help to sell papers.

(5) Lectures may be grouped with film shows, school projects, and visits to works; all these are well worth pursuing, and can produce favourable reactions. Although they can only involve a small proportion of the customers, this often includes those who are likely to show any interest in a public service, and perhaps may be influential in informing public opinion.

Another, and rather specialized, form of public communication required by the manager is that at public enquiries and meetings, where he may be examined upon the policies which he has to follow and the way in which he is implementing them. This field is rather narrow, but there is an increasing trend towards the public examination of all sorts of projects, and social pressure for increased public participation in the decision-making of public bodies. The trend is noticeable in the planning field, where planning authorities are encouraged to consult local bodies, and it may be the manager's task to seek to persuade those bodies that his authority's proposals are reasonable, and to submit them to examination and discussion. The pendulum of social pressures and public opinion may swing against this trend, but a manager must accept an appearance in public of this kind as part of his duties, and if necessary seek training accordingly. He might also remember that a golden rule at such meetings is never to underestimate the intelligence of his audience, nor to overestimate its information.

## INWARD COMMUNICATION

This covers all written and spoken calls and communications coming to the organization. The essential one is that of complaints or urgent queries. A great deal can be done for public relations if these communications are handled quickly, sympathetically, and efficiently, and a wise manager will also make sure that communications from people such as Members of Parliament or of public authorities are not subject to delay or prevarication!

## 13. EPILOGUE

This Chapter has been written, and should be read, in full awareness of the working environment of a manager in the water industry, of the sudden emergencies and urgent panics, the deadlines to be met, and the pressures of everyday responsibilities.

No one can pretend that it is easy in these circumstances to recall and apply, with tranquil and considered wisdom, all that a manager ought to do. Nevertheless he must try, by constant vigilance in the face of the burden and stress of his daily problems, to take the longer view and undertake his broader duties to direct his organization as efficiently as possible, using all the means, knowledge, and techniques that are available to him.

Perhaps as a final word it would be well to recall that generals are always said to be preparing to win the previous war. Managers should take care that they are not organizing for the problems and conditions of their younger and more impressionable days.

## 14. BIBLIOGRAPHY

References have not been entered within the text of this Chapter as so many books, articles, conference reports, etc., pertinent to the practice of management both generally and within the public and nationalized services appear regularly. The reader seeking a list of contemporary literature or relatively short texts on specific aspects of management is advised to make enquiries of the appropriate organizations with offices in London (the British Institute of Management, the Royal Institute of Public Administration, the Industrial Society, etc.). In addition, an extensive series of books on numerous aspects of management is published in paperback form by Messrs. Penguin Books of Harmondsworth, Middlesex.

The titles listed below, although not entirely contemporary, are recognized texts included to serve as an initial guide with some bias towards the detail of management within the public bodies which form the British water industry. No titles have been listed specifically in relation either to the effects of legislation on employment (see Chapter 3), or on the financial factors of concern to the practising manager (see Chapter 5). Many readers will be able to turn to the library service within their own organization for advice, but it is appreciated that some will not have access to such a facility and the importance of these last two subjects should not be overlooked in the pursuit of further reading material.

**Water Industry Management Structures and Constraints**

1. H.M.S.O., London 1972, "The new local authorities, management and structure".
2. H.M.S.O., London 1973, "The new water industry, management and structure".
3. Representative Body, the Commission for Local Administration in England, London 1978, Report for year ending March 31st 1978, "Your local ombudsman".
4. H.M.S.O., 1976, (appendix volume and background papers) a report by the National Economic Development Office, "A study of U.K. nationalized industries".
5. Institution of Water Engineers and Scientists, London 1978, Proceedings of Symposium on "Engineering and the environment: harmony or conflict?"

**Management Techniques**

6. Industrial Society, London: series (on various topics) "Notes for managers".
7. H.M.S.O., series of C.A.S. Occasional Papers (on specific management techniques) published for the Civil Service Department.
8. Rowe, E., 1976, "Management techniques for civil engineering construction", Applied Science Publishers, Barking, Essex.
9. Argenti, J., 1969, "Management techniques", (International Business Management Series), George Allen & Unwin, London.

10. Harris, T. Q., 1970, "I'm O.K.—You're O.K.", (Transactional Analysis), Cape, London. Available also in Pan Paperback (1973)
11. Humble, J., 1972, British Institute of Management, London, "Management by objectives".
12. Mitchell, G. H., 1972, "Operational research: techniques and examples", English University Press, London.
13. Wiest, J. D., and Levy, F. K., 1977, "A management guide to PERT/CPM", Prentice-Hall, Englewood Cliffs, N.J., U.S.A. and London.

**Motivation**

14. Rose, M., 1975, "Industrial behaviour: theoretical development since Taylor", Allen Lane, London.
15. Scott, D., 1970, "The psychology of work", Duckworth, London.
16. Sidney, E., Brown, M., Argyle, M., 1973, "Skills with people", Hutchinson, London.

**Communications**

17. Fowler: "Dictionary of modern English usage", University Press, Oxford.
18. Gowers/Fraser, 1973 (2nd edition): "The complete plain words", H.M.S.O., London.
19. Maude, B., 1974, "Practical communication for managers", Longman, London.
20. Water Research Centre, 1977, Papers and Proceedings of Conference, "Information for the water industry".

**Work and Remuneration**

21. Innes, I., 1973, "Job evaluation", The Industrial Society, London.
22. Johnson, S., and Ogilvie, G., 1972, "Work analysis", Butterworths, London.
23. Anstey, E. *et al,* 1976, "Staff appraisal and development", Allen & Unwin, London.

Chapter 7

# RESEARCH

## 1. INTRODUCTION

THERE is a long tradition of water research in the U.K. particularly in relation to freshwater biology and pollution. Major developments took place in the late 1920s and early 1930s, since when there has been a steady growth in research effort and expenditure. Up to 1974 the dominant source of funds was the Government, but since that time there has been a progressive shift towards funding by the Regional Water Authorities and Water Companies in England and Wales and by the Regional Councils in Scotland. This shift has resulted in increased attention to the rationalization and co-ordination of research work, and this Chapter explains the structure, organization, and level of funding involved. The management of research work is also receiving greater emphasis, and so also is the application of results, this latter feature stemming from the need of funding authorities to demonstrate that they are getting value for money.

Important influences on the level and direction of research in recent years have been the increasing concern for the environment, greater attention to potential health hazards, and concern over the condition of underground water pipes and sewers and the costs involved in their renovation and replacement.

On the international scene, the U.K. is becoming increasingly involved through emerging *European Economic Community* (EEC) legislation, and there is steadily increasing emphasis on information exchange and collaboration with other research institutes, not only in Europe but throughout the world.

## 2. DEVELOPMENT OF WATER RESEARCH IN THE U.K.

### ORGANIZATIONS BEFORE 1974

The beginnings of water research in the U.K. stretch back over more than 50 years.

The *Water Pollution Research Board* was established in 1927 under the *Department of Scientific and Industrial Research* with a research programme covering all aspects of pollution prevention and the purity of water supplies. Work on potable waters was discontinued in 1955 after the setting up of the *Water Research Association* (now part of the *Water Research Centre* (WRC)).

The Board originally supported work carried out at a number of locations before occupying the first laboratory at Minworth. It was moved to temporary accommodation at Watford in 1940 and to its permanent location at Stevenage as the *Water Pollution Research Laboratory* (now part of the Water Research Centre) in 1954. From 1971 to 1974 the Water Pollution Research Laboratory was an establishment of the *Department of the Environment (DoE)*.

The *Freshwater Biological Association* was set up in 1929 as an independent body to carry out fundamental work on freshwater ecology and biology. It is currently grant-aided by the *Natural Environment Research Council*, with laboratories at Windermere in Cumbria, and at Wareham in Dorset.

Another long-established organization is the Water Department of the *Geological*

---

*Survey of Great Britain*, established in 1935, but now part of the Natural Environment Research Council *Institute of Geological Sciences* referred to later.

A further landmark in the history of U.K. water research was the establishment by the water supply industry, in 1953, of the Water Research Association (now part of the Water Research Centre). Originally based at Redhill, Surrey, the Association developed rapidly until it moved in 1961 to its present location at Medmenham in Buckinghamshire. As a Research Association support came from Member subscriptions, including water undertakers, river authorities, consultants, and industrialists. It was grant-aided by the DoE and undertook repayment work for customers.

A boost to water research effort came in 1963 with the advent of the Water Resources Act, which set up the *Water Resources Board* and the River Authorities. The Water Resources Board, which was responsible for preparing a water resource plan for England and Wales, established a Research Division which included an in-house research team with funds available for commissioning research externally. Extensive programmes were developed for examining new ways of investigating water resources more accurately, of operating resources to maximize their yield, and of developing further resources by methods new to this country. Many of these programmes have continued under the successor organizations described later.

In 1964 the *United Kingdom Atomic Energy Authority* commenced a large programme on methods of desalination, much of the fundamental work being done at the *Atomic Energy Research Establishment* at Harwell. The programme was subsequently phased out as it became evident that there was no place for desalination in the development of water resources in England and Wales, except possibly in the very long term. It led, however, to a number of spin-off projects in water and effluent treatment. Harwell also subsequently diversified into other areas of non-nuclear research and maintains expertise of relevance to the water industry at the present time.

Another major development was the setting up of the Natural Environment Research Council under the Science and Technology Act 1965. Its terms of reference were to encourage, plan, and execute research in those physical and biological sciences that relate to man's natural environment and its resources. Funded through the *Department of Education and Science*, the Council supported work by contract to existing establishments, but also set up or incorporated other bodies as Natural Environment Research Council Institutes. At the present time there are ten component and five grant-aided institutes. The *Marine Biological Association* and the *Scottish Marine Biological Association* (which were both founded in 1884) became Natural Environment Research Council establishments to work on the fundamental biology of marine organisms and ecology. The Institute of Geological Sciences was formed in 1965 and incorporated a hydrogeological department to develop research on groundwater and aquifers. At the same time an extensive hydrological research programme was developed at the *Institute of Hydrology*, also a Natural Environment Research Council institute. The Institute of Hydrology programme involves fundamental studies of the behaviour of water in its main phases in the hydrological sciences, and the manner of its movement between these phases. The hydrogeological team of the Institute of Geological Sciences is being moved to the Institute of Hydrology site at Wallingford. In the early 1970s the *Institute of Marine Environmental Research*, the *Institute of Oceanographic Sciences*, and the *Institute of Terrestrial Ecology* were established as Natural Environment Research Council institutes to deal with further aspects of marine and terrestrial ecology.

Another research organization which has played an important part in water research in the U.K. is the *Hydraulics Research Station*. Set up originally in 1947 as the *Hydraulics Research Organization* under the Department of Scientific and Industrial Research, it took over work at the *National Physical Laboratory* and *Imperial College* in 1948, and moved to Wallingford in 1951. It was transferred to DoE after the reorganization of Government departments in 1970. Broadly, the terms of reference of the Hydraulics Research Station are to predict the performance of civil engineering works and their consequences to the environment. A great deal of modelling work is involved, largely physical, much of it on a repayment basis and with overseas sites featuring prominently in the studies. Also under DoE, programmes of relevance to the water industry have developed at the *Building Research Establishment* and the *Transport and Road Research Laboratory*.

Rapid growth took place in the 1960s of the *British Hydromechanics Research Association*, which was originally established in 1947. The work carried out, a high proportion of which is on a repayment basis, is concerned with the application of all aspects of fluid engineering to industrial problems. Other Research Associations also began to develop programmes related to water. In particular, the textile research associations *(Hosiery and Allied Trades Research Association, Cotton, Silk and Man-made Fibres Research Association, Wool Industry Research Association, and British Launderers Research Association)* combined to investigate water use and effluent disposal in their industry and produced an extensive report on their findings[1].

The *Construction Industry Research and Information Association* was established in 1967 to act as a research broker for the construction industry. Topics on water research soon became a component part of the programme carried out by a number of laboratories under contract.

The next major change in the research field which will have long-lasting consequences was the complete review of the framework for Government research and development put forward in a White Paper in 1972. With recommendations from Lord Rothschild, head of the Central Policy Review Staff and a Working Group of the *Council for Scientific Policy* under the Chairmanship of Sir Frederick Dainton, the Government implemented the principle of the customer/contractor relationship for work funded by Central Government. This has led to Government Departments as customers receiving part of the funds formerly channelled to the Research Councils. This money was to be used for work designated by the Departments as important in helping them to discharge their own obligations. Scientific staffs were built up within departments to consider research needs and to supervise contracts. Some of the diverted funds continued to be channelled back through the five Research Councils, but work was also carried out by the Departments' own internal research establishments and by direct contracts to research organizations. The relevant Department for the water industry is the DoE, and soon after it had been established in 1970 a unified research organization was set up under the Director General (Research) to provide co-ordinated research support throughout the Department. The machinery for programme formulation is covered in more detail in Section 5 of this Chapter.

The effects of this new attitude towards funding were being felt during the period before the water industry reorganization in 1974. During this period increasing attention was also being given to the fragmentation of research in the industry.

## EFFECTS OF WATER INDUSTRY REORGANIZATION IN 1974

When reorganization took place in April 1974 research for the water industry was regrouped into a newly constituted Water Research Centre, which incorporated the Water Pollution Research Laboratory, the Water Research Association, and the Research Division of the Water Resources Board. The planning section of the Water Resources Board became the *Central Water Planning Unit* and the data processing section became the *Water Data Unit*, both within the Department of the Environment. Both of these units have continued to operate research programmes and to let contracts on topics relevant to their particular fields of interest. The Water Research Centre, with laboratories at Medmenham and Stevenage, runs a comprehensive research programme covering water supply, waste water disposal, and environmental protection involving fresh and saline waters. It was set up on the basis of a Research Association in the private sector with wide-ranging membership, but with the bulk of its funds coming from the newly constituted regional water authorities, the water companies, and from grants and contracts from DoE. In 1978, the total staff numbered some 500 and the annual budget was of the order of £5 000 000. The mechanism for programme formulation within the Water Research Centre is given in more detail in Section 5 of this Chapter.

In the period immediately after reorganization one of the tasks of the *Regional Water Authorities* was to collate and assess the inherited research projects previously carried out by the component organizations. In the case of the larger authorities, this amounted to sizeable projects and machinery was set up, mostly under the Directorates of Scientific Services, to co-ordinate and appraise the work and to institute approval systems. An increasing number of authorities now prepare and make available details of their research programmes and these are also included in the Water Research Centre's Register of Research in the Water Industry[2].

In Scotland, research projects are in progress within the newly constituted *Regional Councils* and in the *River Purification Boards. The Scottish Development Department* maintains a research programme within the industry and at universities.

In Northern Ireland, research projects are funded and co-ordinated by the *Department of the Environment for Northern Ireland* through its Water Services Divisions.

Although the *Welsh Water Authority* is responsible for most of the locally controlled research projects, the *Welsh Office* makes funds available for work within Wales where Government money is appropriate.

The total effort devoted to research within local authorities and water companies therefore adds up to an appreciable amount and is reflected in the funding levels discussed in Section 4 of this Chapter.

Appendix A, p. 240, summarizes the principal organizations currently involved in water research in the U.K., and their fields of activity.

## PRIORITIES FOR RESEARCH SINCE 1974

The methods of deciding on priorities in research adopted by the water industry and by Central Government are discussed further in Section 5 of this Chapter. The results of these consultations and the prevailing economic climate since reorganization have led to prominence being given to certain areas of research.

Restrictions on capital spending have led to increased emphasis on obtaining more effective use of existing facilities. Research on increasing throughput on treatment plant and on the optimum use of network systems has been important. The very high estimated cost of replacing the ageing underground assets has resulted in an acceleration of effort on improved methods of inspection, renovation, and replacement techniques. Another considerable problem inherited by the water authorities was the safe and effective disposal of sewage sludge. Programmes have therefore been expanded to look at least-cost solutions and the effects on crops and animals of sludge utilization on land.

Work has also expanded in recent years on the possible health effects of drinking water quality. Specific research effort has been devoted to the problem of lead and nitrate which have caused operational difficulties to some authorities. Water re-use and the possible effects of organic compounds has also stimulated programmes involving the identification of compounds and epidemiological and toxicological studies. To assist in advising the industry in this matter, a *Joint Committee on Medical Aspects of Water Quality* was set up in 1976 by the Department of the Environment and the *Department of Health and Social Security*. Work on various aspects of water quality has been enhanced as a consequence of the emergence of EEC legislation on Standards. In order to set sensible limits, the medical and operational implications of concentration limits for different substances have required investigation.

## REGISTERS OF RESEARCH

The Department of the Environment publishes an annual four-part Register of Research[3] which contains information from a wide range of organizations, such as universities, research institutes, and Government research establishments. Part II—Environmental planning, and Part IV—Environmental pollution, include a large number of projects on water research and give information on the scope of the project, the sponsorship and finance, and details of any reports or publications.

A more comprehensive survey of projects carried out by the water authorities and water undertakers appears in the Register of Research in the Water Industry[2] published by the Water Research Centre.

## SURVEY OF RESEARCH ORGANIZATIONS

In 1975 the Natural Environment Research Council published the second edition of a booklet entitled "Hydrological research in the United Kingdom"[4] to mark the end of the International Hydrological Decade (1965-1974); the first edition was published half-way through the decade. The booklet outlines the hydrological interests and expertise of all Government-sponsored agencies in the U.K. over the five-year period.

## 3. OVERSEAS RESEARCH

International co-operation in water research is an increasingly important matter, both to minimize the waste of effort resulting from similar programmes in different countries, and to take the maximum advantage of varied experience in similar fields. Each country has a different system of research organization, varying from a small number of large laboratories with common control, at one extreme, to a very large number of small and specialized units, co-ordinated by committee systems, at the other. Informal contact between scientists of similar interests is a valuable, but limited system, while international conferences can be extremely useful for exchanging results of completed work, but are of little assistance in planning future programmes.

Collaboration between two organizations is comparatively easy to organize, but setting up collaboration between several units working on the same subject is more difficult and involves much effort.

The Commission of the EEC is performing a considerable service in setting up concerted action programmes on specified subjects. In Great Britain, several research organizations are setting up planned co-operation with many institutes both in Europe and elsewhere in the world. For example, the Water Research Centre has set up a European Division to improve co-operation within the EEC.

Some of the principal organizations involved in water research overseas are given in Appendix B, p. 243.

## 4. WATER RESEARCH FUNDING

The organizations listed in Appendix A, p. 240, receive their funds from four main sources:

(1) **Water Industry (Water Authorities and Water Undertakers)**
Water Industry funds are used largely to support work undertaken by the industry itself, and by the Water Research Centre on its behalf.

(2) **Department of the Environment**
The DoE principally supports work at its own laboratories (mainly the Hydraulics Research Station), at those of the Natural Environment Research Council (Institute of Geological Sciences, Institute of Hydrology, Freshwater Biological Association, Institute of Oceanographic Sciences, Institute of Marine Environmental Research, and Marine Biological Association), and at the Water Research Centre.

(3) **Natural Environment Research Council**
Natural Environment Research Council funds received through the Department of Education and Science are mainly allocated to component and grant-aided laboratories and in the form of research grants to universities.

(4) **Ministry of Agriculture, Fisheries and Food/Department of Agriculture and Fisheries for Scotland**
Expenditure is largely in support of work at their own laboratories.

The level of funding from these four sources, and the type of work it supports, are shown in Fig. 7.1.

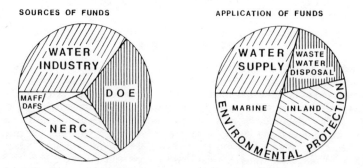

**Fig. 7.1.   Funding of research relevant to the water industry. Total funding in 1977-78 was about £20 million**

NERC : Natural Environment Research Council
MAFF : Ministry of Agriculture, Fisheries and Food
DAFS : Department of Agriculture and Fisheries for Scotland
DoE   : Department of the Environment

A large number of commercial concerns also carry out research in connection with the development and improvement of their products and services, but no details are available of the total expenditure involved. Similarly, the University Grants Committee makes a substantial contribution to university research, but the proportion allocated to studies on water is not separately published.

Work of direct relevance to the water industry is mainly funded either by the industry itself or by the Department of the Environment. Their combined expenditure totalled about £13 000 000 in 1978, or about 1 per cent of the industry's revenue expenditure. (The country as a whole spends about 2½ per cent of its gross national product on research and development.) The water industry and DoE have agreed that the Government should fund work when (a) it is related to areas for which the Government has direct responsibility, or (b) it is required in the national interest, but for various reasons is not being carried out. However, this still leaves "grey" areas where research is required into an issue of importance to the water industry and which also has national implications. It has been part of Government policy following reorganization to transfer an increasing proportion of the responsibility for funding to the water industry. It seems likely, therefore, that these grey areas will increasingly become the responsibility of the industry.

Water industry research expenditure is largely channelled through the Water Research Centre for central issues and, for regional issues, through the Scientific Department of the authority concerned. Natural Environment Research Council funds are, in general, used to promote work of a more fundamental and long-term nature, while Ministry of Agriculture, Fisheries and Food/Department of Agriculture and Fisheries for Scotland expenditure is largely in connection with flood protection and with fisheries.

Both the *World Health Organization* (WHO) and the EEC fund water research projects, the latter normally under broader environmental programmes. However, the money involved (in the U.K.) is small in comparison with the funds from the sources mentioned above.

## 5. PROGRAMME FORMULATION AND MANAGEMENT

The process of research may conveniently be considered as consisting of five stages:—

(i)   problem identification;
(ii)  choice of contractor;
(iii) programme formulation and approval;
(iv)  management and monitoring of the research;
(v)   application of the results.

In practice, the process is somewhat iterative since the programme may need modification on the basis of the emerging results, and research will often reveal new avenues which have to be assessed. The completion of one programme and the application of the results may suggest further stages of exploration.

### PROBLEM IDENTIFICATION

The definition in technological terms of problems in planning, design, operation, and maintenance can be one of the most difficult yet most important stages in the derivation of a research programme. Whereas it is easy to establish that a problem exists, it requires some experience to evaluate the technical information required for its solution. Inadequate attention to this question has led in many cases to poorly defined and inadequately based research programmes.

Another essential requirement is to quantify the occurrence and significance of the problem in operational and financial terms. Such information is often vital in deciding firstly, whether the cost of a research programme can be justified, secondly, the time-scale involved and, thirdly, whether the use of existing knowledge or the derivation of new approaches is required. This is not a task that a research organization can do unaided, although it is an important part of the research task to stay constantly in touch with the practical needs. Working strictly on the Rothschild customer-contractor principle, it should be the task of the practitioner to spell out his requirements and to quantify the benefits. In practice, this is often a task shared by the research organization and the industry it serves.

The water industry has devoted much attention to this question of problem identification and priority assessment assisted considerably by the *Water Industry Standing Technical Committees* and *Advisory Committees* referred to later. Central Government has also been active in this matter in deciding the level of funding and appropriate areas, and has obtained advice from the water industry and its own customer departments. An overall assessment of research needs was published by the water industry soon after reorganization[5]. Attempts have been made to apply cost/benefit analysis to research programmes both to assess the justified level of expenditure and to allocate priorities. By considering revenue and capital spending by the industry, it is possible to calculate the percentage improvement required to pay for given levels of research expenditure. What is more difficult to predict is the improvement in performance likely to result from the research, and the probability of its success. Furthermore, the results of some research will lead to an increase in expenditure to improve reliability or lessen risks, for example in the case of water quality and related health implications. Much of the value of research can therefore be seen as providing assistance in obtaining more effective application of revenue and capital expenditure.

Another approach to the assessment of the value of research is to determine the penalty of not carrying out the work. Although this is a much more subjective approach, it can help in defining the nature of the benefits which are likely to result from investigations.

In general terms the absence of research reduces opportunities for improving cost-effectiveness and reliability, and can lead to increased risks. For example, in the absence of studies of techniques for the detection of unaccounted-for water and waste, water losses could stay high or unnecessary expense could be incurred on over-sized waste inspection teams. Again, without research on the health effects of pollutants, unnecessary risks could be involved or over-restrictive conditions could be imposed on water abstraction. Lack of knowledge on the effects of sewage sludge on crops and animals could lead to non-acceptance of one of the most economic forms of disposal. Absence of research on water and sewage treatment processes would restrict improvements to performance and the development of cheaper high-rate techniques.

## CHOICE OF CONTRACTOR

Although more than one U.K. research organization may be capable of carrying out certain investigations, it is not common practice for funding bodies to seek tenders for work. Because of the co-ordination machinery described below, responsibilities for given areas are broadly defined and contracts are placed after informal discussions between customers and funding bodies. One of the main factors responsible for this situation is the specialized nature of much of the work.

### FORMULATION MACHINERY

Once the primary needs have been established and priority assigned, the initial stages of research programme formulation can be undertaken. The essential task of the research organization selected for the work is to determine the programme of investigation, the level and type of effort required, and the time-scale. Clear and precise objectives are essential and form the cornerstone of any research project.

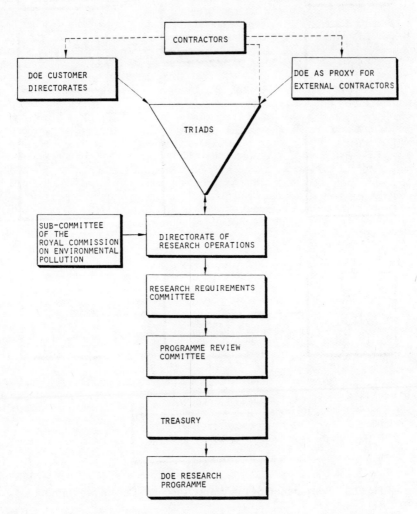

**Fig. 7.2. Formulation of the DoE programme for environmental protection**

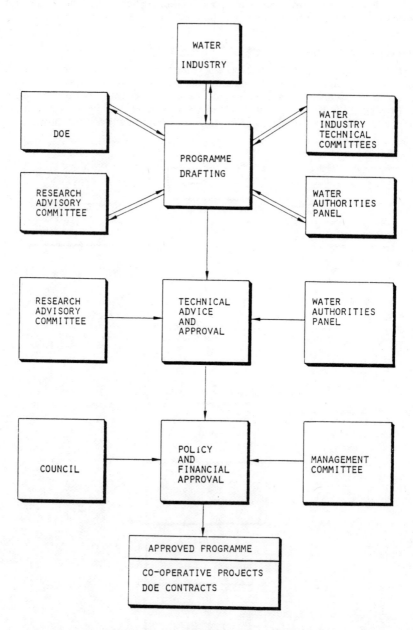

**Fig. 7.3.   Formulation of the Water Research Centre programme**

## Department of the Environment Mechanism for the Environmental Protection Programme

The mechanism for the formulation of the DoE programme which is described in detail in the Report on Research and Development 1977[6], is summarized below, and is shown schematically in Fig. 7.2.

The formulation cycle starts with a review of the overall balance of research across the Department of the Environment (and across the *Department of Transport* as well, since research is a common service to both Departments). An assessment is made of any major issues requiring decisions at this level and guidelines on the resources likely to be available are given to each of the six *Research Requirements Committees*. A Research Requirements Committee corresponds to each of the Department's major policy groupings, one of which is environmental protection.

The *Environmental Protection Research Requirements Committee* is concerned with the broad balance and the priorities of the environmental protection research programme, which comprises 13 subject areas covering particular themes such as water resources, sewage disposal, air pollution, and noise. Eight of these subject areas are concerned with water. Each subject area contains a number of programme items which are coherent programmes of work on specific topics. The Committee considers the allocation of resources to the subject areas and gives advice on the type of programme item for inclusion.

The development of the programme within the subject area requires a flexible dialogue involving three elements: (1) the customer to state the research needs; (2) the contractor to suggest the research required to meet these needs; and (3) the *Directorate of Research Operations* to determine the scope and balance of the programme. Because these three elements are involved, the groups appointed to serve the Research Requirements Committee in this way have been termed Triads.

The task of the Triads is thorough discussion of proposals from customer divisions and from major contractors for inclusion in the programmes within their subject areas. Their output is a series of brief reports to the directorate of research operations introducing and explaining the programme item forms which summarize the programmes. These reports form the basis of proposals from the directorate of research operations to the Research Requirements Committee, which reviews the programme proposals and considers competing priorities in the light of available resources. Its recommendations are then considered by a *Programme Review Committee* and a decision is taken on the scale and allocation of the bids.

Once the programme has been approved by the Programme Review Committee, and the finance authorized by the *Treasury,* contracts are negotiated between the Department and the contractors.

During the development of the proposals external advice on the scope, content, and balance is sought in a number of ways. Many of these are informal, such as contacts with the industry. The *Water Industry Standing Technical Committees* also offer comments on priority areas for Government funding. However, the main channel for formal advice is through a Subcommittee of the Standing Royal Commission on Environmental Pollution.

## Water Research Centre Mechanism

The important stages in the formulation of the Water Research Centre research programme are shown in Fig. 7.3.

For review purposes, the WRC programme is divided into sectors which broadly correspond to the fields of interest of the Water Industry Standing Technical

Committees. External advice on the overall balance and relative priorities is sought through informal contacts with the industry and the Department of the Environment, and formally through two Advisory Committees:

(a) The *Water Authorities Panel* which represents the specific interests of the major water undertakings in the U.K., and of the DoE, and

(b) the *Research Advisory Committee* which represents the more general interests of the Water Research Centre Membership.

Broad guidelines on the budget available are also sought from the *Management Committee* and *Council* at this stage.

The advice of each of the industry's Standing Technical Committees is obtained on the priorities in each sector, and an outline programme is then drawn up. This is considered by the Water Authorities Panel and the Research Advisory Committee in relation to the industry's needs and to complementary work elsewhere, both within the water industry and in other research establishments. Their comments are taken into account and the cost of the programme is then calculated for consideration by the Management Committee and Council. Once the budget has been determined the Water Research Centre sets about drawing up the specific projects in detail.

In parallel with the formulation of the co-operative programme the Water Research Centre is involved in the Department of the Environment programme formulation as a contractor. This is explained above and is shown in Figs. 7.2 and 7.3.

### RESEARCH PROGRAMMES AND REPORTS

Each year the Water Research Centre produces a published Research Programme[7] which outlines the research in progress at the Centre and relates this to the problems facing the industry. Most water authorities make available their research programmes and their progress reports and some refer to research work in their annual reports (Appendix A, p. 240).

The majority of the principal research organizations also produce annual reports summarizing progress during the year (Appendix A).

### STANDING TECHNICAL COMMITTEE REPORTS

The Water Industry Standing Technical Committees produce occasional reports[8-15] on issues of major importance to the water industry, and these documents have a bearing on the formulation of the industry's research requirements.


## 6. MANAGEMENT AND MONITORING OF RESEARCH PROJECTS

The management of research and development work is a very specialized aspect of management science, for which essential requirements are adequate experience in research work at different levels of responsibility and a sound understanding of the relevant areas of technology. These are, of course, additional to the skills necessary for any form of management. The time required for proper exercise of this function is often underestimated, and adequate allowances must be made in forecasting the manning of projects.

One of the principal difficulties involves the management of research teams with a range of disciplinary skills. Responsibilities for project management have to be superimposed on line managements systems which are often based on disciplines. This leads to a formal or pseudo matrix arrangement, and the optimum solution for each specific case depends largely on the personalities of the staff concerned.

An essential starting point for the project manager must be the full specification of the task. Objectives should be clear and brief and should represent clearly defined goals against which the performance of the research team can be judged. An appropriate research team can then be selected. Particular attention should be paid to its size and to the expertise of its members, bearing in mind the relative priority of the project. The programme of research should set out the main elements of the project describing the routes by which the work will proceed. Bar charts are appropriate for detailing the time-scale, and more elaborate presentations such as PERT* diagrams and RPD* diagrams may be necessary for more complicated projects. These latter techniques focus greater effort at the project planning stage and clarify the steps and sequences necessary, their interaction, consequences of delays, the critical path, and other factors.

Regular reviews of progress are an essential feature of research management. Progress reports should be a component of these reviews, and should be structured to consider technical progress, difficulties, changes in direction which may be required as a result of changing research needs, and the implications of the results achieved so far. These reviews will also consider the financial aspects, including effort spent, consumable and capital expenditure, and the costs of any external services.

The effort devoted to projects can be monitored by a time-recording procedure for staff, and for large research organizations these records may be computerized. In some cases the computer print-out can be used as a basis for invoicing the funding agency.

A research organization may need to consider whether a project should be undertaken in-house, or whether to proceed by the use of an external contractor. The following factors could lead to a decision to proceed by the latter method:—

(i)   lack of suitable expertise;
(ii)  lack of laboratory space and facilities;
(iii) insufficient time to acquire staff, equipment, or accommodation;
(iv)  need to retain flexibility by not acquiring specialist facilities on a permanent basis; and
(v)   economic advantages.

The use of an external contractor has advantages, perhaps the most important being that of (iv) above, since the research organization does not become committed to staff and facilities on a long-term basis. These long-term commitments tend to introduce a considerable degree of inflexibility. On the other hand, the main disadvantages are the risk of unsatisfactory work, coupled with the supervision required and the extent to which the resultant expertise eventually lies with another organization which may become a competitor.

A major problem in the management of research is the identification of the stage in a project at which the likely returns do not justify further effort. However, it is important for management to face up to this problem in view of the self-perpetuating nature of most research projects. Compelling arguments can usually be put forward for continuing work, particularly where a sizeable investment has already been made. In many cases, success is claimed to be "just around the corner"; in others, the size of the investment itself generates pressure for additional results, more or less irrespective of their value. Even when a project has achieved its principal goal, arguments are often put forward for further development and refinement.

It is an important function of management continually to assess and compare

*PERT = Programme Evaluation and Review Technique
 RPD  = Research Project Development

priorities so as to ensure the resources available are deployed to maximum effect. However difficult this problem is when tangible benefits can be identified and estimated, it is even worse when the benefits are intangible, which is often the case with projects concerned with water in relation to environmental or health considerations.

## 7. DISSEMINATION AND APPLICATION OF RESEARCH RESULTS

An industry which has defined its needs for research will constantly press for successful results from research programmes initiated to meet these needs. The water industry defines its research needs carefully, in the ways described earlier in this chapter, and this creates a "pull" for results from water research organizations. Nevertheless, such research bodies invariably find it necessary to "push" by devoting considerable effort to promoting the application of their research. The process is therefore a "push-pull" process, but pulling gives the best applications, and the pull is often strongest when the user has closely collaborated with the researcher in defining and pursuing the project. This gap between new knowledge acquired from a research project and its application is only part of the problem of transfer of technology, since there is a wide gap also between existing knowledge and its application. Experience has shown that this transfer of technology is not an easy process, a fact illustrated by reference to the Water Research Centre, which spends about 20 per cent of its total budget on a range of activities designed to transfer knowledge into the water industry.

It is not easy for the industry to adopt changes suggested by the results of research. New methods have to be carefully assessed in an industry where reliability and safety are of utmost importance. Pressures of day-to-day problems restrict the time available for considering new approaches. Finance might not be available to effect the changes required, even if subsequent savings will result. The time-scales for capital investment are often long—maybe five to ten years for a major project—and this builds in delays in applying new processes. Communications between the research worker and practitioner may not be adequate. A further phenomenon which is sometimes referred to as the "not invented here" attitude, also produces resistance to the adoption of results of research.

If a development has been accomplished which is suitable for commercial exploitation, then the normal market forces will often operate. For example, an instrument which measures water flow in pipes, if technically superior to existing devices and at a competitive price, will be purchased by those whose need is seen to justify the cost. But many research results are not of this sort. Mathematical techniques are often the end point of a project, and experience shows that often these results are not taken up by the industry, because the potential user believes that he can do it in a better (i.e. different) way by carrying out his own investigation. Had he been in some way associated with the project, perhaps on a Steering Committee or as a source of data, or in providing facilities for proving trials, he would have been "involved" and might more willingly seek to apply the results.

Experience has shown that many approaches have to be used to assist technology transfer. These include the written word (technical reports, newsheets, and papers), presentations (seminars, conferences, exhibitions, site demonstrations, and training courses), collaborative exercises with the operating agencies, and commercial exploitation through patents and licensing agreements. The method has to be chosen according to the particular case, but in most instances more than one method will be used simultaneously. The main methods are described below:

(1) *Written reports* for operations managers and their staff should be tailored to their particular requirements, containing only the essential features of the work, but clearly setting out the results and methods of application. This differs from the conventional research report and published paper written by scientists for scientists which is, however, an essential requirement for the proper critical review of scientific work. Glossy newsheets have been used effectively to convey the practical message from a piece of work in a form acceptable to busy executive or operational staff.

(2) *Collaborative projects* ensure that a successful technique is applied in at least one location, and this can often become an effective demonstration unit. Some projects require site evaluation in a number of locations to embrace a range of field conditions, thus widening the initial application.

(3) *Meetings* between research personnel and operating agencies present opportunities for direct transfer of ideas. They can take many forms and can be varied to allow for the type of work involved.

(4) *Seminars* allow for informality, but numbers need to be restricted to, say, less than 60 for effective discussion to take place. It is possible with this type of meeting to hold meetings on the same topic at a number of locations, thus allowing participation by a greater number of potential users of the results. The Water Research Centre for example has two series of regional meetings each year, using ten venues throughout the British Isles.

(5) Larger *conferences* have a different role. They attract experts from other countries and so enable approaches and techniques to be debated at an international level. Discussion within the conference sessions tends to be rather more formal than with seminars, but methods can be used to overcome much of this problem. Learned societies and professional bodies play an important part in this form of transfer.

(6) *Discussions* outside the formal sessions are often a most valuable feature for participants. Exhibitions are often run in conjunction with conferences, at which manufacturers and research organizations can mount displays and demonstrations.

(7) *Site demonstrations* can often form an appropriate means of communicating when equipment is a feature of the development. In the case of the Water Research Centre, technical liaison officers assist in this function and offer on-the-spot advice and assistance.

(8) *Training* is a direct means of transferring skills and techniques, but it is also a means of communicating results of certain types of research projects. New techniques in chemical analysis, methods for quality control in analysis, or the use and application of new computer programs are examples where training methods are appropriate.

(9) *Commercial exploitation* becomes particularly important when dealing with hardware developments that can be sold or used on a substantial scale. Professional advice is usually needed when dealing with patenting aspects, and handling licensing arrangements requires skill and experience.

Those who plan and manage the water industry's plant and systems have a responsibility for keeping up-to-date with the best modern information, and putting this into practice where they can. This needs awareness of the latest significant and relevant research results which research organizations of all types are only too willing to promote.

## 8. REFERENCES

1. Wool Industry Research Association, 1973, Report of Textile Research Conference, WIRA, Leeds, "The use of water in the textile industry".
2. Water Research Centre, "Register of research in the water industry", *in press.*
3. Department of the Environment, Annually, "Register of research", DoE, London.
4. Natural Environment Research Council, 1975, "Hydrological research in the United Kingdom, 1970-75", NWC, London.
5. Stott, P., 1975, *Water, 5, 16,* "Water authorities' research needs".
6. Departments of the Environment and Transport, Annually, "Report on research and development", H.M.S.O, London.
7. Water Research Centre, Annually, "Research programme".
8. Department of the Environment/National Water Council, Standing Technical Advisory Committee on Water Quality, Biennial Report, DoE, London.
9. Department of the Environment/National Water Council, Standing Committee on Disposal of Sewage Sludge, 1978, "Sewage sludge disposal data and review of disposal to sea", DoE, London.
10. Department of the Environment/National Water Council, Standing Committee on Sewers and Water Mains, 1976, "Working party on the Hydraulic Design of Storm Sewers; a review of progress, March 1974-June 1975", NWC, London.
11. Department of the Environment/National Water Council, 1976, "Technical Working Group on Waste of Water, First Report published", Standing Technical Committee Reports No. 2, NWC, London.
12. Department of the Environment/National Water Council, Standing Technical Committee on Water Regulations, 1976, "Report No. 8, consultation paper on domestic unvented hotwater systems", DoE, London.
13. Department of the Environment/National Water Council, Standing Committee on the Disposal of Sewage Sludge, 1977, "Report of the Working Party on Disposal of Sludge to Land (Report No. 5)", DoE, London.
14. Department of the Environment/National Water Council, Standing Technical Committee on Water Treatment, 1977, "Desalination", NWC, London.
15. Department of the Environment/National Water Council, Standing Committee on Sewers and Water Mains, 1977, "Sewers and water mains—a National assessment", NWC, London.

### APPENDIX A: Principal U.K. Organizations Involved in Water Research

**Water Industry**

| | |
|---|---|
| *Water Research Centre | Work on all aspects of the hydrological cycle under ten sector headings:<br>Resource development and management<br>Drinking water quality<br>Water treatment<br>Sewers and water mains<br>Waste water treatment<br>Sludge disposal<br>Groundwater pollution<br>River management<br>Tidal waters<br>Quality surveillance |
| *Regional Water Authorities<br>*Scottish Development Department<br>*Department of the Environment for Northern Ireland<br>Scottish Regional Councils<br>*Scottish River Purification Boards | Work on all aspects of the hydrological cycle with emphasis on data collection and on studies relating to regional and local problems. |

**Appendix A**—*continued*

---

**Department of the Environment**

| | |
|---|---|
| *Hydraulics Research Station | Hydraulic design of engineering structures<br>Open channel flow<br>Storm drainage<br>Estuaries and tidal flow<br>Coasts and wave action. |
| *Building Research<br>Establishment | Earthworks and dams<br>Water demand in domestic properties<br>Water saving devices<br>Water supply and drainage systems. |
| *Transport and Road Research<br>Laboratory | TV survey of sewers<br>Soil/pipe interactions<br>Pipe construction methods<br>Tunnels<br>Flexible pipelines. |
| *Central Water Planning Unit<br>(The Unit's programme is<br>determined by a steering<br>committee presided over by the<br>Chairman of the National Water<br>Council) | National and strategic aspects of water services planning and<br>operation in England and Wales. Problems likely to arise in<br>connection with possible long-term developments. |

---

**\*Natural Environment Research Council**

| | |
|---|---|
| *Institute of Hydrology | Hydrological processes (evaporation, interception, run-off, erosion,<br>sediment transport, sub-surface flow)<br>Catchment systems and their modelling<br>Flood studies, resource studies, low flow studies<br>Instrumentation. |
| *Institute of Geological Sciences | Hydrogeological studies:<br>  Well and borehole records<br>  Landfill sites<br>  Groundwater studies including nitrates<br>  Hydrogeological mapping<br>  Special studies of local problems in collaboration with water<br>    authorities.<br>Field units:<br>  Work in relation to reservoir siting, dams, aqueducts, and well<br>    siting. |
| *Freshwater Biological Association<br>(grant-aided) | Fundamental research on ecology of lakes and rivers. |
| *Institute of Terrestrial Ecology | Survey of water bodies<br>Part of the Wash barrage study<br>Effects of àquatic herbicides, insecticides, and metals on aquatic<br>systems. |
| *Institute for Marine<br>Environmental Research | Ecology of estuaries<br>Effects of pollution on ecological systems<br>Model simulations<br>Development of analytical techniques. |
| *Institute of Oceanographic<br>Sciences in the U.K. | Sediment movement<br>Wave analysis<br>Tide and surge modelling. |
| *Marine Biological Association<br>(grant-aided) | Chemical and biological aspects of estuarine processes. |
| *Scottish Marine Biological<br>Association (grant-aided) | Basic studies of the processes governing the inter-relationships<br>between marine plants and animals and their environment,<br>including studies of heated effluent and paper mill effluent, and<br>of farmed fish. |

---

**Appendix A**—*continued*

---

**\*Agricultural Research Council**

| | |
|---|---|
| \*Letcombe Laboratory | Nitrate leaching from soils. |
| \*Grassland Research Institute (grant-aided) | Nitrate leaching from soils<br>Effects of sludge disposal to land. |
| \*Rothamsted Experimental Station (grant-aided) | Nitrate leaching from soils.<br>Evaporation |
| \*Institute for Research on Animal Diseases | Effects of sludge disposal to land. |

---

**Department of Industry**

| | |
|---|---|
| \*Warren Spring Laboratory | Flotation<br>Pumping of non-Newtonian fluids<br>Measurement and characterization of odours<br>Removal of metals<br>Tunnelled outfalls. |
| \*National Engineering Laboratory | Pumps and valves<br>Flow measurement in closed pipes. |
| \*Laboratory of the Government Chemist | Specialized water analyses. |

---

**Research Associations**

| | |
|---|---|
| \*British Hydromechanics Research Association | Design of pump intakes and sumps<br>Pumps and pump systems<br>Pumping of sludges<br>Pressure surges in complex networks<br>Flood defences. |
| \*Construction Industry Research and Information Association (all work is done extramurally) | Design and constructional aspects of treatment works, river systems and pipelines. |
| \*Local Government Operational Research Unit | Sewer records. |

Several of the research associations are working on the treatment of industrial effluents and their subsequent effects on the environment.

---

**\*United Kingdom Atomic Energy Authority**

| | |
|---|---|
| AERE Harwell | General analytical service including trace elements in water<br>Groundwater pollution from landfill sites<br>Tidal energy studies. |

---

**\*Medical Research Council**

| | |
|---|---|
| \*Royal Free Hospital Department of Clinical Epidemiology (grant-aided) | Water quality and cardiovascular disease<br>Health aspects of the re-use of water. |
| MRC Cell Mutation Unit, Sussex University | Mutagenic screening of water samples. |
| MRC Epidemiology Unit, Cardiff | Health aspects of trace elements in water, particularly lead. |

---

**Ministry of Defence**

| | |
|---|---|
| \*Meteorological Office | Rainfall forecasting and measurement<br>Weather radar<br>Long-term climatic change. |

---

**Appendix A**—*continued*

---

### Universities

Research is carried out at a large number of university departments throughout the British Isles on a wide range of water problems. The main centres are in the Universities of:

Birmingham
Cambridge
Lancaster
London—Imperial College
—University College
Newcastle upon Tyne
Strathclyde

---

### Industry

A large number of commercial concerns carry out research in connection with development and improvement of products and services. The major areas involved are:

Water and effluent treatment plant manufacture;
Manufacture of pipes and fittings;
Instrument manufacture;
Chemical industry.

---

*indicates organizations which publish an Annual Report

---

## APPENDIX B: ORGANIZATIONS INVOLVED WITH WATER RESEARCH OUTSIDE THE U.K.*

| Country | Organization |
|---|---|
| Australia | CSIRO (Commonwealth Scientific and Industrial Research Organization) |
| Austria | Bundesanstalt für Wasserbiologie und Abwasserforschung |
| Belgium | CEBEDEAU (Centre Belge d'Etude et de Documentation de l'Eau, de l'Air et de l'Environnement) |
| Brazil | CETESB (Companhia Estadual de Tecnologia de Saneamento Básico e de Defesa do Meio Ambiente) |
| | FEEMA (Fundacão Estadual Engenharia do Meio Ambiente) |
| Canada | CCIW (Canadian Center for Inland Waters) |
| | Freshwater Institute |
| Czechoslovakia | VUUV (Vyzkumny Ustav Upravy Vod) |
| | VUV (Vyzkumny Ustav Vodohospodasky) |
| Denmark | VKI (Vandkvalitetsinstituttet) |
| Finland | NORDFORSK (Scandinavian Council for Applied Research) |
| | Vesihallitus Research Institute |
| France | IRCHA (Institut National de Recherche Chimique Appliquée) |
| | BRGM (Bureau de Recherches Géologiques et Minières) |
| | CEA (Commission de l'Energie Atomique) |
| Germany (FDR) | DVGW (Deutscher Verein des Gas-und-Wasserfaches) |
| | DVWW (Deutscher Verband für Wasserwirtschaft eV) |
| | Engler-Bunte-Institut |
| | WABOLU (Institut für Wasser-, Boden- und Lufthygiene des Bundesgesundheitsamtes) |
| | ATV (Abwassertechnische Vereinigung) |
| Hungary | VTKI (Vizgazdalkodasi Tudomanyos Kutato Intezet) |
| India | NEERI (National Environmental Engineering Research Institute) |
| Ireland | IIRS (Institute for Industrial Research and Standards) |

**Appendix B—**continued

| Israel | TECHNION (Israel Institute of Technology)<br>TAHAL (Water Planning for Israel Ltd)<br>Weizmann Institute of Science |
|---|---|
| Italy | IRSA (Istituto di Recerca sulle Acque)<br>Ente. Naz. Cellulosa e Carta |
| Japan | Institute of Public Health<br>Institute for Environmental Studies |
| Netherlands | KIWA (Keuringsinstituut voor Waterleiding artikelen)<br>RID (Rijksinstituut voor Drinkwatervoorziening)<br>RIZA (Rijksinstituut voor Zuivering van Afvalwater)<br>RIVA (Rijksinstituut voor de Volksgezondheid)<br>TNO (Toegepast Natuurwetenschappelijk Onderzoek) |
| Norway | NIVA (Norsk Institutt for Vannforskning)<br>SIFF (Statens Institutt for Folkehelse) |
| Peru | CEPIS (Centro Panamericano de Ingenieria Sanitaria y Ciencias del Ambiente) |
| Poland | Instytut Ksztatowania Srodowiska |
| Singapore | Singapore Institute of Standards and Industrial Research |
| South Africa | NIWR (National Institute for Water Research) |
| Spain | Empresa Nacional de Ingenieria y Tecnologia SA |
| Sweden | IVL (Institutet for Vatten- och Luftvardsforskning)<br>VAV (Svenska Vatten-och Avloppsverksföreningen) |
| Switzerland | EAWAG (Eidgenössische Anstalt für Wasserversorgung, Abwasserreiniging und Gewasserschutz) |
| Thailand | AIT (Asian Institute of Technology) |
| United State of America | EPA (Environmental Protection Agency)<br>USGS (US Geological Survey (Department of the Interior)) |
| USSR | Academy of Sciences of the USSR |
| United Nations | UNEP (United Nations Environmental Program) |
| WHO | General<br>IRC (International Reference Centre) |
| EEC Commission | (Unit 4 Water Management)<br>DG XII (Directorate-General XII Research, Science and Education. Directorate Cl Environmental and Raw Material Research)<br>JRC (Joint Research Centre) |

*This table is not comprehensive and where further information is required the reader is advised to consult relevant directories, e.g. Pollution Research Index (Francis Hodgson, 1975)
Endoc Directory (Peter Peregrinus, 1978).

# INDEX